ELEMENTS OF
INTERNAL-COMBUSTION
ENGINES

ELEMENTS OF
INTERNAL-COMBUSTION
ENGINES

A. R. ROGOWSKI, S.M.

Associate Professor of Mechanical Engineering
Massachusetts Institute of Technology

New York · Toronto London
McGRAW-HILL BOOK COMPANY, INC.
1953

THE MAPLE PRESS COMPANY, YORK, PA.

PREFACE

There seem to be currently two types of engine texts on the market. One is written primarily for the practicing engine specialist or for the student who expects to go into engine development, research, or design. The other is the technical manual written for the mechanic engaged in engine repair and maintenance.

From discussions with teachers and publishers, it is the author's belief that there exists a large body of engineering students who would appreciate and derive great benefit from a one-term course in the basic theory of the internal-combustion engine, even though they never expect to enter the engine field professionally.

There is hardly a subject known to engineers but what a large number of fully developed and highly practical examples are to be found in the internal-combustion engine—to name a few, combustion, fluid flow, friction, thermodynamics, heat transfer, lubrication, vibration. The internal-combustion engine appears, therefore, to be an ideal educational medium in the use of which the engineering student may learn to apply a wide variety of fundamental principles to the solution of many real engineering problems.

The subject matter of this book has been used successfully in war training programs and in one-term engine courses taken by seniors in mechanical engineering, marine engineering, general engineering, and engineering administration. Emphasis has been placed upon the application of the elementary principles of physics, chemistry, mechanics, etc., to the specific engineering problems connected with estimating and obtaining the maximum power, efficiency, and reliability from the internal-combustion engine.

The problems used in this book were taken from examinations and quizzes in engine theory given by various members of the Sloan Laboratory Staff at MIT. It is hoped that these problems will be found thought-provoking and that they will also serve to illustrate to the student the scope and usefulness of the text material. They may also be of value to the instructor in suggesting quiz questions. Problems of a more routine nature may be considered preferable for general homework or in cases where certain points brought out in classroom discussion are

v

to be emphasized.   Such problems are most effective if designed as the need arises.   Many of the problems given here may easily be simplified or abridged for this purpose.

Being an intermediate-level text, this book contains little that has not appeared elsewhere.   It is hoped that the principal value of this book will be found in the straightforwardness and clarity of the presentation. In this regard, the author is overwhelmingly indebted to the influence of Profs. C. F. Taylor and E. S. Taylor.   Their treatment of air capacity and heat rejection, as developed in their outstanding advanced engine book "The Internal Combustion Engine" (International Textbook Co.), has been followed with minor modifications in this text.

Much credit is due to Donald H. Tsai for his painstaking help with the illustrations.

AUGUSTUS R. ROGOWSKI

CAMBRIDGE, MASS.
FEBRUARY, 1953

CONTENTS

CHAPTER 1

INTRODUCTION

An engine is a device which transforms the chemical energy of a fuel into sensible, or "thermal," energy and uses this sensible energy to perform useful work. In the internal-combustion engine both processes can be considered to take place within the engine cylinder, where the hot products of combustion act directly on the piston.

In the steam engine—the most common *external*-combustion engine—all the energy required to operate the engine must first leave the hot combustion products, then pass through the walls of a heat exchanger or boiler, and enter the working medium, which is usually water or steam. The steam must then flow through pipes to the engine cylinder, where its energy is finally transformed into work upon the piston. The temperature of the steam and of the boiler surfaces must be kept far below that of the furnace gases, or the metal parts of the boiler will melt. Because of this fact, only moderately high temperatures can be obtained in the steam-engine cylinder, which limits the efficiency of this type of engine.

In the internal-combustion engine a relatively small fraction of the energy in the cylinder gases is transferred to the metal parts of the engine. The walls of the combustion space of an air-cooled engine may operate at 400°F while enclosing gases with temperatures of 4000°F or higher. These high gas temperatures and temperature drops available in the internal-combustion engine make possible the high efficiencies obtained with this type of prime mover.

High efficiency and absence of cumbersome auxiliary apparatus, such as furnaces, boilers, and condensers, make the internal-combustion engine relatively light and compact for its output. In addition to these advantages, the internal-combustion engine has become one of the most reliable devices serving mankind. Internal-combustion engines are almost the sole source of power for aircraft and road vehicles. Of the new locomotives ordered in 1950 by American railroads, over 99 per cent were powered with diesel engines. The installed horsepower of internal-combustion engines for marine use throughout the world exceeds that of all types of steam marine power plants combined.

Beginning about the year 1800 many experimental internal-combustion engines were constructed. The first really successful engine did not

1

appear, however, until 1876, when a German engine builder, Dr. N. A. Otto, built his famous "Otto gas engine." The operating cycle of this engine was based upon principles first laid down in 1862 by a French engineer named Beau de Rochas. The majority of modern internal-combustion engines operate according to these same principles, so that the Otto engine may well be considered the ancestor of most modern internal-combustion engines.

The development of the well-known diesel engine was begun about 1893 by Rudolf Diesel. Although this engine differs in many important respects from the Otto engine, the operating cycle of the modern high-speed diesel engine is thermodynamically very similar to the Otto cycle.

Preliminary Nomenclature

Conventional internal-combustion engines have one or more cylinders in which combustion of the fuel takes place. A cross section of an air-cooled engine cylinder with the principal parts labeled is shown in Fig. 1. One end of the cylinder is closed by the *cylinder head*, which usually contains the *inlet valves* for admitting the mixture of air and fuel and the *exhaust valves* for discharging the products of combustion. The valves are normally kept closed by means of *valve springs* and are opened mechanically by means of cams geared to the engine shaft. The passages in the cylinder head leading to or from the valves are called *ports*. The system of pipes which connect the inlet ports of the various cylinders to a common air intake for the engine is called the *inlet manifold*. If the exhaust ports are similarly connected to a common exhaust system, this system of piping is called the *exhaust manifold*.

The *piston* is a close-fitting member shaped like an inverted cup, which slides back and forth in the cylinder and forms a movable wall in the combustion space. The piston travels from a point near the cylinder head called *top center* to a point near the open end of the cylinder called *bottom center*. Passage of the piston from one end of its travel to the other is called *a stroke*. The distance the piston travels during one stroke, *i.e.*, from top to bottom center, is called the length of the stroke or simply "the stroke." The inside diameter of the cylinder is known as the *bore*.

The *crankshaft* is the principal rotating member of the engine. An extension of this shaft is usually the part through which the external work of the engine is done. Crankshafts are shown in Figs. 3 to 5. This shaft is built with one or more eccentric portions called cranks or crank throws, which produce the reciprocating motion of the pistons through link members called connecting rods.

The *connecting rod* connects the *crankpin*, which is part of the crank, with the piston and transmits the forces due to the pressure of the cylinder gases on the piston head down into the crankshaft. To provide for the swinging motion of the connecting rod, the upper end of the rod is fastened to the piston by means of a cylindrical member called the *wrist pin*. The wrist pin may oscillate in bearings in the piston, the upper end of the connecting rod may turn on the wrist pin, or, as is usually the case in aircraft engines, both kinds of motion may be permitted.

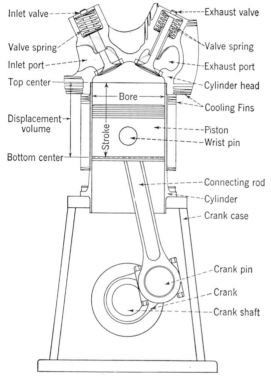

FIG. 1. Cross section of an engine cylinder.

The main body of the engine to which the cylinders are attached and which contains the crankshaft and crankshaft bearings is called the *crankcase*. This member holds the other engine parts in alignment and resists the explosion and inertia forces. It also protects the parts from dirt and serves as part of the lubricating system.

Some familiarity with these parts is a necessary background for an understanding of the basic principles of engine operation. These and other engine parts will be discussed in more detail later in the chapter.

The Four-stroke Cycle

In general, a machine of any kind in performing its function repeats over and over a certain series of operations. The order in which these operations are performed is fixed and all parts of the machine return to their original positions at the end of each series.   One complete series of this kind is called a *cycle*.

The majority of internal-combustion engines operate on what is known as the four-stroke cycle; *i.e.*, each cylinder requires four strokes of its piston, or two revolutions of the crankshaft, to complete the normal series of operations for the cylinder.   The four-stroke cycle of operation has been in use since 1876, when Dr. N. A. Otto, of Germany, built the first four-stroke gas engine.   Engines which employ the four-stroke cycle and which ignite a mixture of fuel and air by means of a timed electric spark or other small hot spot and burn this mixture while the piston remains close to top center (constant-volume burning) are often called Otto-cycle engines.   Diesel engines may use a four-stroke cycle, but because of their unique method of ignition and combustion they are not considered Otto-cycle engines.   The Diesel cycle is discussed in detail in Chap. 13.

The series of operations which make up the normal spark-ignition four-stroke (Otto) cycle used in most aircraft and automobile engines is given below.   It is the same as proposed by Beau de Rochas in 1862.

The *intake*, or *suction*, stroke starts with the piston at top center. The inlet valve opens at about this time, and the motion of the piston toward bottom center draws fresh air (usually mixed with fuel) into the cylinder.   Shortly after the piston reaches bottom center, the fresh mixture stops flowing into the cylinder, and the inlet valve is therefore arranged to close near this point.   The volume swept by the piston during one stroke is called the *displacement volume* of the cylinder.   The volume remaining above the piston at top center is called the *clearance volume*. Figure 2a shows the suction stroke in progress.

The *compression* stroke takes place with all valves closed and is for the purpose of returning the piston to top center so that the cylinder gases may do some work upon it.   During the compression stroke the gases which formerly occupied the *total cylinder volume* are compressed into the clearance volume.   Just before the end of the compression stroke, the mixture is ignited by causing an electric spark to pass between the electrodes of one or more spark plugs located somewhere in the wall of the combustion space.   The burning thus started spreads *progressively* to all parts of the mixture during the next 30 or 40° of crank travel. Since the amount of piston motion per degree of crank travel is small near top center, burning occurs at approximately constant volume.   Near the end of compression, but before burning takes place, the cylinder contents might have had a temperature of 500°F and a pressure of 150 psia. During the burning process most of the chemical energy of the fuel is transformed into sensible energy, producing a temperature rise of approximately 3500° to a final temperature of about 4000°F.   The pressure exerted by these gases—now products of combustion—will be correspondingly increased to about 700 psia. The exact values of cylinder pressure and temperature can be calculated fairly closely when the operating conditions are known (see Chap. 4). Figure 2*b* shows the compression stroke at the instant of ignition.

The next stroke is known as the *power* stroke or *expansion* stroke. During this stroke all valves remain closed, and the hot high-pressure gases drive the piston back to bottom center. Because of their high pressure, the cylinder gases do approximately five times as much work on the piston during the expansion stroke as the piston had to do on the

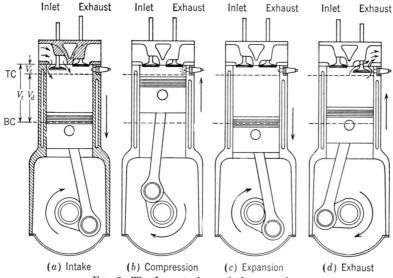

(*a*) Intake   (*b*) Compression   (*c*) Expansion   (*d*) Exhaust

FIG. 2. The four-stroke cycle in operation.

gases during the compression stroke. As the cylinder gases expand and give up their energy to the piston, they become cooler, so that near the end of the expansion stroke the gas temperature may be 2500°F and the pressure around 75 psia. The more the cylinder gases are permitted to expand during the power stroke, the cooler they become, as more of their sensible energy is transformed into useful work on the piston head. In other words, with more expansion, less heat is rejected with the exhaust gases, and the engine cycle becomes more efficient.

The extent of this expansion is approximated by the ratio

$$\frac{\text{volume above the piston at bottom center}}{\text{volume above the piston at top center}}$$

or

$$\frac{\text{clearance volume} + \text{displacement volume}}{\text{clearance volume}}$$

This ratio is called the *compression ratio* and is extremely important because of its effect upon engine performance.

Near the end of the expansion stroke, the exhaust valve opens, and the pressure in the cylinder at this point forces most of the gases out of the cylinder. The high velocity with which the exhaust gases escape is responsible for much of the noise associated with internal-combustion engines. Figure 2c pictures the expansion stroke just before the exhaust valve opens.

During the *exhaust* stroke, the piston returns to top center, sweeping all the spent gases (with the exception of those which occupy the clearance volume) out through the open exhaust valve. The exhaust valve

FIG. 3. Crankshaft of in-line six-cylinder engine.

closes near top center, leaving these "residual" gases in the clearance space at approximately exhaust-port pressure. The residual gases mix with the fresh charge during the next intake stroke. Figure 2d shows the piston in the middle of the exhaust stroke.

It is to be noted here that positive work is done on the piston during only *one* of the four strokes of the cycle. The energy required to keep the shaft turning during the intake, compression, and exhaust strokes is supplied by a flywheel or other mass connected to the engine crankshaft. The flywheel stores the energy received from the gases during the power stroke and releases it during the other three strokes. In multicylinder engines the power strokes are usually arranged to occur at evenly spaced intervals of crankshaft rotation, so that the power stroke of one cylinder may be taking place, for example, during part of the compression stroke of another cylinder. A smaller flywheel is therefore required for multicylinder engines.

It should also be pointed out that there is no particular virtue in compressing the mixture during the compression stroke. If the same weight of fresh charge had been pumped into the cylinder by means of an external pump while the piston was at top center, and the charge subsequently ignited, the work done during the expansion stroke would have been the same as before; and the intake and compression strokes could have been eliminated. However, it is usually preferable to use the same piston to draw in and compress the fresh charge and to receive the energy of the gases after combustion.

FIG. 4. Crankshaft for eight-cylinder V-type engine. (*Courtesy of Oldsmobile Division General Motors Corp.*)

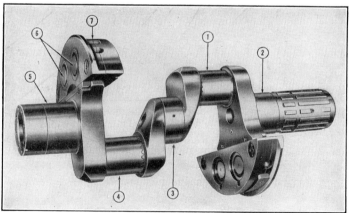

FIG. 5. Crankshaft of two-row radial engine. 1. Front crankpin. 2. Front journal. 3. Center journal. 4. Rear crankpin. 5. Rear journal. 6. Rear vibration damper pins. 7. Rear counterweight. (*Courtesy of Pratt & Whitney Aircraft.*)

Each cylinder of every four-stroke engine completes the series of operations outlined above once every two engine revolutions. A six-cylinder engine, for example, will have only three intake strokes or three power strokes per revolution of its crankshaft.

Engine Types

Engines are commonly classified according to their cylinder arrangement. If the cylinders are attached to the crankcase one cylinder behind the other with their axes parallel, the engine is called an "in-line" engine. Such a row of cylinders is called a *bank*. For greater power, two or more banks of cylinders are often attached to the same crankcase and use the same crankshaft. Engines with two banks of cylinders are called V engines; those with four banks are called X engines. Engines with

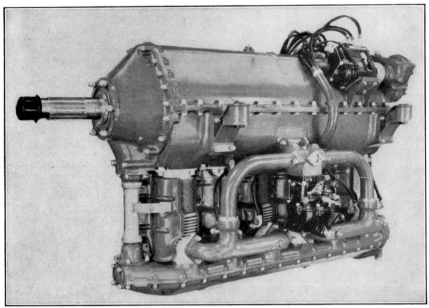

FIG. 6. Six-cylinder inverted in-line engine. (*Courtesy of Fairchild Engine & Aircraft Corp.*)

banks of cylinders naturally require long crankshafts and crankcases. If the cylinders are attached to the crankcase with their axes disposed like the spokes of a wheel, the engine is known as *radial*. Such an engine, with all cylinders operating on a single crank throw, will have a relatively short, stiff crankshaft and compact crankcase. Its frontal area will tend to be large, however. Sometimes two pistons operate in the same cylinder. This arrangement is shown in Fig. 106.

Examples of these engine types may be seen in Figs. 6 to 8. In-line engines are most often liquid-cooled. Radial engines are almost always air-cooled. All the above types of engines are used in aircraft, but automobile engines are almost universally liquid-cooled in-line or V engines.

Engines are also classified according to their thermodynamic cycle or type of combustion. These differences will be discussed in detail in later chapters.

Function and Material of Parts

Although this text does not deal to any extent with details of engine design or construction, it is at least desirable to know the purpose of each important part, the reason for its shape, and why certain materials or

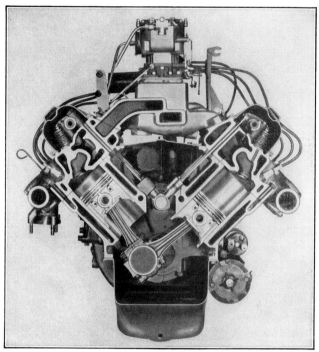

FIG. 7. Cross section of a V-type engine. (*Courtesy of Oldsmobile Division General Motors Corp.*)

processes are used in its manufacture. Since engine design practice is still undergoing continuous change, the discussion will be limited to well-established principles and practice.

Cylinders. The cylinder has several functions. It encloses the burning gases, which may reach temperatures of 5000°F and pressures of 1000 psia or higher in a supercharged engine. It guides the piston and acts as a bearing, taking the side load of the piston, which is the reaction to the torque of the crankshaft. The cylinder usually contains the valve seats and ports and supports the valves and valve-actuating mechanism. The cylinder must be provided either with increased outer surface area in the form of fins or with a water jacket, so that the heat transferred to

FIG. 8. Two-row radial air-cooled engine.

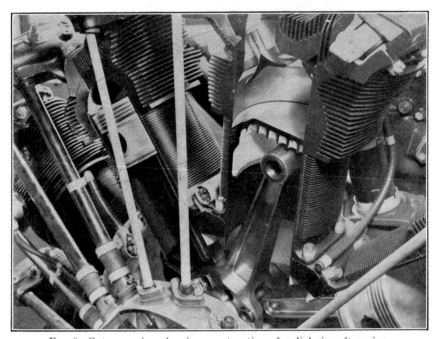

FIG. 9. Cutaway view showing construction of radial aircraft engine.

the cylinder walls by the hot gases can be removed rapidly enough to keep the cylinder temperature within the range of adequate mechanical strength and good lubrication.

When cost is more important than weight, cast iron is often used for cylinders and cylinder heads. This material has good natural lubricating properties, holds its strength at elevated temperature, and is easy to

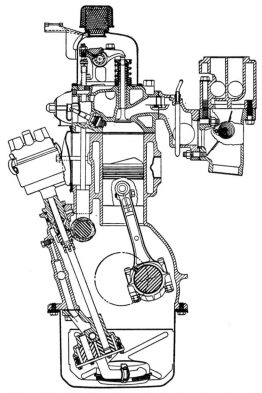

FIG. 10. Cross section of engine showing valve in head construction. (*Courtesy of Buick Motor Division General Motors Corp.*)

machine. Several cylinders can be cast in one block, with cooling passages cast right in around the cylinders. This is standard automobile practice. Aircraft practice is to make the cylinder barrels of thin steel for strength and lightness, hardened inside for wear resistance. When the cylinder is to be air-cooled, fins may be machined on the outside of the cylinder barrel or aluminum fins may be shrunk or cast onto the barrel. When liquid cooling is employed in aircraft engines, the cooling jackets are often cast of aluminum alloy in one block to accommodate several cylinders. The cylinders may then be made of thin steel and inserted in the block.

When the cylinders are fastened separately to the crankcase, the cylinder head is usually made of a finned aluminum-alloy casting or forging, which is screwed onto the cylinder barrel while hot, so that it shrinks to a gastight fit. Aluminum alloy is used because of its high thermal conductivity. The ability of the cylinder head to conduct heat to its fins is very important since both spark plugs and valves are kept cool by contact with the cylinder head. Although aluminum alloy may be made as strong as mild steel, its strength is seriously affected by high tempera-

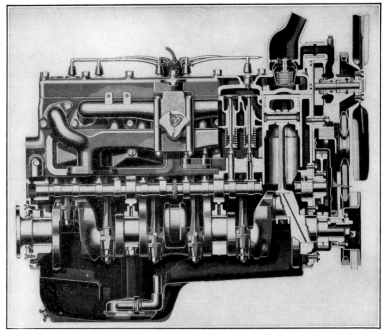

Fig. 11. Cross section of engine showing L-head construction.   (*Courtesy of Chrysler Corp.*)

tures.   Aluminum-alloy cylinder heads are seldom operated much above 500°F.

The gas force acting on a single cylinder head, tending to tear the cylinder from the crankcase, may be as much as 30,000 lb in a large aircraft engine.   The hold-down flange near the bottom of the cylinder must be carefully designed with large fillets to distribute the load as evenly as possible to the crankcase.   In automobile engines the upper crankcase and the crankshaft bearing supports are usually cast integral with the cylinders, so that hold-down flanges are eliminated.   Examples of cylinder and cylinder-head construction are shown in Figs. 9 to 11.

Pistons.   The piston together with its sealing rings must transmit the gas load through the wrist pin to the upper connecting-rod bearing. This assembly must slide freely in the cylinder and at the same time prevent the gases in the combustion space from escaping into the crankcase (blowby). It must transmit enough heat into the cylinder walls or into the oil which splashes up on the underside of the piston to keep the piston head cool. The piston and rings must control the amount of oil on the cylinder walls so that adequate lubrication is maintained without exceeding a reasonable oil consumption.

When weight is not important and speeds and outputs are moderate, cast-iron pistons are often used. Their good lubricating properties and low coefficient of thermal expansion make them easy to fit and maintain.

Fig. 12. Pistons from high-output engines showing rings, wrist pin, and relief on nonthrust areas.

Since the inertia forces of heavy pistons require heavy counterweights on the crankshaft to balance them, it is particularly important to keep the piston light in aircraft engines. Where lightness and good thermal conductivity are important, aluminum-alloy forgings are usually employed. The length of the piston and the side-wall thickness are kept as small as possible. The piston head and path to the wrist-pin bosses are kept heavy to carry the gas loads. The thermal path from piston head to piston rings must be sufficient, as this is the principal avenue of escape for the heat entering the piston head.

Piston rings. The sides of the piston are grooved circumferentially to hold several piston rings. These rings are not continuous but are cut through at one point so that they spring out and press against the cylinder wall regardless of the piston clearance. Piston rings are generally made of cast iron because of the ability of this material to stand up under the conditions of poor lubrication which exist at the upper end of the cylinder. Cast iron also retains its elastic properties at fairly high temperatures. The rings fit their grooves with moderate clearance and, with the help of the lubricating oil, furnish a good seal. The sealing rings are called compression rings and are usually rectangular or slightly tapered in section. The lower rings are used for oil control and are made in a variety of shapes. The ring grooves containing the oil-control rings are often vented to the inside of the piston to carry the oil which has been scraped from the cylinder wall by the rings back into the crankcase. Figure 12 shows typical aircraft pistons and rings.

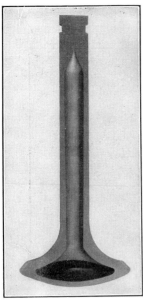

FIG. 13. Section of a sodium-cooled valve. (*Courtesy of Thompson Products Inc.*)

Wrist pins. The wrist pin is made of steel for strength and stiffness. Stiffness is important because the wrist pin is subjected to bending loads and may cause local failure of the piston bosses or of the bearing in the upper end of the connecting rod if it is allowed to deflect. The wrist pin is made hollow for lightness since it is a reciprocating part. Figures 9 and 12 show typical wrist pins.

Valves. The valves are usually mushroom-shaped with conical seating surfaces. They are made of special alloy steels capable of retaining their mechanical strength at high temperatures and able to resist the corrosive and erosive effects of the high-temperature high-velocity cylinder gases. The exhaust valve is of course particularly critical and in high-output engines is often filled with metallic sodium. The sodium melts, and as the valve moves back and forth, the sodium mechanically transfers heat from the valve head to the valve stem. Figure 13 shows such a valve in cross section.

The size, position, and number of valves used in the cylinder head are a compromise between mechanical complexity and the desire of the designer to keep the passages as large as possible. For high output, it appears to be desirable to keep the flow capacity of the inlet valves equal to or slightly greater than that of the exhaust valves. In air-cooled designs, one inlet and one exhaust valve are generally used in a hemispherical cylinder head. They are made as large as possible consistent with the strength of the cylinder head.

In liquid-cooled engines the valves may be operated by means of cams mounted on the cylinder head. This simplifies the intermediate linkage required. Such a system is shown in Fig. 14. In many engines the cams are located in the crankcase. The cam lifts a cam follower con-

FIG. 14. Overhead valves and camshaft of Allison engine. (*Sloan Laboratory.*)

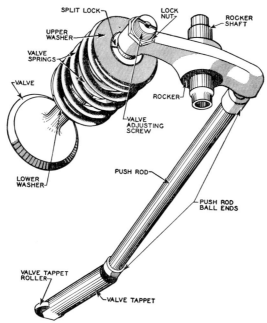

FIG. 15. Overhead-valve, rocker-arm, and push-rod assembly. (*Courtesy of Pratt & Whitney Aircraft.*)

nected to a push rod. The push rod actuates a lever called a *rocker arm*, which depresses the valve stem and opens the valve (see Figs. 7 and 15). In some automotive-type engines, complication is avoided by locating the valves in a pocket in one side of the combustion space with valve stems pointing downward toward the camshaft. This construction is shown in Fig. 11. The bearing for the valve stem is usually made of bronze and is called a valve guide. If the cylinder head is made of aluminum, inserted valve seats are always used. These inserts are made of heat-resistant material similar to the valves. A typical valve-actuating system for an air-cooled engine is shown in Fig. 15.

Fig. 16. Two designs of connecting-rod assembly for V-type engines. (*Sloan Laboratory.*)

Connecting rods. The connecting rod is made from a steel forging for strength and reliability. It is milled to an I or H section for strength and lightness and for ease of manufacture and inspection. The surface is often polished or shot-blasted to improve resistance to fatigue. Inserts of bearing material are pressed or otherwise inserted into each end of the rod. In V-type engines which have two or more banks of cylinders disposed at an angle to each other, or radial engines, which position their cylinders radially about the crankcase, it is common practice to use one crankpin for several connecting rods. Figures 9 and 16 show methods for accomplishing this.

Crankshafts. The crankshaft carries the loads from the connecting rods, in bending and torsion, to the propeller or other power take-off. It is particularly subject to fatigue failures because of its peculiar shape. Stress concentrations are likely to occur at the junction of the crank cheek and crankpin or crank cheek and main journal unless large fillets, wide crank cheeks, or other means are provided to redistribute the stresses. For aircraft use the crankshaft is carefully made of alloy steel and is given a very high surface polish. To facilitate engine assembly, some crankshafts are made in several sections. This construction requires unusual care in manufacturing. Several crankshafts are shown in Figs. 3 to 5.

Crankcases. The crankcase of aircraft engines is sometimes made of an aluminum-alloy forging or casting and sometimes of steel. In automobile engines the upper part of the crankcase is cast in one piece with the cylinder block. The crankcase must be strong and stiff, as it preserves the alignment of the entire engine and carries the cylinder-head gas loads down to the crankshaft bearings, where they are resisted by the piston-head gas loads, carried to the same point by the connecting rod and crankshaft. Because of the large forces involved, the various cross-sectional shapes and sizes are chosen with great care.

SUGGESTIONS FOR FURTHER READING

"Aircraft Powerplant Handbook," U.S. Department of Commerce, Washington, D.C., 1949.

Heldt, P. M.: "High Speed Combustion Engines," P. M. Heldt, Nyack, N.Y., 1946.

Lichty, L. C.: "Internal-combustion Engines," 6th. ed., McGraw-Hill, New York, 1951.

Obert, E. F.: "Internal Combustion Engines," International Textbook, Scranton, Pa. 1950.

Taylor, C. F., and E. S. Taylor: "The Internal Combustion Engine," International Textbook, Scranton, Pa., 1948.

CHAPTER 2

PHYSICAL PRINCIPLES

Perhaps the main objectives in studying the theory of the internal-combustion engine are:

1. An understanding of the processes taking place and the conditions prevailing in an engine cylinder.

2. The ability to predict the changes in power, fuel consumption, and reliability which will result from changes in the operating conditions or changes in the design features of a given engine.

3. The ability to predict the operating characteristics of a new design from test results on a similar engine of a different size.

To achieve these objectives, it is necessary to be familiar with the elementary principles of engineering thermodynamics, physics, and chemistry. This familiarity must include the ability to apply these principles correctly, which implies a fundamental understanding of the derivation of the formulas used and a clear physical picture of the mechanisms involved.

The background material discussed in this chapter is the minimum required by the practicing engineer in internal-combustion engines; yet it is the author's experience that many students do not have a working familiarity with these basic principles. Although a fairly exact treatment has been attempted, emphasis has been placed upon usefulness and clarity.

Fundamental Quantities

Force. In this text the unit of force F will be the pound. A pound is the force required to give an acceleration of one foot per (second)^2 to a mass of one slug of matter.

Gravitational constant. The acceleration which the earth's attraction gives to freely falling masses is called g. The value of g may be taken as 32.2 ft/sec^2 with sufficient accuracy for engineering calculations at any location or altitude thus far attained.

Weight. The weight of a body w is the force in pounds with which the earth attracts the body. The weight of a given body will change with any variation in the value of g.

Mass. The mass of a body M is the quantity of matter in the body. The mass of a given body is therefore the same anywhere in the universe. The unit of mass used in this book will be the *slug*. A body with a mass

18

of one slug will be attracted by the earth with a force in pounds numerically equal to the local value of the gravitational acceleration g.

For example, since $g = 32.2$ ft/sec² on the earth's surface, the earth would attract a mass of one slug with a force of 32.2 pounds; that is, a slug would weigh 32.2 lb. Somewhere out in space where the acceleration due to the earth's gravity is only 10 ft/sec², the slug would weigh only 10 lb, although it would still contain the same quantity of matter as before. The weight w is *always* equal to the number of slugs M times the local value of g; or

$$w = Mg \qquad (1)$$

The pound *mass* is a quantity of matter 1/32.2 times as large as the slug. In places where the acceleration of gravity is 32.2 ft/sec², a pound mass would be attracted to the earth with a force of one pound; *i.e.*, a pound mass weighs almost exactly one pound on the earth's surface.

In this text, therefore, the pound mass (1/32.2 slug) and the "pound weight" (the quantity of matter which the earth attracts with a force of one pound) will be used interchangeably to indicate the same quantity of matter. The gravitational acceleration will be assumed constant at 32.2 ft/sec.²

From (1), it is seen that the mass in slugs

$$M = \frac{w}{g}$$
$$= \frac{w}{32.2} \text{ near the earth's surface} \qquad (1a)$$

The Gas Laws

During the intake and compression strokes, the working fluid of the internal-combustion engine consists principally of air and gasoline vapor. During the expansion and exhaust strokes, the working fluid is mainly nitrogen, carbon dioxide, and water vapor. At the pressures and temperatures existing in the internal-combustion engine all these gases obey the simple gas law

$$pV = NRT \qquad (2)$$

to an approximation sufficiently close for engineering purposes. This law is very simple and *always* applies to *any* gas, regardless of the process to which the gas is subjected, as long as the gas is not near its liquefaction point. In Eq. (2)

p = pressure of the gas in pounds per square foot absolute (psfa)

V = volume occupied by the gas in cubic feet (ft³)

N = number of moles of gas under consideration

R = 1544, a universal constant (nearly the same for all gases), the units of which are ft-lb/(mole)(°R)

T = absolute temperature of the gas in degrees Rankine (°R)

The mole.   A pound-mole of any gas is a quantity of the gas equal to the molecular weight in pounds; thus

$$N = \frac{w}{m} \qquad (3)$$

where w = number of pounds of gas

m = molecular weight of the gas, lb/mole

By substituting $N = 1$ in the gas law [Eq. (2)] it is seen that the volume occupied by one mole of *any* gas is the same at a given pressure and temperature.

Combining Eqs. (2) and (3), the gas law may be written

$$pV = \frac{wRT}{m} \qquad (2a)$$

if desired.   In some texts the quantity R/m is given a separate symbol and is called the *individual gas constant*.   Since m is different for each gas, the individual gas constant will also be different for each gas.

Simplification of the gas law.   When the number of moles w/m of gas under consideration is fixed, both N and R are constant, and from Eq. (2) or (2a)

$$\frac{p_1 V_1}{T_1} = \frac{p_2 V_2}{T_2} = \frac{p_n V_n}{T_n} = \text{const} \qquad (4)$$

This simple relation is *always* true when applied to a constant number of moles of a gas and makes it possible to calculate the effect of changing any two of the variables (pressure, volume, or temperature) upon the remaining one.

Absolute pressure.   The pressure which the atmosphere exerts upon objects at sea level varies slightly from time to time but is approximately 14.7 pounds per square inch.   The ordinary pressure gage, connected to a tank, for example, does not measure the pressure within the tank but instead indicates how much *above atmospheric* pressure the tank pressure is.   To obtain the actual, or *absolute*, tank pressure, the atmospheric pressure must be added to the gage reading.   The absolute pressure is proportional to the number of moles in the tank and may be calculated by the gas law.

Absolute temperature.   If a certain quantity of gas is sealed in a container so that the gas occupies a constant volume and the pressure in the container is plotted at various gas temperatures in Fahrenheit degrees, a straight line will be obtained as in Fig. 17a, but the pressure will not be proportional to the temperature, as the gas law indicates.   For example, changing the temperature from 60 to 120°F will not double the pressure.

If the straight line of Fig. 17a is extended to zero pressure, it will cross the temperature axis at −460°F. If this point is chosen as the origin of the plot and a *new* temperature scale is constructed by adding 460° to each number on the old (Fahrenheit) scale, the pressure will now be proportional to the new temperatures. The new scale is called the *absolute* Fahr-

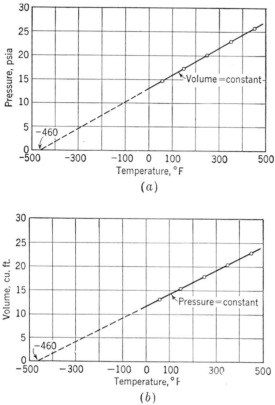

FIG. 17. (a) The effect of temperature on the absolute pressure of a gas held at constant volume. (b) The effect of temperature on the volume of a gas subjected to constant pressure.

enheit or, more commonly, the *Rankine* temperature, and

$$°R = (460 + °F)$$

Note that the size of one degree Rankine is the same as the size of one degree Fahrenheit. Thus a 10° temperature rise is the same in either system.

A similar experiment could have been performed by keeping the pressure of the gas constant and plotting the volume occupied by the gas against the temperature. The extrapolated volume would also have reached zero at $-460°F$, as shown in Fig. 17b.

Proportionality. The word "proportional" may require some explanation at this point. When a relationship exists between two quantities x and y such that for every value of x there is a definite value of y, then y may be plotted as a curve against x and y is known as a "function of x."

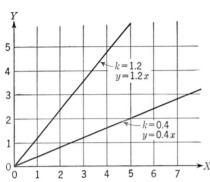

FIG. 18. Plot showing $x \propto y$ in two cases, with different values of the proportionality constant k.

This is written $y = f(x)$. The function may be a complicated one such as $y = 3x^3 - \sin 2x + 7$. However, if the function is a *constant* times x, that is, if $y = kx$, where k is a constant, then whenever x is doubled, y also doubles, etc. When this is true, it is said that y is *proportional* to x, or $y \propto x$. When $y = kx$, the plot of y against x is a *straight line passing through the origin*, as shown in Fig. 18. This is the test for proportionality. If the plot of y vs. x is not straight or is straight but does not pass through the origin, y is *not* proportional to x.

Example 1. Calculate the volume occupied by 1 mole of any gas at standard sea-level conditions (14.7 psia, 60°F temperature).
Solution. From the gas law, $V = NRT/p$.

$$V = \frac{1 \times 1544 \times (460 + 60)}{14.7 \times 144} = 380 \text{ ft}^3$$

Check of units:

$$\frac{\text{mole} \times \dfrac{\text{ft-lb}}{(\text{mole})(°R)} \times °R}{\dfrac{\text{lb}}{\text{in.}^2} \times \dfrac{\text{in.}^2}{\text{ft}^2}} = \text{ft}^3$$

Example 2. A gas occupies a closed tank at 14.7 psia and a temperature of 60°F. Heat is added to the gas until it reaches a temperature of 120°F. What will be its pressure?
Solution. From (2) or (4), since N and V are constant,

$$\frac{p_1}{T_1} = \text{const} = \frac{p_2}{T_2}$$

$$p_2 = 14.7 \times \frac{120 + 460}{60 + 460} = 14.7 \times \frac{580}{520} = 16.40 \text{ psia}$$

Example 3. Air has a molecular weight of 29. What volume will be occupied by 1 lb of air at standard conditions (14.7 psia and 520°R)?

Solution. From (2a)

$$V = \frac{wRT}{mp} = \frac{1 \times 1544 \times 520}{29 \times 14.7 \times 144} = 13.1 \text{ ft}^3$$

or, since for this example RT/mp = constant,

$$\frac{V_1}{w_1} = \text{const} = \frac{V_2}{w_2}$$

From Example 1, the volume of 1 mole (29 lb of air) at standard conditions = 380 ft³.

$$\frac{V}{1} = \frac{380}{29} = 13.1 \text{ ft}^3$$

Specific volume and density. The volume occupied by one pound of substance is known as its *specific volume* v (ft³/lb).

The inverse of the specific volume ($1/v$) is the *weight density*, or *specific weight*, γ, and is the number of pounds of substance in one cubic foot of material (lb/ft³). From the above definitions,

$$wv = V \text{ (ft}^3) \qquad \text{and} \qquad \gamma V = w \text{ (lb)}$$

From the gas law (2a) it is always possible to calculate the weight density, *i.e.*,

$$\gamma = \frac{w}{V} = \frac{mp}{RT} \tag{5}$$

For a given gas, m and R being constant, the density is proportional to the pressure and inversely proportional to the temperature, that is, $\gamma = (p/T) \times$ constant (or $\gamma \propto p/T$).

The mass density ρ is the number of slugs of material in one cubic foot (slugs/ft³). The number of pounds *mass* per cubic foot will *always* be exactly 32.2ρ, and the number of pounds *weight* per cubic foot (γ) will always be $g\rho$. Within engineering accuracy $g = 32.2$ near the earth's surface, so that γ may also be considered equal to 32.2ρ.

Example 4. γ for air at standard conditions is 0.0765 lb/ft³. What is the weight density of air at 5 psia pressure and 600°R?
Solution. From Eq. (5)

$$\frac{\gamma_2}{\gamma_1} = \frac{p_2}{T_2}\frac{T_1}{p_1}$$

$$\gamma_2 = 0.0765 \times \frac{5}{600} \times \frac{520}{14.7} = 0.0226 \text{ lb/ft}^3$$

Mixtures of gases. When two or more gases occupy a single container, *each* gas diffuses and fills the entire space, obeying the gas law just as though the other gases were not present. This principle is called Dalton's law. For example, suppose three gases a, b, and c are mixed in a container of volume V. If the temperature of the mixture is T, then the pressure exerted on the walls of the container by gas a is, by the gas law,

$p_a = N_a RT/V$; the pressure exerted on the walls of the container by gas b is $p_b = N_b RT/V$. The *total* pressure within the container is

$$p_t = p_a + p_b + p_c + \cdots = (N_a + N_b + N_c + \cdots)\frac{RT}{V} = N_t \frac{RT}{V} \quad (6)$$

From the above expressions for p_a and p_b it is seen that

$$\frac{p_a}{p_b} = \frac{N_a}{N_b} \quad (7)$$

and from (6)

$$\frac{p_a}{p_t} = \frac{N_a}{N_t} \quad (7a)$$

These pressures p_a, p_b, etc., which go to make up the total pressure are called *partial pressures*. At a given volume and temperature, the partial pressure of a gas is evidently proportional to the number of moles of *that* gas present, and *independent* of the number of moles of any other gas present. The fraction of the *total* pressure which is contributed by any one of the gases is equal to the ratio of the number of moles of that gas present to the total number of moles present.

Example 5. Octane vapor ($m = 114$) weighing 0.14 lb is mixed with 2 lb of air ($m = 29$) in the inlet manifold of an engine. If the total pressure in the manifold is 14.7 psia and the temperature is 500°R:

(a) What volume will this quantity of mixture occupy?

(b) What will be the partial pressure of the air in the mixture?

(c) What will be the weight density of the air in the mixture, considering that the air occupies the entire volume?

Solution. (a) From Eq. (3),

$$N_a = \frac{2}{29} = 0.069$$
$$N_o = \frac{0.14}{114} = 0.00123$$

From (6),

$$V_t = \frac{(N_a + N_o)RT}{p_t} = \frac{0.0702 \times 1544 \times 500}{14.7 \times 144} = 25.6\,\text{ft}^3$$

(b) Since $V_a = V_t$, from the gas law (2),

$$p_a = \frac{N_a RT}{V_a} = \frac{N_a RT}{V_t} = \frac{0.069 \times 1544 \times 500}{25.6 \times 144} = 14.47\,\text{psia}$$

or from (7a)

$$p_a = p_t \frac{N_a}{N_t} = 14.7 \frac{0.069}{0.0702} = 14.47\,\text{psia}$$

(c) From (5),

$$\gamma_a = \frac{w_a}{V_a} = \frac{m_a p_a}{RT} = \frac{29 \times 14.47 \times 144}{1544 \times 500} = 0.0782\,\text{lb/ft}^3$$

or

$$\gamma_a = \frac{2}{25.6} = 0.0782\,\text{lb/ft}^3$$

Forms of Energy

An engine takes in chemical energy (in the fuel) during the suction stroke, changes most of this into sensible energy during the combustion process, and then transforms part of the sensible energy into mechanical work on the piston head.

During the suction stroke the atmosphere does work on the mixture as it forces it into the cylinder. During the exhaust stroke the products of combustion do work on the atmosphere as they leave the cylinder. In order to understand these processes, it is necessary to study the various forms of energy in some detail.

Energy is defined as the capacity to do work. If a machine or body, because of its position, temperature, or velocity, is capable of doing work on another body, it is said to have energy. Work is done whenever motion takes place against a resistance. The amount of work done is the distance moved, times the magnitude of the resisting force in the direction of the motion. Work and energy may be expressed in the same units. It is common, however, to express work in foot-pounds (the amount of energy required or the amount of work done to move a distance of one foot against a resistance of one pound of force) and to express thermal energy in British thermal units (Btu). One Btu is equivalent to 778 foot-pounds.

When energy is being transferred from one body to another by means of a temperature difference, it is called *heat* and is usually measured in Btu.

Transfer of Energy. It is important to note that heat and work are both energy in transit. If a temperature difference exists between two bodies in contact, it is our experience that the hot body will become cooler and lose some of its ability to do work. The cold body will become hotter and will gain exactly the energy lost by the hot body. To describe this process, we say that heat flowed from the hot body to the cold body. Similarly, when work is done, the system doing the work loses energy and the system upon which the work is being done gains exactly this amount of energy.

Stored energy. In the two cases above, when the process is finished the energy gained by the second body is not called heat or work, since heat is no longer flowing and work is no longer being done. The additional energy which is now stored in the second body may be called internal energy, kinetic energy, etc., depending upon the manner in which it is stored.

Potential energy. Any body possessing weight w (pounds), and elevated a distance of Z feet above a chosen level (called a datum) will do wZ foot-pounds of work in returning to the datum level. In its elevated position the body is therefore said to have *potential energy* equal to wZ ft-lb.

Kinetic energy. Any body of mass $M = w/g$, in slugs, moving with a velocity of u feet per second will do $wu^2/2g$ foot-pounds of work before coming to rest. In its state of motion the body is therefore said to have *kinetic energy* equal to $wu^2/2g$ ft-lb.

Internal energy. A body may possess energy due to the motion or position of, and the attraction between, the particles of which it is made. Thus a box resting on the ground possesses no potential or kinetic energy, but if it is full of spinning tops, it would be considered to have internal energy. In a "permanent" gas (*i.e.*, a gas which is far from its liquefaction point), the internal energy E (Btu) will usually be in the form of (1) translational motion of the molecules of the gas and (2) motion of the atoms within the molecules. These two kinds of internal energy are known as *sensible internal energy*, although only that part which is due to molecular translation can actually be felt as warmth. For a given quantity of a particular permanent gas, the amount of sensible internal energy present is fixed by the temperature of the gas alone.

It is convenient when dealing with sensible internal energy to establish an arbitrary temperature datum (say 520°R) and measure the sensible internal energy of the substance above this datum. For example, if a certain gas is at temperature T, its sensible internal energy is considered to be equal to the amount of work it would be able to do on a piston as it expanded without heat loss to the datum temperature T_0. The symbol for sensible internal energy is E_s, and the units are Btu.

The gas or gases under consideration may also contain chemical energy. A mixture of hydrogen and oxygen at T_0 (datum) would be considered to have no sensible internal energy. If the hydrogen and oxygen were to combine chemically, however, the temperature would rise and the amount of sensible internal energy would suddenly become very great. The symbol for *chemical energy* is E_c and the units are Btu. The sum of the chemical energy of the fuel present and the sensible internal energy is called the *total internal energy* E. That is,

$$E = E_s + E_c \qquad (8)$$

If during any combustion process no heat is allowed to escape from the gases and no work is permitted to be done by the gases, then at any time during the process the increase in *sensible* energy due to combustion is exactly equal to the loss in *chemical* energy as the fuel is used up. The total internal energy therefore remains *unchanged*.

Processes. A change in the condition or state of a substance is called a process. The process may consist of heating, flow from one place to another, expansion, or some other change.

Nonflow Processes

If there is no flow of material into or out of a system (container) during a process, it is called a nonflow process. This is the simplest kind of process, and much can be learned about it by applying the principle of the conservation of energy. This principle tells us that the total energy stored in the substance at the end of a process is equal to the total energy stored in the substance before the process began plus the heat added to the substance from outside the container during the process minus the work done by the substance on or through the boundary of the container during the process. Including the various kinds of energy mentioned on pages 25 and 26,

$$E_{s_2} + E_{c_2} + \frac{wZ_2}{J} + \frac{wu_2{}^2}{2gJ} = E_{s_1} + E_{c_1} + \frac{wZ_1}{J} + \frac{wu_1{}^2}{2gJ} + {}_1Q_2 - \frac{{}_1W_2}{J} \quad (9)$$

where $J = 778$ ft-lb/Btu and is used to keep the units of each term of the equation in Btu

$_1Q_2$ = heat which *entered* the substance through the walls of the container during the process, Btu

$_1W_2$ = work done *by* the substance during the process, ft-lb

The subscripts 1, 2 mean that the heat flowed or the work was done between condition 1 and condition 2, that is, during the process.

Figure 19 shows a nonflow system consisting of a container filled with a gas. Heat may flow into the gas through the walls of the container, and work may be done by the gas on the movable piston.

If the substance is a quiescent gas (without kinetic energy), in a container whose level does not change during the

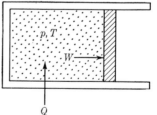

FIG. 19. Diagram illustrating a nonflow system.

process, $u_1 = u_2 = 0$ and $Z_1 = Z_2$, so that expression (9) reduces to

$$_1Q_2 = (E_2 - E_1) + \frac{{}_1W_2}{J} \quad (10)$$

Note that $_1Q_2$ is positive when heat is flowing *into* the gas and $_1W_2$ is positive when work is being done *by* the gas. It is seen from this expression that when heat is added to a quiescent gas, either the energy may be stored in the gas as an increase in internal energy $E_2 - E_1$ or the boundary of the gas may expand against an external resistance (pressure), in which case some or all of the energy may leave the gas in the form of work.

The value of the *sensible* internal energy of a gas above a datum temperature depends only upon the temperature of the gas. The relationship between the change in temperature of a gas and the corresponding change in sensible internal energy is given by

$$wC_v = \frac{dE_s}{dT} \tag{11}$$

where C_v is called the specific heat at constant volume. Note that C_v is *defined* by this expression. For "perfect" gases C_v is constant so that

$$E_{s_2} - E_{s_1} = wC_v(T_2 - T_1) \tag{11a}$$

In actual gases, C_v increases with temperature, so that an average value $\bar{C}_v$ must be assumed for the temperature range under consideration; or $E_{s_2} - E_{s_1}$ may be set equal to $w \int_{T_1}^{T_2} C_v \, dT$ if the relationship between C_v and the gas temperature is known.

If no chemical reaction takes place between condition 1 and condition 2, E_c is constant and, from (8), $E_{s_1} - E_{s_2} = E_2 - E_1$. In this case

$$E_2 - E_1 = wC_v(T_2 - T_1) \tag{11b}$$

Using Eq. (3), (11a) may be written as

$$E_{s_2} - E_{s_1} = NmC_v(T_2 - T_1) \tag{11c}$$

where mC_v is the *molal* specific heat at constant volume.

Equations (11) and (11a) are always true, *regardless of whether the process takes place at constant volume or not.*

The reason for the name "specific heat at constant volume" may be explained as follows. From (11a)

$$C_v = \frac{E_{s_2} - E_{s_1}}{w(T_2 - T_1)} \qquad \text{Btu/(lb)(°R)} \tag{11d}$$

Thus C_v is the number of Btu the sensible internal energy of each pound of gas increases, for each degree increase in temperature. Similarly, $mC_v = (E_{s_2} - E_{s_1})/N(T_2 - T_1)$ [Btu/(mole)(°R)] and is the number of Btu the sensible internal energy of each *mole* of gas increases, for each degree increase in temperature.

Returning to expression (10), the term $_1W_2$ is the work done by the gas during the process. Whenever a gas expands, the gas pressure acting upon the area of the moving gas boundary (the piston, for example) produces a force. As the gas boundary moves, the force acts through a distance and work is done.

$$\text{Work} = \text{force} \times \text{distance}$$
$$= \text{pressure} \times \text{area} \times \text{distance}$$

But,

$$\text{Area} \times \text{distance} = \text{change in volume of the gas}$$

Therefore, the work done by the gas $= p(V_2 - V_1)$. If the pressure is not constant during the process, the work will be equal to $\int p\, dV$, which is the area under the curve of pressure vs. volume.

The constant-volume process. If a gas occupies a closed vessel without movable walls, the volume of the gas is the volume of the container and cannot change; that is, $V_2 = V_1 =$ constant. From (4)

$$\frac{p_2}{T_2} = \frac{p_1}{T_1} \quad \text{or} \quad p_2 = p_1 \frac{T_2}{T_1} \tag{12}$$

This condition is approximated by an engine during the time the cylinder charge is burning, because the burning process takes place quite rapidly, and at this particular part of the cycle the piston is close to top center, where a large movement of the crankshaft is required to move the piston appreciably.

The gas can do no work at constant volume since

$$\text{work} = \text{pressure} \times \text{change in volume}$$

Applying Eq. (10) to this constant-volume process,

$$_1Q_2 = E_2 - E_1 + 0 \tag{13}$$

Thus *all* the heat added through the walls of a constant-volume container is stored in the gas as an increase in internal energy.

If no chemical reaction takes place in a gas which is being heated at constant volume, then from Eqs. (11b) and (13)

$$_1Q_2 = wC_v(T_2 - T_1) \tag{14}$$

or

$$C_v = \frac{_1Q_2}{w(T_2 - T_1)} \tag{14a}$$

that is, C_v is *also* the number of Btu of heat required to raise the temperature of each pound of gas 1°, when the gas is held at constant volume. This is why C_v is called the specific heat at constant volume.

The constant-pressure process. If a gas is free to expand against a constant pressure applied to its boundaries, then from the gas law (4)

$$\frac{V_2}{T_2} = \frac{V_1}{T_1} \quad \text{or} \quad V_2 = V_1 \frac{T_2}{T_1} \tag{15}$$

This condition is approximated by a gas enclosed in a soap bubble. If it is heated and expands, it does so against the constant pressure of the surrounding atmosphere.

If heat is added during a constant-pressure process, part of it goes to increase the internal energy of the gas (as indicated by the rise in temperature) and part of it immediately leaves the gas in the form of work as the gas expands.

Since the work done by the gas in a constant-pressure process is $p(V_2 - V_1)$, Eq. (10) may be written

$$_1Q_2 = (E_2 - E_1) + \frac{p(V_2 - V_1)}{J}$$

$$= \left(E_2 + \frac{p_2V_2}{J}\right) - \left(E_1 + \frac{p_1V_1}{J}\right) \tag{16}$$

The combination $E + pV/J$ occurs so often in thermodynamics that it has been given a name. It is called enthalpy and has the symbol H.

Therefore, in a constant-pressure process

$$_1Q_2 = H_2 - H_1 \tag{17}$$

Sensible enthalpy H_s is defined as $E_s + pV/J$. The relationship between a change in the temperature of a gas and the corresponding change in sensible enthalpy is given by

$$wC_p = \frac{dH_s}{dT} \tag{18}$$

where C_p is called the specific heat at constant pressure. Note that C_p is *defined* by this expression just as C_v is defined by (11).

For perfect gases C_p is constant, but for actual gases an average value $\bar{C}_p$ must be assumed for the temperature range under consideration. From (18)

$$H_{s_2} - H_{s_1} = wC_p(T_2 - T_1) \tag{18a}$$
$$H_{s_2} - H_{s_1} = NmC_p(T_2 - T_1) \tag{18b}$$

If no chemical reaction takes place during the process, E_c = constant, so that $E_{s_2} - E_{s_1} = E_2 - E_1$ and $H_{s_2} - H_{s_1} = H_2 - H_1$. In this case, from Eqs. (17) and (18a)

$$_1Q_2 = wC_p(T_2 - T_1) \tag{19}$$

so that C_p is the number of Btu of heat required to raise the temperature of each pound of gas 1° when the gas is permitted to expand at constant pressure during the process. For a given gas C_p is always larger than C_v because more heat must necessarily be added to raise the temperature of a gas, if at the same time the gas is doing work. The symbol for the ratio C_p/C_v is k.

Relationship between C_v and C_p. From Eq. (18a) and the definition of H_s

$$H_{s_2} - H_{s_1} = wC_p(T_2 - T_1) = (E_{s_2} - E_{s_1}) + (p_2V_2 - p_1V_1)\frac{1}{J}$$

and from (11a)

$$E_{s_2} - E_{s_1} = wC_v(T_2 - T_1)$$

$$\therefore wC_p(T_2 - T_1) = wC_v(T_2 - T_1) + (p_2V_2 - p_1V_1)\frac{1}{J}$$

From the gas law, $pV = wRT/m$.

$$\therefore wC_p(T_2 - T_1) = wC_v(T_2 - T_1) + \frac{wR}{mJ}(T_2 - T_1)$$

from which

$$C_p - C_v = \frac{R}{mJ} \tag{20}$$

and

$$mC_p - mC_v = \frac{R}{J} \tag{20a}$$

TABLE I. VALUES OF MOLECULAR WEIGHT AND SPECIFIC HEAT
FOR COMMON GASES AT ROOM TEMPERATURE

Gas	m, lb/mole	C_v, Btu/(lb)(°R)	k
O_2	32.00	0.155	1.40
N_2	28.02	0.176	1.40
CO_2	44.00	0.151	1.30
H_2O	18.02	0.333	1.33
H_2	2.02	2.41	1.41
CO	28.00	0.177	1.40
Air	28.96	0.170	1.40

The *difference* in the molal specific heats of *all* gases is constant since R and J are both constant, while the difference in the pound specific heats of any given gas is constant but varies with m for different gases. Table I above gives values of m and C_v for common gases.

The work done by the expanding gas during a constant-pressure process is $(p_2V_2 - p_1V_1)(1/J) = (wR/mJ)(T_2 - T_1)$. Therefore from (20)

$$_1W_2 = w(C_p - C_v)(T_2 - T_1) \tag{21}$$

Adiabatic expansion. Many processes occur so rapidly that there is not time available for heat to flow in or out of the substance during the process. Such a process is called adiabatic. If a gas is compressed or expanded adiabatically, applying the principle of the conservation of energy, we have from Eq. (10)

$$_1Q_2 = 0 = (E_2 - E_1) + \frac{_1W_2}{J}$$

or the work done *by* the gas in a nonflow adiabatic process

$$_1W_2 = J(E_1 - E_2) \tag{22}$$

i.e., the energy flowing out of the gas in the form of work came from the store of internal energy of the gas. The work was done at the expense of the internal energy. From Eqs. (11*a*) and (22), the work done by the gas when no chemical reaction is taking place

$$_1W_2 = wJC_v(T_1 - T_2) \tag{23}$$

From the gas law, $T = pVm/wR$.

$$\therefore \; _1W_2 = \frac{mJC_v}{R} (p_1V_1 - p_2V_2)$$

Since

$$R = mJ(C_p - C_v) \tag{20}$$

$$_1W_2 = \frac{C_v}{C_p - C_v} (p_1V_1 - p_2V_2)$$

$$= \frac{1}{k - 1} (p_1V_1 - p_2V_2) \tag{24}$$

where $k = C_p/C_v$. If $_1W_2$ is negative, work is being done *on* the gas. Note that expressions (23) and (24) are good only for nonflow adiabatic expansions or compressions.

During an adiabatic volume change, the pressure and temperature both change, so that although the gas law still applies as always and $pV/T =$ constant, another relationship is required before the final pressures or temperatures can be calculated. If the adiabatic process takes place with negligible internal friction in the gas itself, as is the case when the engine piston moves in the cylinder during the compression or expansion strokes, the relation is

$$pV^k = \text{const} \qquad \text{or} \qquad p_2V_2{}^k = p_1V_1{}^k \tag{25}$$

The proof of this relationship may be found in any text on thermodynamics.

Thus for a frictionless adiabatic process

$$\frac{p_2}{p_1} = \left(\frac{V_1}{V_2}\right)^k \tag{25a}$$

By the gas law (4), $T_2/T_1 = p_2V_2/p_1V_1$. Combining this with (25a),

$$T_2 = T_1 \left(\frac{V_1}{V_2}\right)^k \left(\frac{V_2}{V_1}\right) \qquad \text{or} \qquad T_2 = T_1 \left(\frac{V_1}{V_2}\right)^{k-1} \tag{26}$$

and similarly

$$T_2 = T_1 \left(\frac{p_2}{p_1}\right)^{(k-1)/k} \tag{27}$$

Example 6. Three pounds of air ($m = 29$, $C_v = 0.170$) was heated at constant volume until the temperature increased $100°$.

(a) How much heat was added to the air?

(b) How much work was done by the air?

Solution. (a) From (13) and (14)

$$_1Q_2 = E_2 - E_1 = wC_v(T_2 - T_1)$$
$$_1Q_2 = 3 \times 0.170 \times 100 = 5.10 \text{ Btu}$$

(b) No work was done, as the air could not expand.

Example 7. Three pounds of air ($m = 29$, $C_v = 0.170$) was heated at constant pressure until the temperature increased $100°$.

(a) How much heat was added to the air?

(b) How much work was done by the air?

Solution. (a) From (17) and (19)

$$_1Q_2 = H_2 - H_1 = wC_p(T_2 - T_1)$$

From (20)

$$C_p = \frac{R}{mJ} + C_v$$

$$= \frac{1544}{29 \times 778} + 0.170 = 0.238$$

$$_1Q_2 = 3 \times 0.238 \times 100 = 7.15 \text{ Btu}$$

(b) From (21)

Work done by air $= 3 \times 0.068 \times 100 = 2.05$ Btu

or, from (10)

Work done $= {_1Q_2} - (E_2 - E_1) = 7.15 - 5.10 = 2.05$ Btu

Example 8. Three pounds of air ($m = 29$, $C_v = 0.170$) was compressed adiabatically until the temperature increased $100°$.

(a) How much heat was added?

(b) How much work was done on the air?

Solution. (a) No heat was added, as the process was adiabatic.

(b) From (22) and (11a)

$$_1W_2 = wC_v(T_1 - T_2)$$
$$= 3 \times 0.170 \times -100 = -5.10 \text{ Btu.}$$

Note that $_1W_2$ is negative, meaning that work was done *on* the air.

Flow Process

Steady flow. Figure 20 is a diagram of any device through which a fluid flows at a uniform rate and which absorbs heat and does work, also at a uniform rate. In engines, the gas flow, heat flow, and work output vary throughout each cycle, but if a sufficiently long time interval (such as a minute) be chosen, then even an engine can be considered to be operating under steady-flow conditions.

Applying the principle of conservation of energy to such a system during the chosen time interval, the total energy in the mass of fluid which enters the machine across boundary 1-1 plus the heat added to the fluid through the walls of the machine, minus the work done by the

machine, must equal the total energy left in the equal mass of fluid crossing boundary 2-2 and leaving the machine. Expressed in mathematical
form,

$$E_2 + \frac{p_2 V_2}{J} + \frac{w Z_2}{J} + \frac{w u_2{}^2}{2gJ} = E_1 + \frac{p_1 V_1}{J} + \frac{w Z_1}{J} + \frac{w u_1{}^2}{2gJ} + Q - \frac{W}{J} \quad (28)$$

Equation (28) is known as the general energy equation and is one way of
stating the first law of thermodynamics. Note that the terms of Eq. (28)

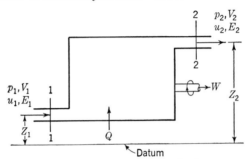

FIG. 20. Diagram illustrating a steady-flow process.

have the same meaning as the corresponding terms of Eq. (9). In fact,
the equation is the same except for one new term, pV/J.

Flow work. The term pV/J is called flow work and must be considered whenever flow takes place. Figure 21 is a detail of the entrance to
the device of Fig. 20.

During the interval of time chosen above, a volume V_1 was forced
across the boundary 1-1. The force resisting this motion was $p_1 \times A_1$,
where A_1 is the cross-sectional area
at 1-1. For steady flow, the force
causing the motion would also be
$p_1 A_1$. The distance the force moves,
L, is just sufficient to get volume
V_1 across the boundary; that is,
$LA_1 = V_1$. The flow work done on
volume V_1 by the atmosphere, or
external pump, is therefore $F \times L =$
$p_1 A_1 L = p_1 V_1$, and as volume V_1
enters the machine, it will carry

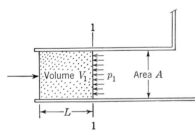

FIG. 21. Detail of entrance passage
illustrating flow work.

this additional energy with it. Similarly, as an equal mass with
volume V_2 leaves the machine during the same time, it carries away
with it the energy $p_2 V_2$, which is the work the fluid within the machine
had to do on the rejected mass to force it across boundary 2-2.

In applying the general energy equation it is often possible to leave out
one or more terms, as was done in Eq. (10) for cases of zero flow. The

general energy equation (28) and its abridged form, Eq. (9), are perhaps the most useful relationships in engineering thermodynamics.

With gases the gravity forces are small, so that the term wZ/J may usually be neglected. The flow velocity of gases in the internal-combustion engine is low enough so that in most cases the term $wu^2/2gJ$ may also be ignored. A few examples will be given to illustrate the application of the general energy equation. Applications of Eq. (9) are given in Examples 6 to 8

Example 9. An airplane supercharger (air compressor) uses 100 hp to compress 5,000 lb of air per hour. If the heat loss from the air is negligible and the inlet temperature is 520°R, calculate the outlet temperature of the air. (The definition of horsepower is given on page 36.)

Solution. Taking point 1 before and point 2 after the supercharger, from (28)

$$E_2 + \frac{p_2 V_2}{J} = E_1 + \frac{p_1 V_1}{J} - \frac{W}{J}$$

or

$$H_2 - H_1 = -\frac{W}{J}$$

where W = work done *by* the gas. Since no chemical reaction is taking place,

$$H_2 - H_1 = H_{s_2} - H_{s_1} = -\left[\frac{-100 \times 33,000 \times 60}{778}\right] = 254,000 \text{ Btu}$$

From (18a)

$$H_{s_2} - H_{s_1} = wC_p(T_2 - T_1) = 254,000 \qquad C_p \text{ for air } = 0.238$$
$$T_2 - T_1 = \frac{254,000}{5,000 \times 0.238} = 213° \text{ temperature rise}$$
$$T_2 = 520 + 213 = 733°\text{R}$$

Notice that no knowledge of the mechanism or of the compressor efficiency is required for the solution of this problem.

Example 10. A gas flows slowly through a pipe which contains a small orifice. The pressure and temperature before this orifice are 50 psia and 600°R, respectively. The pressure after the orifice is 20 psia. Calculate the temperature of the air after the orifice.

Solution. Taking point 1 before and point 2 after the orifice, and noting that no work or heat is entering or leaving through the pipe walls,

$$E_2 + p_2 V_2/J = E_1 + p_1 V_1/J \qquad \text{or} \qquad H_2 = H_1$$

Since $H_2 - H_1 = 0$, then

$$T_2 = T_1 = 600°\text{R}$$

Thus in a pure throttling process, the gas temperature after the throttle is the same as the initial gas temperature.

Example 11. The temperature of the atmosphere as recorded by a thermometer placed at the nose of a bombing airplane reads 6°F higher than a thermometer in a free balloon near by. Calculate the probable speed of the bomber.

Solution. Taking the bomber as a reference point, the air well ahead of the bomber can be considered to have a velocity relative to the bomber of u_1, while that at the nose of the bomber will have been brought to rest. From (28)

$$E_2 + \frac{p_2 V_2}{J} = E_1 + \frac{p_1 V_1}{J} + \frac{w u_1^2}{2gJ}$$

$$u_1^2 = \frac{2gJ}{w}(H_2 - H_1)$$

From (18a)

$$u_1^2 = 2gJC_p(T_2 - T_1)$$
$$u_1^2 = 2 \times 32.2 \times 778 \times 0.238 \times 6 = 71,500$$
$$u_1 = 267 \text{ fps}$$

Power and Efficiency

Work. Energy has already been defined as the capacity to do work, and *work* might be defined as the energy expended when motion takes place in opposition to a force (see page 25). Work thus represents energy being transferred from one place to another. Whenever 778 ft-lb of work is done on a system, the energy of the system will be found to have increased 1 Btu; or if 778 ft-lb of work is done by a system, the system will lose 1 Btu of energy.

Power is the *rate* of doing work. It is generally useless to do a certain piece of work unless it can be done within a reasonable length of time. For example, in an airplane, it may be required to move a distance of 200 miles against the resistance of the air, within 1 hr. When work is done at the rate of 550 ft-lb/sec or 33,000 ft-lb/min, the quantity of power being developed is known as one horsepower.

Efficiency. It is common practice in engineering to establish a figure of merit for a device by comparing the actual performance of the device with the performance it would have had under some arbitrary set of ideal conditions. The ratio of actual performance to ideal performance is called the *efficiency* of the device. Since the ideal performance is usually unattainable, the efficiency is usually less than 1.

In internal-combustion engines, one of the most important efficiencies is the *thermal efficiency*.

$$\text{Thermal efficiency } \eta = \frac{\text{work delivered by engine}}{\text{chemical energy received by engine in the fuel}}$$

In this case, the arbitrary ideal is to have the work done by the engine equal to the chemical energy received by the engine in the fuel. Thus

$$\eta = \frac{\text{work output}}{\text{fuel energy input}} = \frac{\text{work output}}{e_c \times w_f \text{ input}} \tag{29}$$

where e_c = chemical energy *per pound* of fuel (see discussion below)
w_f = pounds of fuel

Obviously the output and input may be measured over any convenient interval such as 1 cycle or 1 min. The output and input energies must be expressed in the same kind of units, since η is a number without units (see page 40).

The quantity e_c is commonly measured by permitting the fuel to react with excess oxygen in a strong container called a "bomb." The chemical energy of the fuel is calculated from the rise in temperature of the bomb and the surrounding cooling water. Since conditions in a bomb and in an engine are very different, it is certain that the amount of energy obtainable by the combustion of 1 lb of fuel in an engine will be somewhat different from this value. In spite of this fact, the use of e_c in the expression for energy input results in a satisfactory ideal for use in comparing the performance of one engine with another.[1]

With work output W in foot-pounds and e_c in Btu per pound of fuel

$$\eta = \frac{W}{J e_c w_f} \tag{30}$$

$$\therefore W = w_f J e_c \eta \tag{30a}$$

and since

$$\text{hp} = \frac{(W/\text{min})}{33,000},$$

$$\text{hp} = \frac{(w_f/\text{min}) J e_c \eta}{33,000} \tag{31}$$

Power. The power of an engine is seen from (31) to depend upon (1) the rate at which chemical energy is supplied to the engine (Btu/min input) and (2) the efficiency η with which the chemical energy supplied is converted into work output.

In order to change the chemical energy of a fuel into sensible internal energy in the engine cylinder, it is necessary to supply oxygen for its combustion. The oxygen required is obtained from the air supplied to the engine. For the proper combustion of a given fuel, the amount of air which must be present is fixed within narrow limits by the chemical nature of the fuel.

The ratio

$$F = \frac{w_f}{w_a} \tag{32}$$

is called the fuel-air ratio. The subscripts f and a refer to fuel and air, respectively. With ordinary vaporized liquid fuels, the space taken up

---

[1] The value of e_c used in engine calculations is the energy which would have been obtained from the bomb test if the water formed by the combustion had not condensed in the bomb. This is called the lower heating value of the fuel or the lower heat of combustion.

by the fuel in the cylinder is almost negligible, and most of the displacement volume is used on the intake stroke to bring air into the cylinder.

Air capacity. The amount of work which an engine cylinder can produce in each cycle depends from (31) on the amount of fuel taken into the cylinder on the intake stroke, but since the amount of fuel which may be *usefully* introduced depends upon the amount of oxygen present for its combustion, *the limiting factor to the work output per stroke is the air capacity of the cylinder.* For example, the amount of oxygen in 1 lb of air is sufficient for the complete combustion of about 0.067 lb of gasoline. This is known as the chemically correct fuel-air ratio F_{cc}. If e_c for gasoline is 19,000 Btu/lb, an engine cylinder which contains 0.002 lb of air could burn $0.002 \times 0.067 = 0.00134$ lb of gasoline with a chemical energy of $0.00134 \times 19,000 = 2.55$ Btu. If the cylinder could hold 0.004 lb of air, then twice the fuel could be burned and twice the energy, or 5.10 Btu, would be present.

Because of the importance of the air capacity of an engine, Eq. (30a) and (31) are often rewritten, using (32) and putting $w_a \times F$ in place of w_f, thus:

$$W = w_a J F e_c \eta \tag{33}$$

$$\text{hp} = \frac{(w_a/\text{min}) J F e_c \eta}{33,000} \tag{34}$$

Thus for a given value of fuel-air ratio and thermal efficiency the horsepower developed will be *proportional to the amount of air* the engine can take in per minute.

Specific fuel consumption. From Eq. (31)

$$\frac{1}{\eta} = \frac{(w_f/\text{min}) J e_c}{\text{hp} \times 33,000} = \frac{(w_f/\text{hr}) J e_c}{\text{hp} \times 33,000 \times 60} \tag{35}$$

$(w_f/\text{hr})/\text{hp}$ is the pounds of fuel used per hour for each horsepower developed, or the pounds of fuel required per horsepower-hour of work done. This quantity is called the specific fuel consumption (sfc). From (35) sfc $= (33,000 \times 60)/J e_c \eta$, or

$$\text{sfc} = \frac{2,545}{e_c \eta} \quad \text{lb fuel/hp-hr} \tag{36}$$

Since e_c, the heating value, is constant for a given fuel, the specific fuel consumption is inversely proportional to the thermal efficiency. Fuel costs and weights can be immediately calculated from the sfc so that it is often used in preference to thermal efficiency in practical engine work.

Indicated quantities. If the work output W in (29) or (30) is the work done by the cylinder gases on the piston, it is known as *indicated* work. The efficiency is called the *indicated thermal efficiency* η_i, and the horsepower obtained from (31) using η_i is called the *indicated* horsepower (ihp). If the work output at the engine shaft is used in (29) or (30), then the efficiency is called the *brake thermal efficiency* η_b, and the power from (31) using η_b is called the *brake* horsepower (bhp).

Example 12. One pound of gasoline contains 19,000 Btu of chemical energy. If 30 per cent of the energy can be converted into useful work,

(a) How high would the energy of 1 lb of gasoline raise a 1,000-lb weight?

(b) If the weight is raised in 2 min, how much power will have been developed?

Solution.

(a)
$$19{,}000 \text{ Btu} = 19{,}000 \times 778 = 14{,}780{,}000 \text{ ft-lb}$$
$$\text{Height} = \frac{14{,}780{,}000}{1{,}000} \times 0.30 = 4430 \text{ ft}$$

(b)
$$\text{Power} = \frac{14{,}780{,}000}{2} \times 0.30 = 2{,}217{,}000 \text{ ft-lb/min}$$

or

$$\frac{2{,}217{,}000}{33{,}000} = 67.2 \text{ hp}$$

Example 13. An engine has a thermal efficiency of 25 per cent and develops 160 hp. If the chemical energy of the fuel is 19,000 Btu/lb,

(a) How many pounds of fuel does it use per hour?

(b) How many pounds of fuel would be saved every 24 hr if the efficiency is raised to 28 per cent?

Solution. (a) From (36)

$$\text{sfc} = \frac{2{,}545}{19{,}000 \times 0.25} = 0.535 \text{ lb/hp-hr}$$
$$\text{Lb of fuel used/hr} = 0.535 \times 160 = 85.7 \text{ lb}$$

(b)
$$\text{Lb of fuel used/hr at 28\% efficiency} = 85.7 \times \frac{0.25}{0.28} = 76.5$$
$$\text{Lb saved in 24 hr } (85.7 - 76.5) \times 24 = 221 \text{ lb}$$

Example 14. How many pounds of air per hour does a 2,000-hp engine require if $e_c = 19{,}000$ Btu/lb, the thermal efficiency is 30 per cent, and the fuel-air ratio is 0.08 lb fuel/lb air?

Solution. From (34)

$$\text{Lb of air/hr} = \frac{2{,}000 \times 33{,}000 \times 60}{778 \times 0.08 \times 19{,}000 \times 0.30}$$
$$= 11{,}160 \text{ lb air/hr}$$

or from (36)

$$\text{sfc} = \frac{2{,}545}{19{,}000 \times 0.30} = 0.447 \text{ lb fuel/hp-hr}$$
$$0.447 \times 2{,}000 = 894 \text{ lb fuel/hr}$$
$$\frac{894}{0.08} = 11{,}160 \text{ lb air/hr}$$

Units and Conversion Factors

In engineering work it is often necessary to convert a quantity from one system of units to another. For example, a foreign report mentions a pressure of 100 kg/cm^2, and it is desired to convert this figure quickly to pounds per square inch. The factors required to do this are called conversion factors. The use and calculation of conversion factors are facilitated by a knowledge of units and dimensions.

A *quantity* is anything that can be measured. Certain physical quantities such as force F, length L, and time T are called *fundamental quantities* because it is difficult or impossible to express them in terms of other quantities.

An example of a physical quantity which is usually considered a *secondary*, or *derived*, *quantity* is velocity u, which can be expressed in terms of length and time as L/T. The expression of a physical quantity in terms of the fundamental quantities is called the *dimension* of a quantity. For example, the dimension of velocity is L/T. The dimension of acceleration would be L/T^2, and the dimension of pressure would be F/L^2. From Newton's law, $F = Ma$ so that $M = F/a$ The dimension of M in terms of F, L, and T is therefore $\dfrac{F}{L/T^2} = \dfrac{FT^2}{L}$. Mass itself is sometimes considered a fundamental quantity.

A *unit* is a *standard amount* of a physical quantity. For example, we have a board which has the physical quantity of length. If it is measured by comparing its length with the standard yard for a unit, it may be exactly twice as long (2 units long). If compared with the standard foot, it will be 6 times as long and it will be 72 times as long as the standard inch. Although the physical length of the board is the same in each case, the *numerical value* of the length varies inversely as the size of the unit used to measure it. Expressed mathematically, if Q is the actual magnitude (size) of any physical quantity to be measured and $[Q]$ is the size of the unit being used to measure the quantity, then the numerical value of the quantity (*i.e.*, the number of units N which is contains) is $Q/[Q]$. If the measuring is done using units of sizes $[Q]_1$ in the first case and $[Q]_2$ in the second case, then since the quantity Q being measured is constant,

$$N_1 = \frac{Q}{[Q]_1} \qquad N_2 = \frac{Q}{[Q]_2}$$

so that

$$N_1[Q]_1 = N_2[Q]_2 \tag{37}$$

As an example, suppose we have a certain constant force Q. We can find out how many pounds it is equal to by comparing *its* magnitude with the magnitude of a pound unit $[Q]_1$. The number N_1 we get will be the number of times the unit $[Q]_1$ (1 lb) can be contained in Q. $N_1 = Q/[Q]_1$. If N_1 is found to be 2,500, then the magnitude of Q is 2,500 lb. If $[Q]_2$ is the size of one dyne, the value of Q in dynes would be $N_2 = Q/[Q]_2$.

From Eq. (37)

$$N_2 = N_1 \frac{[Q]_1}{[Q]_2}$$

$[Q]_1$, the size of the pound force, is 4.45×10^5 times as great as $[Q]_2$, the size of the dyne force.

$$\therefore \frac{[Q]_1}{[Q]_2} = 4.45 \times 10^5$$

and

$$N_2 = 2,500 \times 4.45 \times 10^5 \text{ dynes}$$

If $[Q]_3$ is the size of one ton, the value of the force Q in tons would be $N_3 = N_1 \frac{[Q]_1}{[Q]_3}$.

$$N_3 = 2,500 \times \frac{1}{2,000} = 1.25 \text{ tons}$$

The ratio between the sizes of two different units of the same quantity such as $[Q]_1/[Q]_2$ is called a *conversion* factor. $\dfrac{12 \text{ in.}}{1 \text{ ft}}, \dfrac{1 \text{ min}}{60 \text{ sec}}$ are conversion factors. Conversion factors have no dimensions.

Conversion of quantities having the same dimensions from one system of units to another is often necessary. The easiest way to do this is to assign the units of $[Q]_1$ to N_1 and multiply N_1 by the appropriate conversion factors as we did in the example above. The units of N_1 and the conversion factors will then cancel to give the desired units of N_2. For example:

1. An airplane is traveling with a velocity of 500 ft/sec (N_1). How many miles per hour (N_2) is this? Notice that both ft/sec and miles/hr are velocities and therefore have the same *dimensions* length/time, or L/T, but the *units* are not the same.

$$N_2 = \frac{500 \text{ ft}}{1 \text{ sec}} \times \frac{1 \text{ mile}}{5,280 \text{ ft}} \times \frac{3,600 \text{ sec}}{1 \text{ hr}} = \frac{341 \text{ miles}}{1 \text{ hr}}$$

Note that the feet and seconds cancel out.

2. A freely falling body accelerates at a rate of 32.2 ft/sec² (N_1). How many miles per hour will its speed increase each minute (N_2)?

Here again the quantities ft/sec² and miles/hr-min have the same dimensions L/T^2 but different units.

$$N_2 = \frac{32.2 \text{ ft}}{\text{sec}^2} \times \frac{1 \text{ mile}}{5,280 \text{ ft}} \times \frac{60 \text{ sec}}{1 \text{ min}} \times \frac{3,600 \text{ sec}}{1 \text{ hr}} = \frac{1,318 \text{ miles/hr}}{\text{min}}$$

Notice that the conversion factors selected are such that all but the desired units for N_2 will cancel. Since the conversion factors are dimensionless, the dimensions of N_2 are the same as those of N_1.

Homogeneous equations. The addition of dissimilar physical quantities as, for example, 5 lb/in.^{2} + 3 miles/hr + 6 ft^3 serves no useful purpose. All fundamental engineering formulas are therefore homogeneous, *i.e.*, all terms of the equation have the same dimensions. Such formulas are true regardless of the size of the units used, but of course the same system of units must be used throughout, and the answer will be in these units.

In the general energy equation, $wu^2/2g$ represents energy. The dimensions of w are F, of u^2 are L^2/T^2, and of g are L/T^2.

The dimensions of this term are therefore

$$\frac{FL^2T^{-2}}{LT^{-2}} = FL, \text{ or force} \times \text{distance}$$

If the units used are pounds, feet, and seconds, the units of $wu^2/2g$ are

$$\frac{\text{lb-ft}^2/\text{sec}^2}{\text{ft/sec}^2} = \text{ft-lb}$$

If the units used are dynes, centimeters, and seconds, the units of $wu^2/2g$ would be

$$\frac{\text{dyne-cm}^2/\text{sec}^2}{\text{cm/sec}^2} = \text{dyne-cm}$$

which is energy also. The term pV has the dimensions $\dfrac{F}{L^2} \times L^3 = FL$, also, and if pound, foot, and second units are used, the units of pV are

$$\frac{\text{lb}}{\text{ft}^2} \times \text{ft}^3 = \text{ft-lb}$$

When the engineer substitutes numbers in a formula and calculates a numerical answer, the numbers used represent the number of units of each quantity present. The numerical answer which the engineer obtains is useless unless he is absolutely certain what kind of units to assign to this answer. There is usually no reason for doubt. All that is necessary is to:

1. Make sure that the expression is homogeneous—each term must have the same *dimensions*.

2. Use the same size units throughout, or convert them to the same size units by means of suitable conversion factors; for example, p (lb/in.^{2}) $\times \dfrac{144 \text{ in.}^2}{1 \text{ ft}^2}$ is the same as p (lb/ft^2).

All unfamiliar calculations should be checked for dimensions and units. Many foolish errors will thus be avoided. For example:

1. One formula for the weight of fuel flowing per second through a carburetor orifice is $w_f = AC \sqrt{2g\gamma \, \Delta p}$, where A is the area of the passage and C is a number without dimensions or units. Check for dimensional homogeneity.

$$\frac{F}{T} = L^2 \sqrt{\frac{L}{T^2} \frac{F}{L^3} \frac{F}{L^2}} = L^2 \sqrt{\frac{F^2}{T^2 L^4}} = \frac{F}{T}$$

Therefore the equation is homogeneous.

Since g is usually expressed in feet per second per second, we shall use the foot-pound-second system of units. Putting in the units of the right-hand side of the equation,

$$\text{ft}^2 \sqrt{\frac{\text{ft}}{\text{sec}^2} \times \frac{\text{lb}}{\text{ft}^3} \times \frac{\text{lb}}{\text{ft}^2}} = \frac{\text{lb}}{\text{sec}}$$

If the equation is known to be homogeneous, the dimensional check should still be made. Notice that Δp must be expressed in pounds per square foot, A in square feet, etc., in order to cancel the feet.

If the value of g in inches per second per second

$$(= 32.2 \text{ ft/sec}^2 \times 12 \text{ in./1 ft} = 386 \text{ in./sec}^2)$$

and inches are used throughout, the same numerical answer would be obtained.

2. The formula for centrifugal force is

$$\text{Force} = Mr\omega^2$$

where M = mass

r = radius

ω = radians per second

(a) What are the units of slugs in terms of force, length, and time?
From formula (1) (page 19)

$$w = Mg \qquad M = \frac{w}{g} = \frac{\text{lb}}{\text{ft/sec}^2} = \frac{\text{lb-sec}^2}{\text{ft}}$$

(b) What are the units of ω?

$$\omega = \frac{\text{rad}}{\text{sec}} = \frac{1}{\text{sec}}$$

(Radians have no dimensions since a radian is an angle, and an angle is measured by a ratio of two lengths L/L.)

(c) Check the centrifugal-force formula for homogeneity.

$$F = \frac{FT^2}{L} \times L \times \frac{1}{T^2} = F$$

(d) In what units should r be expressed?

r should be expressed in feet if g is in foot units (32.2 ft/sec²), *i.e.*,

$$\text{lb} = \frac{\text{lb-sec}^2}{\text{ft}} \times \text{ft} \frac{1}{\text{sec}^2}$$

SUGGESTIONS FOR FURTHER READING

"Aircraft Powerplant Handbook," U.S. Department of Commerce, Washington, D.C., 1949.

Heldt, P. M.: "High Speed Combustion Engines," P. M. Heldt, Nyack, N.Y., 1946.

CHAPTER 3

THE AIR-CYCLE APPROXIMATION

Importance of thermal efficiency. It is commonly supposed that thermal efficiency has to do only with the quantity of fuel an engine uses per unit of work output. Although this is certainly a most important aspect of efficiency, the subject is much more complex and far-reaching than this.

We have seen on page 38 that, with a constant fuel-air ratio, the power output of an engine is proportional to the product of air capacity and thermal efficiency [Eq. (34)]. If the engine is operating under conditions of maximum air capacity (wide-open throttle and suitable engine speed), a poor thermal efficiency would mean a correspondingly low engine power. If the power output is less than the operator requires and a higher thermal efficiency cannot be obtained, then a larger engine with higher air capacity will be necessary. This large engine, if of similar design, will have a higher first cost, will be heavier, and will take up more space than a smaller engine of high thermal efficiency, which would develop the same maximum power with less air capacity. In addition to the above, the larger engine with larger air capacity draws in more fuel as well, making the fuel costs high, the weight of fuel to be consumed greater, or the range of the vehicle less. Equation (35) shows this effect directly.

$$\text{Thermal efficiency } \eta = \frac{\text{work output}}{\text{chemical energy input}}$$

The difference between the energy input and work output, which we shall call rejected energy, represents for the most part sensible energy leaving the engine through the cylinder walls or in the exhaust gases. The heat entering the cylinder walls must be carried away by the cooling system, or the cylinder and cylinder wall will become too hot for proper strength and lubrication. The hotter the exhaust gases, the more likely is the exhaust valve to overheat and fail. It is therefore extremely important to keep the rejected energy low.

$$\text{Rejected energy} = \text{energy input} - \text{energy output}$$
$$= \frac{\text{energy output}}{\eta} - \text{energy output}$$
$$= \text{energy output} \times \left(\frac{1}{\eta} - 1\right) \tag{38}$$

45

For a given output it is clear that the rejected energy will increase rapidly as the efficiency is lowered, putting a strain on the cooling system and engine structure. An engine of low efficiency is therefore very likely to be an unreliable engine as well. For example, consider two engines, each of which delivers 100 Btu of useful work to its output shaft. One has an efficiency of 30 per cent; the other has an efficiency of 25 per cent.

	Engine 1	Engine 2
Efficiency......................................	0.30	0.25
Output, Btu/min............................	100	100
Input (fuel energy), Btu/min................	333	400
Waste or rejected energy, Btu/min...........	333 − 100 = 233	400 − 100 = 300

Theoretical cycles. Because thermal efficiency has such important effects, it is necessary to know how it is affected by engine design, adjustment, and operating conditions. To do this, we must know what happens within the engine cylinder during one cycle of operation.

Exact conditions existing within the actual engine cylinder are very difficult to determine, but by making certain simplifying assumptions it is possible to approximate these conditions more or less closely. The approximate engine cycles thus calculated are called *theoretical cycles*.

The simplest theoretical cycle is called the *air-cycle approximation*. The air-cycle approximation used for calculating conditions in a spark-ignition engine is called the *constant-volume air cycle*. A typical diagram of cylinder pressure vs. cylinder volume above the piston, as calculated by the air-cycle approximation, is shown in Fig. 22.

Air-cycle approximation. In the constant-volume air-cycle approximation the following simplifying assumptions are made:

1. The gas in the engine cylinder is a perfect gas; *i.e.*, it obeys the gas law and has a constant specific heat.

2. The physical constants of the gas in the cylinder are the same as those of air at moderate temperature; *i.e.*, the molecular weight of the cylinder gas is 29, and the specific heat at constant volume is 0.170 Btu/(lb)(°F).

3. The compression process 1-2 and expansion process 3-4 (Fig. 22) are adiabatic—no heat is gained or lost—and they take place without internal friction in the gases.

4. A quantity of heat equivalent to the sensible energy produced by a combustion process is assumed to flow into the gas *while the piston remains at top center*. (Constant-volume combustion, 2-3.)

5. At the end of expansion and *while the piston remains at bottom center*, sufficient heat is rejected by the gases to bring the temperature and pres-

sure in the cylinder back to those existing in the cylinder at the start of compression. (Process 4-1.)

6. The cycle may be considered closed, with the same "air" always remaining in the cylinder to repeat the cycle, or the gases in the cylinder at 1 may be removed by an exhaust stroke to point 0 and an equal quantity of fresh air at the same temperature and pressure may be assumed drawn in on the intake stroke back to point 1. Since the inlet and exhaust processes are considered frictionless, the work done by the piston in expelling the exhaust gases is exactly equal to the work done

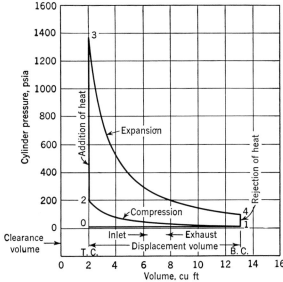

Fig. 22. Typical constant-volume air-cycle pressure-volume diagram. 1 lb of air, $p_1 = 14.7$ psia, $T_1 = 520°R$, $r = 6.5$, $\Delta T = 1,280 \left(\dfrac{r-1}{r}\right) \times 0.170$

on the piston by the atmosphere during the inlet stroke, so that the net work is still represented by the area 1-2-3-4 (see page 53).

Because of the many simplifying assumptions, it is evident that the air-cycle approximation does not closely represent the conditions within the actual cylinder. Although the quantities calculated from this approximation are considerably in error, the trends shown are usually correct, so that the general effect on the efficiency of such variables as inlet pressure or compression ratio may be calculated. Because of the simplicity of the air-cycle calculation it is often used to obtain rough answers to complex engine problems.

Air-cycle calculation. Air-cycle calculations of pressure, temperature, and efficiency may be made using the actual quantity of air which would fill a given cylinder or by assuming the cylinder large enough to hold 1 lb of air.   The resulting values will be the same in either case, because the pressures and temperatures depend only upon the initial conditions at point 1, the volume *ratios*, and the quantity of heat added at point 2 *per pound of air.*

As an example of an air-cycle calculation, assume an engine cylinder containing air at $p_1 = 14.7$ psia, $T_1 = 540°$R.   Let the compression ratio $r = 6$.

The volume of each pound of air contained in the cylinder v_1 (specific volume) will be, from the gas law,

$$v_1 = \frac{V_1}{w} = \frac{RT_1}{mp_1} = \frac{1{,}545 \times 540}{29 \times 14.7 \times 144} = 13.6 \text{ ft}^3/\text{lb}$$

$$v_2 = \frac{v_1}{r} = \frac{13.6}{6} = 2.26 \text{ ft}^3/\text{lb}$$

Since the process from 1 to 2 is a frictionless adiabatic compression,

$$p_2 V_2{}^k = p_1 V_1{}^k \tag{25}$$

and since $v_1/v_2 = V_1/V_2 = r$,

$$p_2 = p_1 \left(\frac{v_1}{v_2}\right)^k = p_1(r)^k$$

As $k = 1.4$ for air,
$p_2 = 14.7 \times 6^{1.4} = 181$ psia

$$T_2 = T_1 \left(\frac{v_1}{v_2}\right)^{k-1} = T_1 \left(\frac{V_1}{V_2}\right)^{k-1} \tag{26}$$

$T_2 = 540 \times 6^{0.4} = 1100°$R

From (14)

$$T_3 - T_2 = \frac{Q}{wC_v}$$

where Q/w is the heat added per pound of air in the cylinder.

If gasoline is used for a fuel, 0.067 lb of gasoline is required to use up the oxygen present in 1 lb of air.   If the heating value of gasoline is taken as 19,000 Btu/lb, then the heating associated with 1 lb of fresh air is $0.067 \times 19{,}000 = 1280$ Btu/lb air.

If all the air in the cylinder is considered to be "fresh" air,

$$T_3 = 1{,}100 + (1{,}280/0.170) = 8630°\text{R}$$

An actual engine draws in only a displacement volume of fresh charge during each inlet stroke, mixing this with the residual gas which was left occupying the clearance space at the end of the preceding exhaust stroke. Because of this it is more common in air-cycle calculations to assume that only that part of the air occupying the displacement volume is "active." In our case this would be five-sixths of the total weight of air in the cylinder since $V_d/V_{total} = (r - 1)/r$. If this method is used, we will have for each pound of cylinder contents only $\frac{5}{6} \times 1280 = 1068$ Btu. Thus

$$T_3 = 1,100 + \frac{1,068}{1 \times 0.170} = 7380°R$$

Using this value of T_3 in Eq. (4) and remembering that $V_2 = V_3$,

$$p_3 = p_2 \left(\frac{T_3}{T_2}\right) = 181 \times \frac{7,380}{1,100} = 1,208 \text{ psia}$$

Using the adiabatic relationships from point 3 to point 4,

$$p_4 = p_3 \left(\frac{V_3}{V_4}\right)^k = 1,208 \left(\frac{1}{6}\right)^{1.4} = 98 \text{ psia}$$

$$T_4 = T_3 \left(\frac{V_3}{V_4}\right)^{k-1} = 7,380 \left(\frac{1}{6}\right)^{0.4} = 3620°R$$

The efficiency of any cycle is $\eta = $ output/input, where input and output are expressed in the same kind of units. The input to our cycle is 1068 Btu/lb of cylinder contents. The work output of the cycle must be equal to the heat per pound added to the cycle between (2) and (3) minus the heat per pound rejected from the cycle between (4) and (1).

$$\text{Work output} = 1,068 - C_v(T_4 - T_1)$$
$$= 1,068 - 0.170(3,620 - 540) = 544 \text{ Btu/lb}$$
$$\eta = \frac{544}{1,068} = 0.51$$

Air-cycle efficiency. It may be shown that the efficiency as calculated from the air-cycle approximation is *independent* of the amount of heat input to the cycle but depends only upon the compression ratio r and the value of k.

$$\text{Heat input from 2 to 3} = wC_v(T_3 - T_2)$$
$$\text{Heat rejected from 4 to 1} = wC_v(T_4 - T_1)$$

so that

$$\text{Work of the cycle} = wC_v[(T_3 - T_2) - (T_4 - T_1)] \tag{39}$$

and

$$\eta = \frac{\text{output}}{\text{input}} = \frac{wC_v[(T_3 - T_2) - (T_4 - T_1)]}{wC_v(T_3 - T_2)}$$
$$= 1 - \frac{T_4 - T_1}{T_3 - T_2} \tag{40}$$

Multiplying the numerator of the second term by T_1/T_1 and the denominator by T_2/T_2, we have

$$\eta = 1 - \frac{T_1\left(\dfrac{T_4}{T_1} - 1\right)}{T_2\left(\dfrac{T_3}{T_2} - 1\right)} \tag{40a}$$

Since processes 1-2 and 3-4 are assumed to be frictionless adiabatics,

$$\frac{T_1}{T_2} = \left(\frac{V_2}{V_1}\right)^{k-1} = \left(\frac{1}{r}\right)^{k-1}$$

and

$$\frac{T_4}{T_3} = \left(\frac{V_3}{V_4}\right)^{k-1} = \left(\frac{1}{r}\right)^{k-1}$$

$$\therefore \frac{T_1}{T_2} = \frac{T_4}{T_3}$$

and transposing,

$$\frac{T_4}{T_1} = \frac{T_3}{T_2} \tag{41}$$

Substituting (41) in (40a), the parentheses cancel, and

$$\eta = 1 - \frac{T_1}{T_2} = 1 - \left(\frac{1}{r}\right)^{k-1} \tag{42}$$

For comparison, this relationship is plotted in Fig. 23 with a similar curve of η vs. r from an actual engine operating at constant fuel-air ratio and rpm. It is seen that the general shape of the two curves is quite similar; in fact the ratio $\dfrac{\eta_{\text{actual}}}{\eta_{\text{air cycle}}}$ is nearly constant. The actual efficiencies are, however, much lower than the air-cycle efficiencies owing to various losses which will be discussed in later chapters.

Effect of engine variables. If a series of air cycles is calculated for various compression ratios, it will be observed that p_3, the maximum pressure of the cycle, increases rapidly as the compression ratio is increased (see Fig. 24). Since engine parts must be built strong enough to withstand this pressure, the disadvantages of increased weight (and other difficulties) soon overcome the advantages of improved thermal efficiency, so that spark-ignition engines are seldom built with compression ratios of more than 8.

The temperature T_4, which corresponds to that of the cylinder gases about to be exhausted, will be found to *decrease* as the compression ratio is raised, in spite of the fact that there is a slight increase in T_3. This reduction in T_4 is due to the greater expansion of the cylinder gases during the power stroke and is a sign of the increased efficiency of the cycle. With more of the input energy going into useful work, less will be left in the exhaust gases. A lower T_4 has the practical advantage of reducing the tendency of the exhaust valve to burn. The above trends are to be found in all actual engines, although the magnitudes will be considerably lower.

The effect of changing the inlet pressure p_1 or the inlet temperature T_1 may be observed by reworking the example of page 48 with different

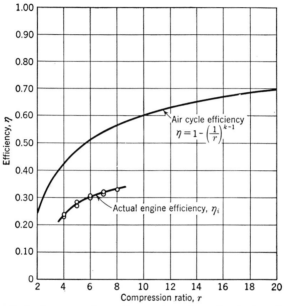

Fig. 23. The effect of compression ratio on air-cycle and actual engine efficiencies.

values of these quantities. It will be found that if p_1 is increased, the other pressures around the cycle will increase but the temperatures and efficiency will be unaffected. Changes in T_1 will affect mainly the cyclic temperatures. A change in the amount of heat Q added at top center will affect both temperature and pressure at points 3 and 4 but will not change the efficiency.

In an actual engine a change in p_1 would have a small effect on the cyclic temperatures, and a variation in T_1 would affect the cyclic pressures. The principal effects, however, are as predicted by the air-cycle calculations. The efficiency of an actual engine, unlike the air-cycle efficiency, is somewhat affected by changes in cyclic pressures and temperatures and is greatly affected by the fuel-air ratio. These effects are considered in more detail in Chap. 4.

Power output. In order to estimate the power output of an engine operating on the air cycle, the energy input per cycle must be multiplied by the number of cycles per minute and by the air-cycle efficiency corresponding to the compression ratio being used [see Eq. (42)].

For example, an engine cylinder of 173 in.³ (0.1 ft³) displacement volume with a compression ratio of 6 operating on the air cycle with $p_1 = 14.7$ psia and $T_1 = 540°R$ would have the same pressures, tempera-

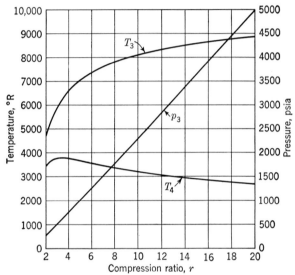

FIG. 24. The effect of compression ratio on the pressures and temperatures of the air cycle. $p_1 = 14.7$ psia, $T_1 = 520°R$.

tures, and efficiency as the cycle shown on pages 48 and 49 and the total cylinder volume would be

$$V_d \frac{r}{r-1} = 0.1 \times \frac{6}{5} = 0.12 \text{ ft}^3$$

Wt of air/cycle $= 1 \times \dfrac{0.12}{13.6} = 0.00883$ lb/cycle

Heat input $= 1{,}068 \times 0.00883 = 9.43$ Btu/cycle

$$T_3 = 1{,}100 + \frac{9.43}{0.00883 \times 0.170} = 7380°R \text{ (same as before)}$$

Work output $= 9.43 \times 0.51 = 4.81$ Btu/cycle

If this cylinder operates at 2,000 rpm (1,000 cycles/min) the horsepower output is

$$\frac{4.81 \times 778 \times 1{,}000}{33{,}000} = 113.5 \text{ hp}$$

Note that since the pressures and temperatures at the various points in the cycle are the same whether the cylinder is assumed to contain 1.0 lb or 0.00883 lb, by the gas law the specific volume will be the same at corresponding points in the cycle in both cylinders. Thus the p-V diagram for the large cylinder would be very large, but the p-v diagram for both cylinders would be identical. The area of the p-v diagram would represent the work done per cycle per pound of air in the cylinder.

Mean effective pressure. Horsepower output alone is not a satisfactory criterion of engine performance since any design of engine, no matter how inefficient, can be made to deliver a given horsepower merely by increasing its size and the number of its cylinders. A better indication of engine performance may be obtained from the *mean effective pressure (mep)*, which is *the amount of work done per cycle in each cylinder, divided by the displacement volume of the cylinder.*

$$\text{mep} = \frac{W/\text{cycle}}{V_d} \qquad (43)$$

This quantity is usually expressed in inch-pounds per cubic inch (in.-lb/in.^{3}), which is dimensionally the same as pounds per square inch, and is an indication of how hard each cubic inch of cylinder displacement is working. The magnitude of the mep depends upon how completely each cubic inch of displacement volume is filled with combustible mixture and how efficiently its chemical energy is converted into work. The meps of engines of similar design, operating under similar conditions, will be nearly the same regardless of the relative sizes of the engines.

Work output of engine in in.-lb/min $= \text{hp} \times 33,000 \times 12$

Work output/cycle in in.-lb $= \dfrac{\text{hp} \times 33,000 \times 12}{n}$

where $n =$ the number of cycles per minute. For a four-stroke-cycle engine $n =$ no. cylinders $\times$ (rpm/2). From (43), therefore,

$$\text{mep} = \frac{\text{hp} \times 33,000 \times 12}{n V_d} \qquad (44)$$

where $V_d =$ the displacement volume of *one* cylinder (displacement/cycle) in cubic inches.

The area enclosed between points 1-2-3-4 of the p-V diagram (Fig. 22) also represents the work done per cycle since the area is the product of pressure $\times$ volume (lb/in.^{2} $\times$ in.^{3} = in.-lb). If this area is divided by the length of the diagram (which represents $V_1 - V_2$, the displacement volume), the result will also be $\dfrac{\text{work/cycle}}{V_d}$, the mep in inch-pounds per cubic inch or pounds per square inch.

If an engine operated on the cycle shown in Fig. 25, *i.e.*, if it had a *constant* pressure during the power stroke and no pressure at all in the cylinder during the rest of the cycle, the p-V diagram would be rectangular and the mep, which is still the area of the diagram divided by V_d, would then be equal to the ordinate of the diagram.   This leads to another useful definition of mep: *the constant pressure which would have to act upon the piston for one stroke, to equal the actual work output of one complete cycle.*

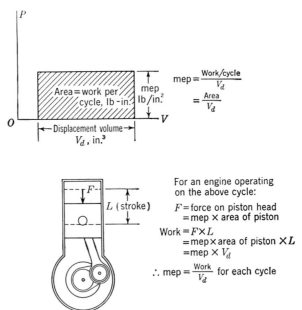

$$\text{mep} = \frac{\text{Work/cycle}}{V_d}$$
$$= \frac{\text{Area}}{V_d}$$

For an engine operating on the above cycle:

F = force on piston head
  = mep × area of piston

Work = $F \times L$
  = mep × area of piston × L
  = mep × V_d

∴ mep = $\dfrac{\text{Work}}{V_d}$ for each cycle

Fig. 25. Explanation of mep.

The equivalence of the two definitions of mep may be shown as follows:
The actual work of one cycle is equal to the work of one power stroke at a pressure equal to the mep.   That is,

$$\text{Work/cycle} = \text{mep} \times \text{piston area (in.}^2) \times \text{stroke (in.)}$$

Since n = cycles per minute,

$$\text{Work/min} = \text{mep} \times \text{piston area} \times \text{stroke} \times n$$

and since piston area × stroke = V_d,

$$\text{hp} = \frac{\text{mep} \times V_d \times n}{33,000 \times 12} \tag{44a}$$

which is the same as Eq. (44).   From (44) it is seen that the mep is indicative of the power developed per cubic inch of cylinder displacement at a given engine speed.

For the air-cycle example of page 49,

$$\text{Work/cycle} = 1{,}068 \times 0.51 \times 778 \times 12 \text{ in.-lb}$$
$$\text{Displacement volume} = (13.6 \times \tfrac{5}{6}) \times 1{,}728 \text{ in.}^3$$

From (43)

$$\text{mep} = \frac{1{,}068 \times 0.51 \times 778 \times 12}{(13.6 \times \tfrac{5}{6}) \times 1{,}728} = 260 \text{ psi}$$

or for the *actual* cylinder of the example on page 52,

$$\text{mep} = \frac{4.81 \times 778 \times 12}{0.10 \times 1{,}728} = 260 \text{ psi}$$

Note the conversion factors required to change Btu per cubic foot to inch-pounds per cubic inch, and note that the mep is the same for both cylinders.

PROBLEMS

1. Two engines each have an output of 100 hp. Engine A has an efficiency of 0.25, and engine B has an efficiency of 0.30. Calculate:

(a) The fuel consumption of each engine in pounds per hour.

(b) The ratio of the fuel consumed in B to that consumed in A.

(c) The ratio of the fuel wasted in B to that wasted in A.

(d) If the weight of each engine is proportional to (input hp)$^{3/2}$, find the ratio of the weight of B to the weight of A.

2. It is desired to increase the efficiency of an engine operating on the constant-volume air cycle by either (1) raising the compression ratio from 6 to 8 or (2) increasing the inlet pressure from 14.7 to 20 psia. Which procedure will give:

(a) The highest pressure of the cycle?

(b) The highest efficiency?

(c) The highest mep?

3. The *Lenoir cycle* consists in the following processes:

1-2 Intake stroke at constant pressure starting from zero volume.

2-3 Explosion at constant volume.

3-4 Reversible adiabatic expansion to the initial pressure.

Write an expression for the efficiency of the Lenoir air cycle in terms of C_p/C_v, T_2, T_3, and T_4.

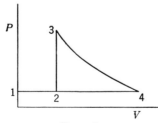

PROB. 3.

4. Calculate an air cycle with:

$p_1 = 14.7$ psia

$T_1 = 520°R$

$r = 6$

Heat added $= 1200$ Btu/lb of active air

5. Recalculate Prob. 4 with p_1 raised to 29.4 psia. Note the effect on p_{max}, T_{max}, efficiency, and mep.

6. Recalculate Prob. 4 with $T_1 = 720°R$. Note the effect on p_{max}, T_{max}, efficiency, and mep.

7. Recalculate Prob. 4 with $r = 8$. Note the effect on p_{max}, T_{max}, T_4, efficiency, and mep. What is the significance of T_4?

8. A special engine is built which has a 3-in. stroke for intake and compression, and a 6-in. stroke for expansion and exhaust. The clearance volume is 20 in.^{3}, and the total volume above the piston at the end of the intake stroke is 100 in.^{3} Combustion is at constant volume. Assuming standard sea-level conditions:

(*a*) Draw the theoretical cycle on the p-V plane.

(*b*) Calculate the air-cycle efficiency of this cycle assuming 1000 Btu/lb active air in the cylinder at the start of compression.

9. What is the ratio (*a* to *b*) of the efficiencies and meps of air cycles *a* and *b* under the following conditions:

Cycle a	Cycle b
$r = 6$	$r = 6$
$p_1 = 12$ psia	$p_1 = 14.7$ psia
$T_1 = 100°F$	$T_1 = 60°F$
Cylinder contains 0.030 lb air	Cylinder contains 0.020 lb air
38.4 Btu added at constant volume/cycle	19.4 Btu added at constant volume/cycle

CHAPTER 4

THE FUEL-AIR-CYCLE APPROXIMATION

In the air-cycle approximation it was assumed for simplicity that the cylinder contained nothing but air and that this air was a perfect gas and had a constant specific heat. Heat was added at constant volume between 2 and 3 and rejected at constant volume between 4 and 1. Compression and expansion were assumed to be frictionless adiabatic processes.

If the actual physical properties of the cylinder gases before and after burning are taken into account, a surprisingly close approximation to the actual pressures and temperatures existing within the engine cylinder may be obtained. The meps and efficiencies calculated by this approximation are, in the case of well-designed engines, only a few per cent above the actual values obtained by tests. This theoretical cycle based on the actual properties of the cylinder gases is called the *fuel-air-cycle approximation* and represents a nearly attainable ideal for comparison with actual performance.

Use of the fuel-air cycle. While the air cycle shows the general effect of compression ratio on engine efficiency, fuel-air cycles may be calculated for various fuel-air ratios, inlet pressures, and temperatures as well. When this is done, it is found that engine efficiency, based on the work done on the piston, is not affected to any extent by inlet conditions but is principally affected by compression ratio and fuel-air ratio. Figure 29 shows how the fuel-air-cycle efficiency varies with these two quantities. This information is useful to the designer because a well-tuned engine working in the normal range of fuel-air ratios will have an efficiency (based on piston work) about 85 per cent as high as that calculated in Fig. 29. Multiplying this corrected efficiency by the fuel energy input per unit of time will give a very close approximation of the power to be expected from the actual engine.

Engineers must also design the cylinder structure to withstand the probable peak pressure (p_3), and the exhaust valves to withstand the temperature at the start of the exhaust process (T_4). Effect of compression ratio and fuel-air ratio on these quantities is shown in Figs. 31 and 32.

In general, the effect of many of the common engine operating variables on the pressures and temperatures within the engine cylinder may be better understood by an examination of the fuel-air-cycle approximation.

Material on the actual calculation of fuel-air cycles will be found on pages 62 to 65. Although a study of this material is not necessary for an appreciation of the fuel-air cycle, it makes it possible for the student to calculate the effect of inlet pressure, inlet temperature, and compression ratio on the efficiency, mep, and pressures and temperatures around the cycle.

Scope of the fuel-air cycle. The fuel-air-cycle calculations take into consideration:

1. The actual composition of the cylinder gases.

2. The variation in the specific heat of these gases with temperature.

3. The fact that fuel and air do not completely combine chemically at high temperatures.

4. The variation in the number of molecules present in the cylinder as the pressure and temperature change.

Assumptions. In the constant-volume fuel-air cycle the following assumptions are made for the sake of simplicity:

1. The fuel is completely vaporized and perfectly mixed with the air.

2. Burning takes place instantaneously at top center (constant volume).

3. There is no heat exchange between the gases and the cylinder walls.

4. Compression and expansion are frictionless as well as adiabatic.

Composition of the cylinder gases. The ratio of fuel to air is often changed during engine operation. This not only affects the composition of the gases before combustion but also changes the relative amounts of carbon dioxide, water vapor, carbon monoxide, etc., in the combustion products. To avoid laborious calculation, fuel-air cycles are computed with the aid of thermodynamic charts embodying the characteristics of the cylinder gases. A separate thermodynamic chart for the unburned mixture must be constructed for each fuel-air ratio of interest. A corresponding thermodynamic chart must also be constructed for the products of combustion of each fuel-air mixture. Such charts are shown in Figs. 26 and 27[1] for a fuel-air ratio of 0.0782. About five such sets of charts would be sufficient to cover the useful range of fuel-air ratios.

Variation of specific heat. Gases having more than one atom to the molecule all show an increase in specific heat at high temperatures, as shown in Fig. 28. The specific heat is the amount of heat required to raise the temperature of a unit mass one degree. It is thought that as the temperature is raised, larger and larger fractions of the heat input go to produce motion of the atoms *within* the molecules. Since temperature is the result of motion of the molecule *as a whole*, the energy which goes into moving the atoms does not contribute to the temperature rise, so

[1] Figure 27 will be found in the pocket at the back of the book.

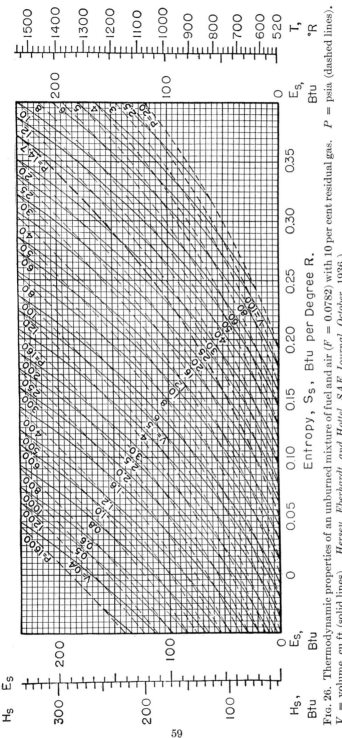

Fig. 26. Thermodynamic properties of an unburned mixture of fuel and air ($F = 0.0782$) with 10 per cent residual gas. P = psia (dashed lines). V = volume, cu ft (solid lines). *Hersey, Eberhardt, and Hottel, SAE Journal, October,* 1936.)

that smaller final temperatures and pressures are obtained. Since at high temperature a given addition of heat results in a smaller increase in temperature, the specific heat is said to increase with temperature.

Chemical equilibrium. If a mixture of a hydrocarbon fuel and excess air is ignited and the conditions are such that the resulting temperature does not exceed about 3000°R, the reaction will go essentially to completion with the fuel completely used up. The products of combustion will

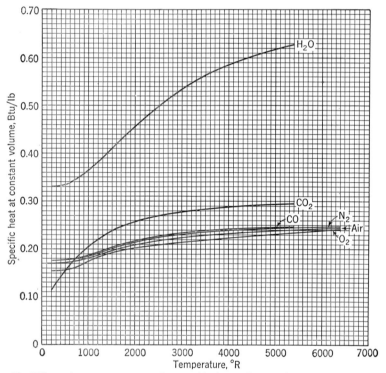

FIG. 28. Effect of temperature on the specific heat of several common gases at constant volume. (*Data from "Gas Tables" by J. H. Keenan and J. Kaye, Wiley.*)

be carbon dioxide (CO_2) and water vapor (H_2O), neither of which has heating value or chemical energy in the usual sense. However, if the burning process results in high enough temperatures, the combination of fuel and air will be incomplete and, even though excess air is present, the combustion space will contain uncombined fuel in the form of chemical substances having heating value, such as carbon monoxide (CO), molecular hydrogen (H_2), and atomic hydrogen (H). In other words, an equilibrium is established between uncombined fuel, air, and combustion products. The incomplete combustion of fuel and air at high temperatures results in lower values of T_3 and p_3 than would otherwise be expected.

The effect of chemical equilibrium is generally small compared with the effect of variable specific heat but acts in the same direction, preventing the chemical energy present from being converted into sensible energy until later in the expansion stroke when the temperature is lower.

Combustion and burning. To help our thinking with regard to chemical equilibrium in fuel-air cycles and in actual engine cycles, *combustion* will be defined as the chemical reaction between a fuel and oxygen. Combustion, therefore, proceeds until the point of chemical equilibrium is reached. The equilibrium point is affected mainly by temperature but is also somewhat affected by pressure. At high temperature, even with excess oxygen present, considerable fuel may remain uncombined; *i.e.*, the combustion will be incomplete. If the temperature is lowered in some manner, the equilibrium point will shift so that more fuel will combine with the oxygen.

Burning, on the other hand, is that part of the combustion process associated with the travel of a flame front across the cylinder. When the flame reaches the far end of the cylinder, the charge is all "burned"—the burning process is over—and chemical equilibrium has been established throughout the cylinder. The combustion of the fuel will be incomplete, however, because of the high temperature.

By the time the piston reaches bottom center on the power stroke, the temperature of the gases will have been so reduced by the work which they have done on the piston that a new equilibrium point will be established where practically all the fuel will be used up and combustion will be complete. In cycles containing excess fuel, both fuel and oxygen will be present after burning, owing to the high temperature, but at the end of expansion the oxygen will be used up by completely combining with the fuel.

Number of molecules. The number of molecules present in the cylinder after combustion depends upon the fuel-air ratio and upon the temperature and pressure existing in the cylinder. For a given temperature, by the gas law $pV = NRT$, the pressure varies with the number of molecules or moles present. This has a direct effect upon the amount of work which the cylinder gases do on the piston.

Because of the effects of variable specific heat and chemical equilibrium, the fuel-air-cycle p-V diagram (Fig. 36) is smaller in area than the corresponding air-cycle diagram. Point 3 on the fuel-air diagram is lower than point 3 on the air-cycle diagram because the temperature rise from point 2 (and therefore the pressure rise) is less. As the piston moves toward bottom center on the expansion stroke, work is done and the gas temperature falls, permitting further chemical reaction (combustion) between fuel and air. This releases sensible energy, which would have been present at top center except for chemical equilibrium.

The energy which had been stored in the atoms at high temperature now also appears as molecular translation, so that the fuel-air-cycle expansion line approaches the air-cycle expansion line as the piston moves toward bottom center.

Construction of the Fuel-Air Charts

Charts for unburned mixture.   Figure 26 is a chart for use in the calculation of the pressure, temperature, and energy of the cylinder contents *before burning takes place*, *i.e.*, between points 1 and 2 in the engine cycle.   The particular chart shown is constructed for a mixture of octane vapor and air in the ratio of 0.0782, plus small amounts of residual gas.   The chart may be used without appreciable error for any reasonable amount of residual gas.   Octane has nearly the same carbon-hydrogen ratio and molecular weight as motor gasoline and so will have the same thermodynamic behavior.

The weight basis of the chart is as follows:

Let F = fuel-air ratio and f = wt of residual gas/total wt of chart contents. The total charge or the total weight of material under consideration in the chart is $(1 + F)$ lb; *i.e.*, the material in the chart originally came from 1 lb of air and F lb of fuel.   This amount of material is sometimes called a "chart quantity."

Part of the fuel and air present is assumed to have combined chemically, since the *fresh* charge in an actual cylinder is always contaminated with residual gases.

Since f = wt of residual gas$/(1 + F)$,

$$\text{Wt of residual gas in chart} = f(1 + F) \text{ lb} \tag{45}$$

The fresh charge, which is the weight of *fresh* air and *unburned* fuel in the chart, is the difference between the total charge weight and the residual gas weight.

$$\text{Fresh charge} = (1 - f)(1 + F) \text{ lb} \tag{46}$$

For every $(1 + F)$ lb of fresh charge, 1 lb is fresh air; thus

$$\text{wt of fresh air in chart} = (1 - f)(1 + F) \frac{1}{1 + F} = (1 - f) \text{ lb} \tag{47}$$

Similarly

$$\text{Wt of fresh fuel in chart} = (1 - f)F \tag{48}$$

For example, if f = 0.06 and F = 0.0782,

Total wt in chart = $1 + F$ =	1.078 lb
Wt residual = $f(1 + F)$ = 0.06 × 1.0782 = 0.0647 lb	
Wt fresh charge = $(1 - f)(1 + F)$ = 0.94 × 1.0782 = 1.0135 lb	
	1.078 lb
Wt fresh air = $1 - f$ = (1.00 − 0.06) = 0.94 lb	
Wt fresh fuel = $(1 - f)F$ = 0.94 × 0.0782 = 0.0735 lb	
Wt of fresh charge = 1.0135 lb	

At moderate temperatures the sensible internal energy E_s and sensible enthalpy H_s of the fuel-air mixture depend *only* upon the temperature.   The ordinate scale of Fig. 26 includes these three quantities, with the datum for zero E_s arbitrarily set at 520°R.   The abscissa scale is entropy, which is a thermodynamic quantity which does not change during a frictionless adiabatic process.   Compression from 1 to 2 would therefore appear as a *vertical* line on the chart. Within the body of the chart are solid lines of constant volume and dashed lines of constant pressure.

The volumes read from the chart are the volumes associated with one chart quantity, or $(1 + F)$ lb of total charge, and the units for H_s and E_s are Btu/$(1 + F)$ lb, or Btu per chart quantity. The chart volume is similar to a specific volume. The charts may of course be used to calculate the conditions of any quantity of gas desired. The ratio

$$V_{chart}/V_{actual} = \frac{\text{total wt in chart}}{\text{actual wt of gases under consideration}} = \frac{1 + F}{\text{actual wt of gases}}$$

The density γ in pounds per cubic foot of the gases in the chart is

$$\frac{\text{lb in chart}}{\text{ft}^3 \text{ in chart}} = \frac{1 + F}{V_{chart}}$$

Chemical energy of the unburned mixture. The ordinate of the unburned charts (Fig. 26) gives only the *sensible* internal energy of the mixture before combustion. The chemical energy of this mixture is due to the unburned fuel present in the mixture and to the combustibles present in the residual gases. Because the chart shown ($F = 0.0782$) has more than the chemically correct amount of fuel, the chemical energy of the hydrogen and carbon monoxide in the cool residual gases amounts to about 300 Btu per chart quantity of residual, or $300/(1 + F)$ Btu/lb of residual gas.

From (45) the weight of residual gas present is $f(1 + F)$ lb. If this is multiplied by the heating value of the residual gas, $300/(1 + F)$ Btu/lb, the chemical energy in the unburned mixture due to the residual gas present is seen to be $f(1 + F) \dfrac{300}{1 + F} = 300f$.

From (48) the weight of fresh fuel present is $(1 - f)F$ lb. If this is multiplied by the heating value of octane, which is 19,270 Btu/lb, the chemical energy in the unburned mixture due to the fresh fuel present is found to be

$$(1 - f)0.0782 \times 19,270 = (1 - f)1,507.$$

The total chemical energy present in one chart quantity of unburned mixture of this particular fuel-air ratio is therefore $E_c = (1 - f)1,507 + 300f$.

Charts for products of combustion. Figure 27[1] is a chart for calculating the condition of the cylinder gases *after burning has taken place*. The basis of this chart is also $(1 + F)$ lb of total weight. In this case, however, the material is *all* combustion products. The ordinate scale in Fig. 27 is *total* internal energy E. The proportion of the total energy which is sensible is shown only at the lower temperatures. The body of the chart is similar to Fig. 26 except that the lines of constant temperature are not horizontal.

Fuel-air-cycle calculation. The use of these charts to calculate a fuel-air cycle is best illustrated by an example. Let us take for comparison the same initial conditions as the air-cycle example of page 48, that is, $p_1 = 14.7$ psia, $T_1 = 540°$R, $r = 6$.

Point 1. On the unburned chart (Fig. 26) at the intersection of the constant-pressure line $p = 14.7$ psia and the horizontal temperature line $T = 540°$R, read $V_1 = 13.8$ ft^3 and $E_{s_1} = 8$ Btu.

Point 2. Adiabatic compression to $1/r = \frac{1}{6}$ of the original volume. The entropy is the same as at 1. Following a vertical line on the chart from point 1 to $V_2 = 13.8/6 = 2.3$ ft^3, read $p_2 = 170$ psia, $T_2 = 995°$R, $E_{s_2} = 100$ Btu.

---

[1] Figure 27 will be found in the pocket at the end of the book.

The fraction of residual gas present in the unburned mixture is unknown but may be approximated from the relationship $f = T_1/2{,}500r$. From this,

$$f = 540/(2{,}500 \times 6) = 0.036.$$

Before combustion the chemical energy present in the mixture

$$E_c = (1 - 0.036)1{,}507 + 300 \times 0.036 = 1461 \text{ Btu}$$

The total internal energy at 2

$$E_2 = E_{s_2} + E_c$$
$$E_2 = 100 + 1{,}461 = 1561 \text{ Btu}$$

Point 3. Burning takes place at constant volume, $V_3 = V_2 = 2.3$ ft³, and no work is done by the gases between 2 and 3 because the piston did not move. The total internal energy must therefore be the same as it was at 2, that is, $E_3 = E_2 = 1{,}561$.

The gases have been converted to combustion products; so using Fig. 27, the chart for combustion products, at $V_3 = 2.3$ ft³ and $E_3 = 1{,}561$, read $p_3 = 900$ psia, $T_3 = 4950°$R.

Point 4. Expansion from point 3 at constant entropy to $V_4 = V_1 = 13.8$ gives $p_4 = 98$ psia, $T_4 = 3270°$R, $E_4 = 1{,}000$.

Point 5. When the exhaust valve opens, most of the gases leave the cylinder. The portion which remains in the cylinder expands adiabatically to exhaust pressure. Continuing down the same isentropic line from point 4 to $p_5 = 14.7$ psia, we find $V_5 = 63$ ft³ for each chart quantity, $T_5 = 2190°$R.

When the piston returns to top center at the end of the exhaust stroke, the volume occupied by the remaining products of combustion is only $V_2 = 2.3$ ft³. Since a chart quantity of residuals at condition 5 requires 63 ft³ of space, there will be only $V_2/V_5 = 2.3/63 = 0.0365$ of a chart quantity of residuals left in the cylinder. During the next suction stroke, enough fresh charge is drawn in to make the total cylinder contents at point 1 again equal to one chart quantity; therefore $f = 0.0365$, which checks our original estimate. If f had been 10 per cent or so in error, the cycle would have been repeated using the new value of f.

Work, efficiency, and mean effective pressure. The work done per cycle, per chart quantity, is equal to the difference between the work done by the *piston* on the *gas* during compression and the work done by the *gas* on the *piston* during expansion. The work of an adiabatic process is done at the expense of the internal energy [see Eq. (22)], so that

$$\text{Work of cycle} = (E_3 - E_4) - (E_2 - E_1) = (E_3 - E_4) - (E_{s_2} - E_{s_1})$$
$$= (1{,}561 - 1{,}000) - (100 - 8) = 469 \text{ Btu}$$

The energy input to the cycle is the chemical energy brought in by the fuel only. The chemical energy in the residual gas at the end of the exhaust stroke is the same as it was at the start of the previous inlet stroke so that it does not represent a gain or loss of energy.

$$\text{Energy input} = \text{wt of fuel} \times \text{heating value of fuel} = (1 - f)F \times 19{,}270$$
$$= (1 - 0.036)1{,}507 = 1450 \text{ Btu}$$

$$\eta = \frac{\text{work output}}{\text{heat input}} = \frac{469}{1{,}450} = 0.323$$

$$\text{mep} = \frac{\text{work/cycle}}{V_d} \quad \text{in.-lb/in.}^3$$

$$= \frac{469 \times 778 \times 12}{(13.8 - 2.3) \times 1{,}728} = \frac{469 \times 778}{11.5 \times 144} = 220 \text{ psi}$$

As in the air cycle, the efficiency and mep of the fuel-air cycle are independent of the size of the engine.   An engine whose cylinder contains one-thousandth of a chart quantity will have one-thousandth the work done, one-thousandth the energy input, and one-thousandth the displacement volume.

Notice that the pressures, temperatures, efficiency, and mep are all lower than the corresponding air-cycle values.

Effect of Engine Variables

Fuel-air cycles have been calculated for constant p_i and T_i, but for varying fuel-air ratios and compression ratios.   The curves of thermal

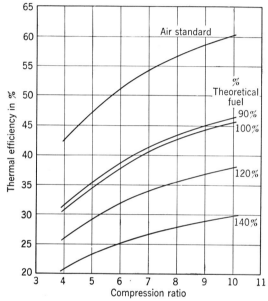

Fig. 29. The effect of compression ratio on the efficiency of the constant-volume fuel-air cycle with $p_{ex} = p_i = 14.7$ psia, $T_i = 520°$R.

efficiency vs. compression ratio resulting from these calculations are shown in Fig. 29.   The fuel-air-cycle efficiency is seen to increase with compression ratio in the same manner as the air-cycle efficiency, principally for the same reason.   The ratio of fuel-air-cycle efficiency to air-cycle efficiency is roughly constant for a given fuel-air ratio.   If efficiency is plotted against fuel-air ratio at constant compression ratio, a curve similar to Fig. 30 results.   As the mixture is made lean (less fuel), the temperature rise between points 2 and 3 will be less as the energy input is less.   Under these conditions the specific heat of the gases will be more nearly constant.   Also at the lower temperatures more of the fuel will combine with the air at top center; i.e., the combustion reaction will come to equilibrium at point 3 with a larger fraction of the fuel energy in the form of sensible energy.

With lower specific-heat and chemical-equilibrium losses, the efficiency is higher and, in fact, approaches the air-cycle efficiency as a limit as the fuel-air ratio is reduced.

On the rich side of the chemically correct fuel-air ratio the efficiency falls even more rapidly with increasing fuel-air ratio. This is because, in addition to the effects noted above, there is insufficient air completely to utilize all the fuel present, regardless of chemical equilibrium. The exhaust gases of rich mixtures will therefore contain combustibles in the form of CO and H_2 which represent a *direct* waste of fuel.

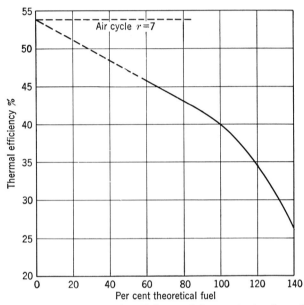

Fig. 30. Effect of fuel-air ratio on the efficiency of the constant-volume fuel-air cycle $p_{ex} = p_i = 14.7$ psia, $T_i = 520°$R.

The effect of fuel-air ratio on p_3 and T_3 is shown in Fig. 31. In the lean region, when more fuel is used, more sensible energy is produced, increasing the temperature rise from points 2 to 3. At the chemically correct fuel-air ratio, there is just enough fuel present to use up all the oxygen, but owing to chemical equilibrium both fuel and oxygen will be present in the cylinder. The use of additional fuel (richer mixtures) will affect chemical equilibrium in such a way as to cause more complete combustion at point 3, and therefore more fuel will combine with oxygen at this point. T_3 continues to rise because of this effect until a fuel-air ratio of about 0.072 is reached.

When oxygen and carbon combine to form carbon dioxide (CO_2), a definite amount of sensible energy appears. If the *same weight of oxygen* is caused to combine with *twice as much fuel* to form carbon monoxide (CO), only about 60 per cent as much sensible energy will be obtained. At the richer fuel-air ratios this condition overcomes the effect of more complete combustion, and T_3 becomes less as shown.

From the gas law, the pressure of a gas confined in a given space depends upon its temperature and the number of molecules it contains.

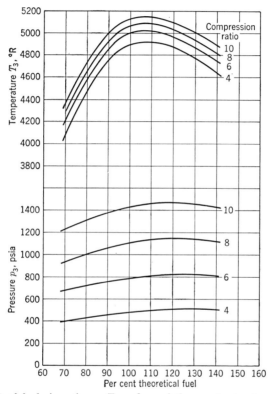

FIG. 31. Effect of fuel-air ratio on T_3 and p_3 of the constant-volume fuel-air cycle with $p_{ex} = p_i = 14.7$ psia, $T_i = 520°$R.

The curve of p_3 vs. F tends, therefore, to follow the curve of T_3 vs. F, except that more molecules are formed by the combustion of rich mixtures. Because of the increasing number of molecules p_3 does not start to decrease until the mixture is somewhat richer than for maximum T_3. Maximum p_3 occurs at a fuel-air ratio of about 0.083.

Both p_3 and T_3 increase with compression ratio, principally because p_2 and T_2 are higher at higher compression ratio.

As shown in Fig. 32, T_4 is a maximum at the chemically correct fuel-air ratio. After expansion, the temperature of the gases is low enough so

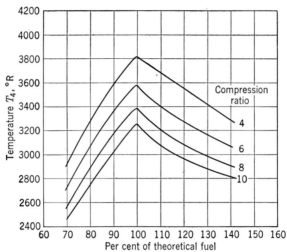

FIG. 32. Effect of fuel-air ratio on T_4 of the constant-volume fuel-air cycle with $p_{ex} = p_i = 14.7$ psia, $T_i = 520°$R.

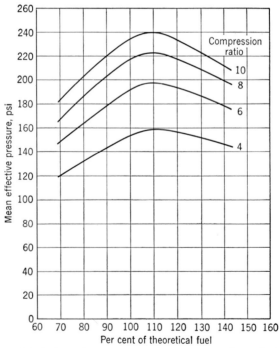

FIG. 33. Effect of fuel-air ratio on mep of the constant-volume fuel-air cycle with $p_{ex} = p_i = 14.7$ psia, $T_i = 520°$R.

that the chemical-equilibrium point is far to the right; *i.e.*, at the chemically correct fuel-air ratio both fuel and oxygen will be completely used up.

Since the effect of chemical equilibrium is not important at point 4, the use of less fuel than the chemically correct ratio simply means less fuel to react and thus a smaller temperature rise. The use of more fuel than is chemically correct results in more of the oxygen combining to form CO instead of CO_2, with less sensible energy developed and again a smaller temperature rise. T_4 is *lower* at a high compression ratio because the increased expansion causes the gas to do more work on the piston, leaving less heat to be rejected at the end of the stroke. This effect is also present in the air-cycle approximation (see Fig. 24).

The mep of the fuel-air cycle has a maximum at a fuel-air ratio a little richer than the chemically correct, since the average pressures during the power stroke would be affected by the same factors that influence p_3 and p_4. Figure 33 also shows the mep increasing with compression ratio because of the higher cyclic efficiency at high compression ratio.

The results obtained from fuel-air-cycle calculations approximate very closely those obtained by actual measurements on running engines. The principal discrepancy between actual engine performance and the performance as predicted by the fuel-air-cycle approximation is due to the fact that the burning process in an actual engine cylinder is not instantaneous. Under certain conditions the time required for combustion will cause the actual efficiency to fall considerably below the fuel-air-cycle figure (see Chap. 5).

SUGGESTION FOR FURTHER READING

Hershey, R. L., J. E. Eberhardt, and A. C. Hottel: Thermodynamic Properties of the Working Fluid in Internal Combustion Engines, *J. SAE*, vol. 39, no. 4, October, 1936.

PROBLEMS

1. Calculate a fuel-air cycle in which $p_1 = 14.7$ psia, $T_1 = 520°R$, $r = 6$, and $F = 0.078$. Find temperatures and pressures at all points of the cycle. Calculate η and mep.

2. Recalculate Prob. 1 at $p_1 = 29.4$ psia $= p_{ex}$.

3. Recalculate Prob. 1 at $T_1 = 720°R$.

4. Recalculate Prob. 1 at $r = 8$.

5. A medium composed of fuel vapor, air, and residual gas is compressed in a cylinder having a compression ratio of 7. Compare the compression line with that of a perfect gas compressed in the same cylinder from the same initial pressure and temperature. Assume adiabatic compression in either case. Discuss the reasons for the differences, if any.

6. For a chart of the thermodynamic properties of the combustion products of an 0.0605 mixture of octane vapor and air, $E_c = (1 - f)1,165$. A similar chart has been constructed for a fuel having a heating value of 19,000 Btu/lb. The fuel-air ratio is 0.1016.   On this chart at $T = 1400°R$ and $p = 8$ psia, $V = 80$ ft^3, $E_s = 192$, $E = 1,026$, $H_s = 310$.   Derive the expression for E_c for this chart.

7. A mixture of fuel and air, $F = 0.078$, compressed to:

(a) $p_2 = 100$ psi, $T_2 = 600°R$, burns at constant volume.   What are p_3, T_3 after burning?

(b) $p_2 = 100$ psi, $T_2 = 1500°R$.   What are p_3, T_3 after burning at constant volume? Explain the difference in the temperature rise obtained in part (a) and part (b).

8. A medium composed of 0.0180 lb of octane vapor, 0.230 lb of fresh air, and 0.016 lb of combustion products is compressed isentropically in a cylinder and then burned at a constant volume of 0.553 ft^3.   Given that $p_1 = 14.7$ psia, and $T_1 = 520°R$, find:

(a) The work of compression, foot-pounds.

(b) The pressure and temperature after combustion.   Use the thermodynamic charts.

9. A medium consisting of 1 lb fresh air, 0.078 lb fresh octane vapor, and 20 per cent residual gas by weight is enclosed in an apparatus consisting of a cylinder and piston.   Initial conditions are $p = 10$ psia, $T = 780°R$.   If the medium is compressed at constant temperature (no chemical reaction) to one-fifth the initial volume, find the final pressure and volume.   Use thermodynamic charts, and show reasoning clearly.

10. A machine has been constructed for research in detonation, which will rapidly compress a mixture of fuel and air.   After compression the piston is locked at top center.

A mass of 0.004 lb of fuel-air mixture ($F = 0.0782$) is compressed from $p = 14.7$ psia and $T = 600°R$ to 7.50 per cent of its original volume in this machine.   While the piston remains stationary at the end of its travel, the pressure in the cylinder drops 40 psi because of heat loss to the walls.   The charge then detonates.

(a) Draw the p-V diagram.

(b) Using the charts, calculate the number of Btu lost by the charge during the delay period.

(c) Calculate the final pressure and temperature after detonation.

CHAPTER 5

THE ACTUAL ENGINE CYCLE

We have seen that an engine with $r = 6$ operating on the air cycle will convert 51 per cent of its input heat into useful work on the pistons. The remainder is rejected at the end of the power stroke and represents the energy lost in the hot exhaust gases. By increasing the compression ratio, and therefore the expansion ratio as well, more work is done by the gases, T_4 will be lower, and less energy will be thrown away.

When the losses due to chemical equilibrium and variable specific heat and the gain due to the larger number of molecules after combustion are added to the exhaust heat loss, we have the fuel-air-cycle approximation which in the example on page 64 converted 32 per cent of the input heat into useful work.

An actual four-stroke-cycle spark-ignition engine operating at $r = 6$ and $F = 0.0782$, as in the above fuel-air-cycle example, will have losses of very nearly the same magnitude and from the same causes as were predicted by the fuel-air-cycle approximation. In addition to the above, the actual engine will have other losses which were not considered in the theoretical cycles. The indicated thermal efficiency of a well-adjusted actual engine with $r = 6$ and $F = 0.078$ should be about 28 per cent. An examination of the actual engine cycle will show the reasons for the difference in efficiency.

Time Required for Combustion

Flame travel. In the fuel-air-cycle approximation, ignition of the charge is assumed to take place at top center, followed by instantaneous burning of the charge (constant-volume burning). In an actual spark-ignition engine, the spark ignites only that very small portion of the charge immediately adjacent to it. The flame then spreads progressively throughout the mixture, much as a fire spreads through a field of grass. The crankshaft will usually travel 40° or more between the time the spark occurs and the time the charge is completely burned. If ignition takes place at top center, burning will end and peak pressure will be reached after the piston has moved a considerable distance from its top-center position. Because of the work done by the gases on the moving piston during burning, and because the volume occupied by the gases at peak

71

pressure is larger than the clearance volume, the peak pressure will be less than it would have been at top center.   An actual indicator diagram with ignition at top center is shown in Fig. 34 with the corresponding fuel-air-cycle diagram for comparison.   A considerable area of the diagram is lost, and thus the actual power and efficiency are low.   If the ignition is made to take place early on the compression stroke, it is possible to have burning completed just as the piston reaches top center.

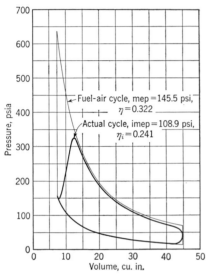

In this case a much better looking diagram is obtained, but additional work is required to compress the burning gases, so that once more the work area is less, and power and efficiency are lost.   The diagram for this condition is shown in Fig. 35 with the fuel-air cycle drawn for comparison.

A moderate ignition advance is the best compromise, resulting in small losses on both the expansion and compression strokes.   When the ignition advance is optimum, a diagram similar to Fig. 36 is obtained.   If through engine adjustment or design, the number of crankshaft degrees required for the flame to cross the combustion space is large, the loss in area of the indicator diagram will be great even though the ignition is made to occur earlier.   These losses, due to the motion of the piston during combustion, are called "burning-time losses" or merely "time losses."

Fig. 34. An actual indicator diagram with ignition at top center and the corresponding fuel-air-cycle indicator diagram.   CFR engine, $3\frac{1}{4}$ bore $\times$ $4\frac{1}{2}$ stroke, $r = 6$, 1,300 rpm, $T_i = 560°R$, $p_i = 14.1$ psia, $p_e = 14.8$ psia, $F = 0.0782$, air $= 0.00122$ lb/cycle, heating value of fuel $= 18,900$ Btu/lb. (*Sloan Laboratory.*)

At full throttle with a "best-power" fuel-air ratio and optimum ignition advance, the time losses may account for a loss in efficiency of about 5 per cent, or only enough to drop the efficiency from a fuel-air-cycle value of 32 per cent to 30.5 per cent.   The time losses *can* become quite large, however, if:

1. The fuel-air ratio is made very rich or very lean.
2. The throttle is closed, making the cylinder pressures low.
3. The ignition advance is not optimum.

The factors which control the time required for flame travel across the combustion space are:

1. The velocity of the flame front.

2. The distance from the point of ignition to the opposite side of the combustion space.

The flame-travel distance may be made less by locating the spark plug near the center of the cylinder head or by using more than one spark plug. A hemispherical combustion space with a spark plug on each side is often used to reduce the time required for combustion.

The motion of the flame front relative to the unburned mixture depends upon how rapidly the heat in the flame front can be transferred to the

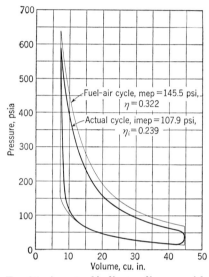

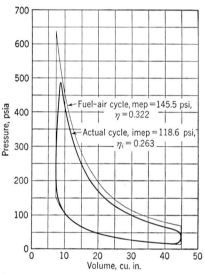

FIG. 35. An actual indicator diagram with early ignition and the corresponding fuel-air-cycle indicator diagram. Same data as in Fig. 34, ignition advance 35°BTC. (*Sloan Laboratory.*)

FIG. 36. An actual indicator diagram with optimum ignition advance and the corresponding fuel-air-cycle indicator diagram. Same data as in Fig. 34, ignition advance 17°BTC. (*Sloan Laboratory.*)

adjacent unburned mixture; for when the nearby mixture is brought to ignition temperature, it, in turn, becomes the flame front. Heat conduction from one layer of moving gas to the next appears to be similar to conduction from a moving gas to a surface, in that the conduction depends upon:

1. The temperature of the burning gas.

2. The density of the gas.

3. The relative motion between the burning and unburned gas.

Effect of Engine Variables on Flame Speed

Fuel-air ratio. Changes in fuel-air ratio have a marked effect on the temperature of the flame. With lean mixtures less chemical energy is present to be transformed into sensible energy, so that the flame temperature is low.   Very rich mixtures burning to CO instead of CO_2 produce less sensible energy.   A slightly rich mixture results in maximum flame temperature and therefore maximum flame speed.   Figure 31 shows the trend of maximum gas temperature T_3 with fuel-air ratio.   For any given spot in the cylinder, the flame temperature will show a similar trend when plotted against fuel-air ratio.

Inlet pressure.   Changes in the *inlet pressure*, which occur whenever the engine is throttled or supercharged, affect the density of the cylinder gases.   Supercharged engines have high flame speeds.

Compression ratio.   Increased *compression ratio* reduces the clearance volume and therefore increases the density of the cylinder gases during the burning process.   Engines of high compression ratio have high flame speeds.

Engine speed.   In order to study the effect of engine speed on flame speed, it is necessary to introduce the term "piston speed."

Piston speed $s = 2 \times$ stroke $\times$ rpm and is therefore the average velocity of the piston.   The velocity of the air entering the cylinder through the inlet valve would be roughly approximated by $s(A_p/A_v)$ where A_p is the area of the piston head and A_v is the effective area of the inlet valve.

High inlet-air velocity, which is induced by high piston speed, results in small vortices in the incoming air.   This turbulence is believed to persist during burning, providing relative motion between portions of the flame front and the unburned mixture.   This motion increases the heat transfer and therefore the flame speed.   Flame speeds in engine cylinders operating at normal piston speeds are of the order of 100 fps, while flame speeds in similar mixtures of fuel and air which do not have turbulence may be only 3 or 4 fps.   The importance of turbulence in the combustion chamber can hardly be exaggerated.

Flame speed does not increase quite as rapidly as piston speed, so that the time losses are larger at high piston speeds, particularly if the ignition timing is not advanced to help compensate for the difference.   Fortunately, at normal piston speeds (2,500 fpm) time-loss effects due to the inability of the flame speed to increase in proportion to engine speed are very small.

Engine size.   Large engines tend to run at low rpm, while small engines tend to run at high rpm (see Chap. 8).   In fact, engines of similar design tend to operate at the same piston speed regardless of size, as the long stroke of the large engine makes up for its low rpm.   If the designs are similar, the ratio A_p/A_v will be the same, so that, at the same s, the inlet velocity, turbulence, and flame speed will be approximately the same in all the engines of a group of similar engines.

At the same flame speed, completion of the burning process takes a longer time in the large engine because the distance across the combustion space is greater. Since the rpm of the large engine is low, the crankshaft takes longer to complete a revolution. The result is, that the *number* of *crank degrees* required for burning will be about the *same* regardless of the size of the engine. The optimum ignition advance will therefore be approximately the same, and the time losses will be approximately the same percentage of the energy input, in each engine of the group.

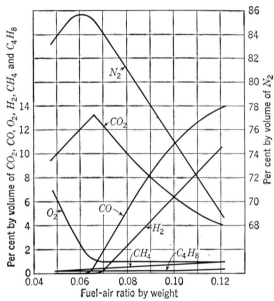

Fig. 37. Composition of the exhaust gases of a typical gasoline engine at various fuel-air ratios. (*H. C. Gerrish and J. L. Meem, NACA T.R. 757.*)

Residual gas. The effect of dilution of the fresh charge with residual gas is to reduce the flame speed and increase the time losses. The amount of residual gas present depends upon the size of the clearance space and the exhaust pressure, while the amount of fresh mixture present depends principally upon the inlet pressure. Engines with high compression ratios (small clearance volumes) and high inlet pressures will have higher flame speeds because of less residual-gas dilution, in addition to the effect of density mentioned above.

Other Actual-cycle Losses

Imperfect mixing of the charge. It is impossible to obtain perfect homogeneity in the mixture of fuel vapor, air, and residual gas present in the cylinder before ignition takes place. Under these circumstances it is possible to have excess oxygen in one part of the cylinder and excess fuel in another part. The fuel, unable to find oxygen, appears in the exhaust as carbon monoxide and hydrogen, representing a loss in efficiency. The composition of the exhaust gases of a typical gasoline engine at various fuel-air ratios is shown in Fig. 37. Note that it is necessary to use a lean mixture to eliminate fuel waste, while a rich mixture is required to utilize all the oxygen.

Even if fuel and oxygen eventually combine during the expansion stroke so that no unburned fuel is actually exhausted, there will be a loss in efficiency since the sensible energy is not present at top center to contribute to the pressure rise at that point.

In a cylinder with poor mixing, the *average* fuel-air ratio may correspond to the best-power value for the fuel-air cycle, *i.e.*, a slight excess of fuel. However, in order to use up all the oxygen present in the cylinder and develop maximum power, still more fuel must be added to the mixture so that the *leanest* part of the combustion space will also contain some slight excess of fuel. Much of the fuel in the *rich* part of the cylinder will then be wasted, because it has no oxygen with which to combine. The flame speed in the rich part of the charge will be low, increasing the time losses.

For maximum economy it is necessary completely to use up all the fuel in the cylinder. To do this, there must be excess air in all parts of the cylinder. If the mixing is imperfect, the fuel-air ratio in the *leanest* part of the cylinder may be too lean to burn. If the spark plug is in this part of the cylinder, combustion will not start and *all* the fuel will be wasted. If combustion does take place, burning will be slow in the lean part of the charge, increasing the time losses.

Imperfect mixing of fuel and air in the inlet manifold may result in a given cylinder receiving a different fuel-air ratio on succeeding suction strokes. The general effect is much the same as imperfect mixing in the cylinder, since for maximum power additional fuel must be supplied in order to use up all the air received by the cylinder on the lean suction strokes. Economical fuel-air ratios cannot be employed, because the unusually lean suction strokes would burn too slowly or would not ignite at all.

Another type of imperfect mixing in the manifold may cause certain cylinders *continuously* to operate leaner than the others. The result of this type of imperfect mixing can be calculated quite simply and will be treated under Distribution (Chap. 9).

With a well-designed inlet system, properly heated, the effect of imperfect mixing on engine efficiency is probably quite small. With fuels of low volatility and with poorly designed manifolds, the effects of poor mixing can be quite serious.

Heat loss to the cylinder walls. During the combustion process and subsequent expansion stroke, the temperature of the cylinder gases is high, and a considerable amount of heat flows from the hot gases through the cylinder walls and cylinder head into the cooling fins or water jacket. Some heat enters the piston head and flows through the piston rings into the cylinder wall or is carried away by the engine oil which splashes onto the under side of the piston. For each 100 Btu of fuel energy entering the engine, it has been estimated that about 8 Btu is lost in this way before the exhaust valve opens. If this 8 Btu were returned to the cylinder gases *at top center*, with a thermal efficiency of 30 per cent for the engine cycle, $8 \times 0.3 = 2.4$ Btu of work would be recovered. Much of

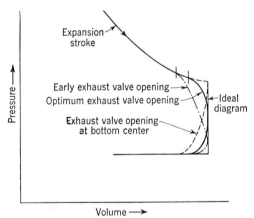

FIG. 38. Effect of exhaust-valve timing on exhaust blowdown loss.

this heat is actually lost late in the expansion stroke when it is about to be thrown away in the exhaust gases anyway. Returning the heat to the cylinder gases at these points would not result in much additional work being done on the piston.

It is estimated that if, in some manner, *all* heat loss from the gases could be prevented, only about 20 per cent of the heat lost during combustion and expansion would appear as useful work. The effect of heat loss would thus be to reduce the work done, by $8 \times 0.20 = 1.6$ Btu for each 100 Btu of fuel-energy input to the engine. This would reduce the thermal efficiency of 30.5 per cent of page 72 to 29 per cent. Heat loss will be dealt with more fully in Chap. 12.

Exhaust blowdown loss. Cylinder pressure near the end of the expansion stroke will depend upon the initial inlet pressure but may be as much as 100 psia. If the exhaust valve were opened at bottom center, the piston would have to do work against high cylinder pressures during part of the exhaust stroke. If the exhaust valve is opened too early, part of the expansion stroke is lost. The best compromise is to open the exhaust valve 40 to 70° before bottom center, reducing the cylinder pressure about halfway to atmospheric before the exhaust stroke begins. These effects are shown in Fig. 38, where it is seen that the optimum exhaust-valve timing results in rounding the end of the indicator diagram. With proper designing and timing of the exhaust valve the blowdown loss is ordinarily quite small.

Power and Efficiency of the Actual Cycle

Actual indicated thermal efficiency. On page 64 (previous chapter), we took as an example a fuel-air cycle which converted 32 out of every 100

TABLE II

Energy Input

    (a) Chemical energy in the fuel.................................. 100.0 Btu

Energy Losses

    (a) Unrecoverable energy loss to the exhaust gases due to the impossibility of further expansion of the gases in the engine cylinder (as calculated from the fuel-air cycle).... 68

    (b) Burning-time losses (which increase the exhaust temperature because the gases convert less energy into useful work on the piston)............................. 1.5

    (c) Direct-heat losses from the cylinder gases (estimated) 8.0 Btu

    Most of this heat would have been lost to the exhaust anyway and is merely transferred to the engine cooling system. That part of the direct-heat loss which would have become useful work if it had not escaped through the cylinder walls is................................ 1.6

    (d) Mixing and blowdown losses (which mostly increase the exhaust-gas temperature)........................... 1.0

        Total losses................................... 72.1 Btu   72.1 Btu

        Net work.. 27.9 Btu

Btu of fuel-energy input into useful work on the piston. The other 68 Btu was lost in the hot exhaust gases. On page 72 it was estimated that burning-time losses would account for about 1.5 Btu less useful work being done. This lost energy will also appear in the exhaust gases. On page 77 it was shown that about 1.6 Btu of useful work was sacrificed by permitting 8 Btu to flow into the walls of the combustion space during combustion and expansion. If we assume that mixing and blowdown losses waste 1 Btu, then the total loss in useful work will be $1.5 + 1.6 + 1 = 4.1$ Btu more than for the fuel-air cycle, or $68 + 4 = 72$ Btu altogether. The indicated thermal efficiency of a typical engine with $r = 6$ and in good adjustment would thus be about

$$\frac{100 - 72}{100} = 28 \text{ per cent}$$

($^{28}\!/_{32}$ = 87.5 per cent of the efficiency of the corresponding fuel-air cycle). These figures are to be taken only as typical values, since the efficiency of an actual engine will vary considerably with design, adjustment, and operating conditions. A summary is shown in Table II.

Compression Ratio. The effect of compression ratio on the thermal efficiency of an actual engine is the same as that predicted by the air-cycle and fuel-air-cycle approximations. This is shown in Fig. 23.

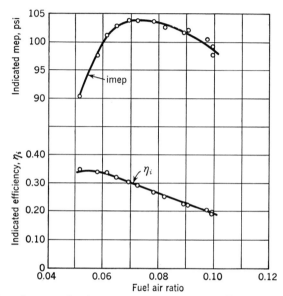

FIG. 39. Indicated mean effective pressure and indicated efficiency of a typical automobile engine. Ford V-8 engine, 1935 model, $3\!\frac{1}{16} \times 3\!\frac{3}{4}$, compression ratio = 6.3, full throttle, constant p_i and p_e, 3,000 rpm, best-power spark advance. (*Fawkes et al.,* *MIT thesis,* 1941.)

Fuel-Air Ratio. If burning-time losses were absent, the curve of thermal efficiency vs. fuel-air ratio for the actual engine would be similar to Fig. 30, for the fuel-air cycle, but slightly lower.

Very rich and very lean mixtures result in lowered burning rates and increased time losses. The effect of these losses is to lower the efficiency at the rich end of the curve and reverse the rising trend noted in Fig. 30 at the lean end. The efficiency curve thus has a maximum, which in most engines occurs at a fuel-air ratio somewhat leaner than chemically correct (F = about 0.055) as shown in Fig. 39. A typical curve of mep vs. fuel-air ratio for an actual cycle (Fig. 39) is similar to that for the fuel-air cycle (Fig. 33) but is modified principally by the effects of time losses and poor mechanical mixing of fuel and air. The fuel-air ratio for maximum power occurs at F = 0.078 approximately for most engines.

Near the peak, the curve is usually quite flat, so that small changes in fuel-air ratio in this region have little effect on engine power, although the efficiency is greatly affected.

It is apparent from Fig. 39 that maximum economy cannot be obtained without some sacrifice in maximum power, and vice versa.

Friction. The curves of Fig. 39 are for indicated power and efficiency. The horsepower at the engine shaft will always be less than the horsepower developed on the piston, owing to mechanical and fluid friction, and similarly the thermal efficiency of the engine based upon the shaft output will always be less than the indicated thermal efficiency. The shaft horsepower is called the brake horsepower (bhp), and the efficiency calculated from the shaft output is called the brake thermal efficiency (η_b). The effect of friction is studied in Chap. 6.

SUGGESTION FOR FURTHER READING

Bouchard, C. L., C. F. Taylor, and E. S. Taylor: Variables Affecting Flame Speed in the Otto-cycle Engine, *J. SAE*, vol. 41, no. 5, November, 1937.

PROBLEMS

1. A new type of spark-ignition engine has been built which will operate without serious time losses at a fuel-air ratio of 0.03 and a compression ratio of 6.0. Assuming that the cyclic efficiency is 70 per cent of the efficiency of fuel-air cycle, what will the sfc be? (Fuel supplied has a "lower calorific value" of 19,000 Btu/lb.)

2. By supercharging it is possible to increase the air capacity of an engine from 1,000 lb/hr to 1,300 lb/hr. Under these conditions the compression ratio must be lowered from 7.5 to 6 to avoid detonation. Estimate from the curves of constant-volume fuel-air cycle characteristics:

(*a*) The per cent change in indicated thermal efficiency.

(*b*) The per cent change in indicated horsepower (ihp).

3. An engine operating at a compression ratio of 5 and $F = 0.060$ has an indicated specific fuel consumption (isfc) of 0.45 lb/ihp-hr. Using appropriate curves of constant-volume fuel-air-cycle characteristics, estimate the isfc of this engine with a compression ratio of 7 and $F = 0.070$. Show all steps clearly.

4. An inventor has an engine which operates smoothly with a compression ratio of 8 and a fuel-air ratio of 0.05.

(*a*) He claims an over-all thermal efficiency of 45 per cent. Is this reasonable? (Base your answer on the information obtained from curves of constant-volume fuel-air-cycle characteristics. Do not calculate a cycle.) Set down clearly your reasoning.

(*b*) What would his maximum probable indicated thermal efficiency be with a fuel-air ratio of 0.08?

(*c*) If his engine gave 100 ihp at 0.05 fuel-air ratio, what would its probable power be with a fuel-air ratio of 0.08? (Use information from curves of constant-volume fuel-air-cycle characteristics.)

5. A spark-ignition engine ($r = 6.0$) operates satisfactorily at a chemically correct fuel-air ratio (0.067) at 14.7 psia inlet and exhaust pressures and 60°F inlet temperature. Its indicated thermal efficiency is 0.31, and its imep is 135 psi.

By increasing the fuel-air ratio to 0.09, it is possible to supercharge the engine to an inlet pressure of 17.5 psia without encountering trouble, other conditions being kept constant. Make an estimate of the indicated thermal efficiency and imep under the new conditions.

Base your solution upon the curves of constant-volume fuel-air-cycle characteristics.

6. An engine cylinder is redesigned with a larger inlet valve, so that the same air capacity can be obtained in the cylinder with less pressure in the inlet manifold (less supercharger work). Under the above conditions, assuming p_1, T_1 are the same as before, what will be the effect of this change on the value of the optimum spark advance, and why?

7. In an engine of 3 in. bore and 4 in. stroke operating at 4,000 rpm, the crankshaft moves 42° between ignition and peak pressure. Show by calculation or reasoning whether the corresponding period in a geometrically similar engine of 5 in. bore operating at 3,000 rpm would require a number of crank degrees larger or smaller than 42.

8. The following changes are made on an engine, one at a time. In each case no detonation occurs. Indicate whether the spark advance should be increased, decreased, or left unchanged, in order to preserve best power. Explain.

(*a*) Mixture increased from best power to a richer ratio.

(*b*) Octane number of gasoline increased.

(*c*) ihp increased at constant speed, by adjusting throttle.

(*d*) ihp increased in proportion to speed, by adjusting throttle.

(*e*) Location of spark plug changed from center to side of combustion chamber.

(*f*) A long exhaust pipe with muffler added to engine.

9. (*a*) An engine cylinder operating with a rich mixture still contains oxygen after the flame has passed through the entire charge. Give two basic reasons for such a condition. (Do not say incomplete combustion.)

(*b*) The above engine also shows oxygen in the exhaust gas. This is due to _____.

10. A nine-cylinder engine with a total piston displacement of 1,820 in.³ takes in 0.008 lb fuel every two engine revolutions. Assuming a heating value of the fuel of 19,000 Btu/lb and a thermal efficiency of 28 per cent, calculate the mep.

11. An indicator card has been taken on a cylinder with 5 in. bore and 6 in. stroke running at 2,000 rpm. The vertical scale of the card is 1 in. = 100 psi. The horizontal scale of this card is 1 in. = 1 in. of piston travel. The area of the card is 9 in.² Calculate the imep and ihp of a six-cylinder engine of this type, at 2,000 rpm.

12. In a four-stroke engine with a compression ratio of 6, the work done by the piston on the gases during the compression stroke was 1,000 ft-lb. The work done by the gases on the piston during the expansion stroke was 5,000 ft-lb.

(*a*) If the cylinder has a total volume of 240 in.³, what was the mep?

(*b*) If the heat input per suction stroke was 16 Btu, what was the thermal efficiency of this engine?

(*c*) If an engine had nine of these cylinders and operated at 2,000 rpm, how much ihp would the engine develop?

13. An aircraft engine gives 2,400 hp at take-off, under which conditions its efficiency is 18 per cent. The fuel-air ratio is 0.10, and the heating value of the fuel is 19,000 Btu/lb. What volume of atmospheric air (0.0765 lb/ft³) is required per minute?

CHAPTER 6

ENGINE FRICTION

The importance of friction. The power available at the drive shaft of an actual engine is always less than the power produced at the piston head by the cylinder gases. The difference is due to the internal friction of the engine. In other words:

$$bhp = ihp - fhp \qquad (49)$$

where bhp = brake horsepower (shaft horsepower)

      ihp = indicated horsepower (horsepower delivered to the piston by the cylinder gases)

      fhp = friction horsepower (engine horsepower lost in internal friction)

From the fuel-air-cycle analysis a close estimation of indicated thermal efficiency can be made. From considerations of engine size, speed, and fuel-air ratio (see Chap. 8) the energy input to the engine per unit of time may be calculated. The ihp of the engine is equal to the product of energy input per unit of time and the indicated thermal efficiency and may therefore be readily computed. A discussion of ihp, leading to expressions (31) and (34), may be found in Chap. 2.

The bhp, on the other hand, can be estimated only when the engine friction is known. A knowledge of the factors affecting friction in the internal-combustion engine is therefore very necessary.

Although the *general* effect on engine friction of changes in engine variables such as engine speed and mep is well known, it is at present impossible to predict *accurately* the friction mep (fmep) which an engine will possess under a particular set of operating conditions. Engine friction can be measured in the laboratory, and such measurements are often used to estimate the probable brake output of the particular engine or of similar engines, under different conditions of operation.

Total Engine Friction

The total friction loss in an engine may be conveniently divided into mechanical friction and pumping friction.

Mechanical friction.   Mechanical friction is the sum of the resistance to motion of all the engine parts and thus represents the power required to keep the mechanical parts of the engine in motion.

Types of mechanical friction.   When two surfaces slide over each other, the friction force opposing the motion is usually affected by the force with which the surfaces are pressed together.   If F is the friction force in pounds and W the load or force acting normal to the surfaces in pounds, then

$$f = \frac{F}{W} \tag{50}$$

where f is called the coefficient of friction (see Fig. 40a).

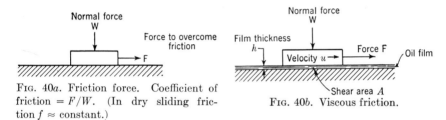

FIG. 40a. Friction force.   Coefficient of friction $= F/W$. (In dry sliding friction $f \approx$ constant.)

FIG. 40b. Viscous friction.

Coulomb friction.   If f is constant over the range of loads and rubbing velocities encountered, the type of friction is known as coulomb friction. The friction produced by the sliding of smooth, unlubricated surfaces over each other is usually close to pure coulomb friction.   Due to the peculiar lubrication conditions existing on the upper cylinder wall, the friction of the piston rings is believed to be mostly of the coulomb type. Under coulomb-friction conditions the magnitude of the coefficient of friction f depends principally upon the materials of which the surfaces are made and the mechanical roughness of the surfaces.

Viscous friction.   If the sliding surfaces are separated by a film of lubricant (see Fig. 40b), then the friction force is produced not by interference of surface irregularities but by a shearing or sliding of the layers of oil film over each other.   In this case the friction force is proportional to the area of oil film being sheared and to the velocity of one surface relative to the other and inversely proportional to the thickness of the oil film.   Mathematically,

$$F \propto \frac{Au}{h}$$

where F = friction force
  A = oil-film area in shear
  u = shearing velocity
  h = thickness of the oil film

The proportionality constant is called the *viscosity* of the oil, and is often given the symbol μ (mu). The viscosity is thus a measure of the resistance to shear possessed by the oil film.

Note that in

$$F = \frac{\mu A u}{h} \tag{51}$$

there is no load term. The friction force is thus *independent* of the roughness of the parts, or of the material of which they are made, and independent of the load W, except in so far as the load tends to squeeze out the oil film and reduce the value of h. Much of the viscous friction present in an engine comes from the various bearings. The clearance space between shafts and bearings is filled with oil. When the load increases, the shaft tends to move sideways in the bearing, reducing the film thickness on one side and increasing it on the other. For moderate loads it is sufficiently accurate to assume that the *average* film thickness remains unchanged. The friction loss in a well-lubricated, moderately loaded bearing is therefore nearly independent of load.

In the average engine operating at full throttle about 70 per cent of the total engine friction is mechanical. A large fraction of the mechanical friction is caused by the piston sliding on the cylinder wall. The remainder of the mechanical friction is due to the bearings and to auxiliaries such as fans, pumps, magnetos, etc.

Piston Friction

Satisfactory lubrication of the piston is difficult to attain. The lower piston skirt may operate a large part of the time with sufficient oil film so that conditions of viscous friction may be said to apply; however, the piston rings and ring lands slide on the upper cylinder barrel where the oil film is at least partially burned away during combustion. It is thought that the rings operate for the most part in the coulomb range.

Viscous piston friction may be reduced by using an oil of lower viscosity and by keeping the area of the piston side walls as small as possible. Figure 12 shows examples of pistons having small oil-film-shear areas. Because of the velocity term in Eq. (51) the viscous portion of the piston friction force will increase with engine speed.

The coulomb portion of the piston friction force will not be affected by speed but *will* be influenced by the gas pressures in the cylinder. The gas force on the piston head is balanced by the load on the connecting rod. Since the connecting rod is usually at an angle to the cylinder axis, a resultant side force is produced. As the cylinder pressures are increased, the side load will become greater, increasing the coulomb friction of piston skirt and lands (see Fig. 41). An increase in the side force may also increase the viscous friction of the piston because of the reduction in thickness of the oil film on the thrust side of the piston.

There is considerable experimental evidence to show that piston-ring friction is influenced by the gas pressures in the cylinder. The cylinder gases work behind the topmost piston rings and force them out against the cylinder wall, increasing the coulomb friction (see Fig. 42).

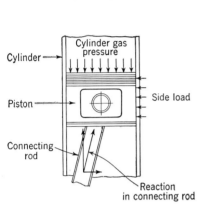

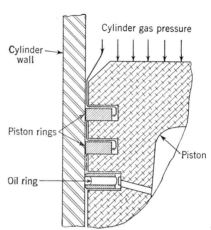

Fig. 41. Diagram showing side load on the piston due to cylinder-gas pressure.

Fig. 42. Diagram showing the cylinder-gas pressure behind top piston rings.

In summation it may be said that the piston friction will increase markedly with engine speed and somewhat less noticeably with mep.

Bearing and Auxiliary Friction

Bearing-friction forces, being viscous, will increase with engine speed according to Eq. (51) but will be practically independent of mep. The friction *forces* associated with fans and pumps vary approximately as the square of the speed. The friction of engine auxiliaries would in general be independent of the engine mep.

Pumping Friction

The work required to induct the fresh charge on the suction stroke and to expel the products of combustion on the exhaust stroke is known as pumping-friction work. In the pressure-volume diagram of Fig. 43, the area 1-2-3-4 is proportional to the indicated work of the cycle, *i.e.*, it represents the difference between the work done *by* the piston during compression and the work done *on* the piston during expansion. The area 4-6-7-1 is known as the pumping loop and is proportional to the pumping-friction work of the cycle.

Effect of engine speed on pumping friction. It is of course necessary to have a pressure drop across the engine valves to cause a flow of gas into or out of the engine. If the inlet- and exhaust-port pressures were both atmospheric, for example, the cylinder pressure during the exhaust stroke would have to be somewhat greater than atmospheric, while the cylinder pressure during the inlet stroke would be less than atmospheric. Thus the work done by the piston in expelling the exhaust gases would be greater than the work done by the atmosphere on the piston during

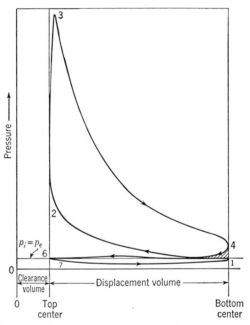

Fig. 43. Indicated and pumping work areas in the pressure-volume plane.

the intake stroke, and the pumping work would reduce the useful output of the engine.

If the engine is operated at higher rpm, the piston will drive the exhaust gases out through the exhaust valve more rapidly and attempt to draw in the fresh charge more rapidly also. The pressure drop across the inlet and exhaust valves will therefore increase, raising the cylinder pressure during exhaust and lowering it during intake. The pumping friction will therefore be greater, as shown by the increased area of the pumping loop. Figure 44 shows pumping loops taken at high and low engine speed for comparison.

Effect of inlet pressure on pumping friction. The mep of spark-ignition engines is controlled by varying the quantity of fresh charge (energy input) admitted to the cylinder on the intake stroke. This is done by throttling the inlet manifold so as to vary the pressure at the inlet ports. When it is desired to reduce the engine power, the throttle is partially closed; this reduces the inlet pressure, and therefore the cylinder pressure during the suction stroke. Lowering the suction line on the p-V diagram in this way increases the size of the pumping loop, but since the quantity of gas in the cylinder is less under throttled conditions, the pressures in the

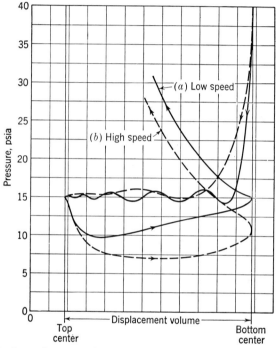

FIG. 44. Effect of speed on pumping friction. CFR engine, $3\frac{1}{4} \times 4\frac{1}{2}$, compression ratio = 6.5, p_i = 14.7 psia, p_e = 14.7 psia, T_i = 150°F, fuel-air ratio = 0.08, best-power spark advance (a) at 1,200 rpm, (b) at 2,400 rpm. (*French and Grisdale, MIT thesis,* 1948.)

cylinder at the end of expansion and during the *early* part of the exhaust stroke will also be reduced. This lowering of the exhaust-stroke pressure tends to reduce the area of the pumping loop, partially compensating for the reduced intake-stroke pressure (see Fig. 45). Because of this, and because lower inlet density reduces the pressure drop through the inlet valve, reducing the inlet pressure 1 psi usually increases the pumping mep only about $\frac{1}{2}$ psi. When supercharging is employed (raising the inlet pressure), the pumping loop is correspondingly reduced.

To summarize, it may be stated that in general the pumping friction will be increased by operation at high engine speeds or with the throttle partly closed. Pumping will also be adversely affected by restricted valves which give high pressure drops or by improper timing of the valves.

Total friction.[1] Experience indicates that in most engines the curve of full-throttle total fmep vs. rpm is linear or slightly concave upward and approaches a value of 5 or 10 psi at zero rpm and reaches values of 20 to 40 psi at high speeds (see Fig. 46).

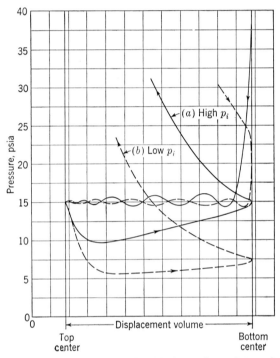

Fig. 45. Effect of inlet pressure on pumping friction. Same data as in Fig. 44 except (a) $p_i = 14.7$ psia, 1,200 rpm, (b) $p_i = 7.4$ psia, 1,200 rpm.

Since fhp is the product of fmep and rpm, the fhp rises rapidly at higher engine speeds. Because of this characteristic of engine friction, it is usually more economical to operate when possible at low rpm to reduce friction losses and open the throttle wider to make up for the smaller number of power strokes. This is equivalent to shifting into high gear in an automobile or increasing the propeller pitch in an airplane.

[1] Total friction may be roughly estimated for part-throttle conditions by correcting the full-throttle total friction obtained from a curve such as Fig. 46, for the effect of inlet pressure as discussed above. Thus:

$$\text{Part-throttle fmep} \approx \text{full-throttle fmep} + 0.5(14.7 - p_i)$$

where p_i = inlet pressure in pounds per square inch absolute.

Measurement of engine friction. The most common way to determine engine friction is to shut off the ignition and rotate the engine shaft by means of an electric motor. The power required to "motor" the engine is called the motoring fhp and is calculated from the torque reaction on the electric motor. This is a simple method of measuring total engine

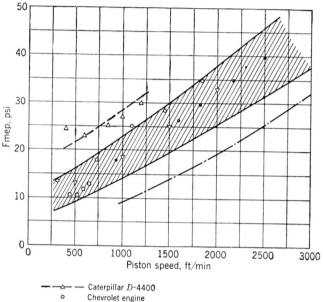

Caterpillar D-4400
Chevrolet engine
Ford 85 hp V-8 engine, MIT tests
Dodge diesel, MIT tests
Sulzer diesel, 8 cylinders, 2-stroke, 19.6 in.×35.3 in., single-acting, including scavenging pump. From Sulzer indicator cards
Allison 12-cylinder aircraft engine, Allison tests
Shaded area—Range for automobile engines from manufacturers' data

Fig. 46. Motoring fmep of a number of engines, full throttle, no supercharger, normal water and oil temperatures, $p_i = p_e = 14.7$ psia. (*From "The Internal Combustion Engine," by Taylor and Taylor. Courtesy of International Textbook.*)

friction but is somewhat inaccurate because the temperatures, pressures, and lubrication conditions are not the same as when the engine is firing. The most accurate method of measuring engine friction is to take an indicator diagram, similar to Fig. 43. From this diagram the ihp and pumping fhp can be obtained. The bhp being developed by the engine can be obtained by measuring the torque which must be applied to the engine shaft to keep the engine speed constant. Then since

$$\text{ihp} - \text{total fhp} = \text{ihp} - \text{pumping fhp} - \text{mechanical fhp} = \text{bhp} \quad (52)$$

the mechanical fhp and the total fhp can be calculated.

Mechanical efficiency. A convenient quantity for use in friction calculations is the *mechanical efficiency*, which is defined as

$$\eta_{mech} = \frac{bhp}{ihp} = \frac{bmep}{imep} \tag{53}$$

Combining this expression with Eq. (49),

$$\eta_{mech} = \frac{ihp - fhp}{ihp} = 1 - \frac{fhp}{ihp} \tag{54}$$

$$\eta_{mech} = 1 - \frac{fmep}{imep} \tag{54a}$$

From Eq. (31)

$$ihp = \frac{(w_f/\min)Je_c\eta_i}{33,000} \tag{31a}$$

where η_i = indicated thermal efficiency and

$$bhp = \frac{(w_f/\min)Je_c\eta_b}{33,000} \tag{31b}$$

where η_b = brake thermal efficiency. Dividing (31b) by (31a),

$$\frac{bhp}{ihp} = \eta_{mech} = \frac{\eta_b}{\eta_i} \tag{55}$$

Similarly from (36)

$$isfc = \frac{2,545}{e_c\eta_i} \tag{36a}$$

where isfc = indicated specific fuel consumption in pounds fuel per indicated horsepower-hour and

$$bsfc = \frac{2,545}{e_c\eta_b} \tag{36b}$$

where bsfc = brake specific fuel consumption in pounds fuel per brake horsepower-hour. Therefore, dividing (36a) by (36b),

$$\frac{isfc}{bsfc} = \frac{\eta_b}{\eta_i} = \eta_{mech} \tag{56}$$

from (55) or (56)

$$\eta_b = \eta_i \times \eta_{mech} \tag{55a}$$

so that (36b) could be written

$$bsfc = \frac{2,545}{e_c\eta_i \times \eta_{mech}} \tag{36c}$$

Example 1. An engine is used on a job requiring 150 bhp. The mechanical efficiency of the engine is 80 per cent, and the engine uses 110 lb fuel/hr under the conditions of operation. A design improvement is made which reduces the engine friction by 7 hp. Assuming the indicated thermal efficiency remains the same, how many pounds of fuel per hour will be saved?

Solution:

$$\text{isfc} = \text{lb fuel/ihp-hr} = \frac{2{,}545}{e_c \eta_i} \tag{36a}$$

$$\text{Lb fuel/hr} = \text{ihp} \times \frac{2{,}545}{e_c \eta_i}$$

$$= \text{ihp} \times \text{isfc}$$

But η_i = constant so that isfc = constant and lb fuel/hr $\propto$ ihp.

$$\text{ihp} = \frac{\text{bhp}}{\eta_{\text{mech}}} \tag{53}$$

Before the change

$$\text{ihp} = \frac{150}{0.80} = 187.5$$

$$\begin{aligned}\text{fhp} &= \text{ihp} - \text{bhp} \\ &= 187.5 - 150 = 37.5\end{aligned} \tag{49}$$

New fhp $= 37.5 - 7.0 = 30.5$

New ihp $= 150 + 30.5 = 180.5$

New fuel rate $= 110 \text{ lb fuel/hr} \times \dfrac{180.5}{187.5} = 105.9 \text{ lb fuel/hr}$

Saving $= 110 - 105.9 = 4.1 \text{ lb/hr}$

Alternate solution. Before the change,

$$\text{bsfc} = {}^{110}\!/_{150} = 0.732 \text{ lb fuel/bhp-hr}$$

$$\text{bsfc} = \frac{\text{isfc}}{\eta_{\text{mech}}} \tag{56}$$

isfc = const so that bsfc $\propto \dfrac{1}{\eta_{\text{mech}}}$

New ihp $= 180.5$ (from first solution)

New $\eta_{\text{mech}} = \dfrac{150}{180.5} = 0.83$

New bsfc $= 0.732 \times \dfrac{0.80}{0.83} = 0.705$

New lb fuel/hr $= 150 \times 0.705 = 105.9 \text{ lb/hr}$

Saving $= 110 - 105.9 = 4.1 \text{ lb/hr}$

Example 2. An engine with indicated thermal efficiency of 28 per cent has an fhp of 18 at 1,500 rpm and 45 at 2,500 rpm. If the bhp required at each speed is 70 and the heating value of the fuel is 19,000 Btu/lb, calculate the bsfc at both speeds.

Solution:

$$\text{isfc} = \frac{2{,}545}{19{,}000 \times 0.28} = 0.478 \text{ lb/ihp-hr}$$

$$\eta_{\text{mech}} \text{ at 1,500 rpm} = \frac{70}{70 + 18} = 0.795$$

$$\text{bsfc} = \frac{0.478}{0.795} = 0.600 \text{ lb/bhp-hr at 1,500 rpm}$$

$$\eta_{\text{mech}} \text{ at 2,500 rpm} = \frac{70}{70 + 45} = 0.608$$

As the indicated thermal efficiency is not apt to be much affected by engine speed, it will be assumed constant.   The isfc will therefore still be 0.478

$$\text{New bsfc} = \frac{0.478}{0.608} = 0.785 \text{ at 2,500 rpm}$$

Lubrication

When relative motion takes place between mechanical surfaces in contact, friction forces are set up which oppose the motion. This friction is mostly due to the interference of minute irregularities in the surfaces.   Motion under these conditions means excessive wear of the parts in any event, as the irregularities are torn away to form new irregularities.   Efficiency suffers because the energy used to overcome friction represents a part of the input to the machine which can never be converted to useful work.   In addition, the heat produced at the surfaces, as work is done against the friction forces, may heat the parts to the point where melting or seizure takes place, destroying the parts.

Purpose.   The purpose of lubrication is to minimize the effects of relative motion, by supplying some fluid or semifluid substance which will separate the moving surfaces and thereby remove this source of friction.

Complete separation is often difficult to achieve, but when an unbroken film of lubricant is present, a great reduction in friction as well as virtual elimination of wear is obtained.   The small amount of friction which exists between well-lubricated surfaces is due to the resistance to shear of the oil film (see page 83).

Bearing friction.   When a shaft turns in a bearing, some of the lubricant adheres to the shaft and is carried around with it.   As the clearance under the shaft is smaller than on the entering side, the oil being carried in cannot all be accommodated at this point.   Viscous resistance to the return flow of this oil builds up a hydrodynamic pressure in the oil film which is great enough to float the shaft out of contact with the bearing, as shown in Fig. 47.

To find the friction loss in a moderately loaded cylindrical bearing, expression (51) may be applied as shown in Fig. 48 by setting

$A = \pi DL$

$u = \pi DN$, where N is the shaft rpm

$h = c/2$, where c is the diametral clearance between bearing and shaft

$F = $ the sum of the tangential friction forces acting on the shaft

Then

$$F = \frac{\mu \pi DL \times \pi DN}{c/2} = \frac{2\pi^2 \mu D^2 LN}{c} \tag{57}$$

$$\text{Friction power loss, ft-lb/min} = Fu = \frac{2\pi^3 \mu D^3 LN^2}{c} \tag{58}$$

Note that the friction power loss of a bearing depends upon the oil viscosity, the rpm, the size, and the geometry but *not* upon the loading.

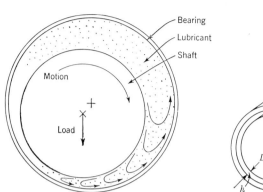

Fig. 47. Action of oil film in plain cylindrical bearing.

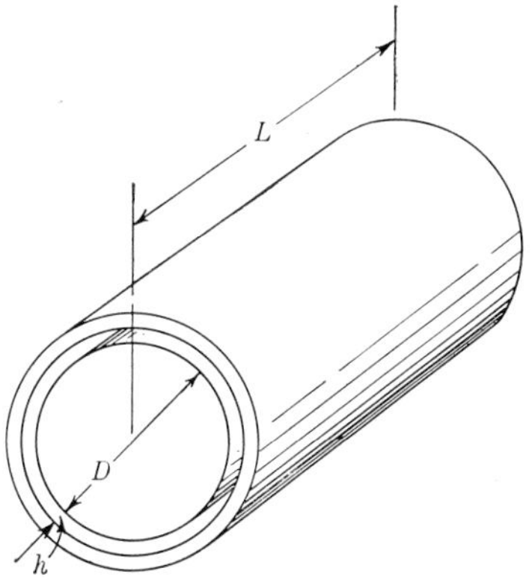

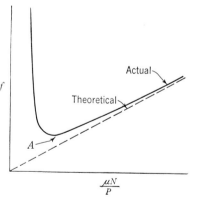

Fig. 48. Cylindrical bearing.

Let P = the loading per unit of projected area of the bearing = W/LD. Then $W = PLD$, and from expressions (50) and (57)

$$f = \frac{F}{W} = \frac{2\pi^2 \mu D^2 LN}{PLDc} = \frac{2\pi^2 \mu N}{P}\frac{D}{c} \tag{59}$$

or for a given bearing or a series of similar bearings

$$f \propto \frac{\mu N}{P}$$

At low values of $\mu N/P$ the hydrodynamic pressure in an actual bearing will not be sufficient to support the shaft load, the oil film becomes incomplete, and the coefficient of friction rises above the value given by (59) as shown in Fig. 49.

The viscosity of oil decreases with an increase of temperature. To keep a constant oil viscosity in a bearing, it is necessary to replace this oil, as it becomes heated by the friction work, with fresh cool oil. In practice an oil pump is usually employed to take oil from a relatively cool reservoir such as the crankcase or from an oil-cooling

Fig. 49. Friction of a plain bearing.

radiator and force it into the bearing. The displaced hot oil flows from the ends of the bearing and is often thrown up on the cylinder wall by the motion of the crankshaft, lubricating the piston before falling back into the crankcase.   Note that the oil-pump pressure serves merely to supply fresh oil for cooling the bearing and to make up for end leakage.   The pressure in the bearing which keeps the shaft from touching the bearing is due entirely to the action of the oil film.

Conditions to the right of point A in Fig. 49 tend to be stable, as a temporary increase in oil temperature reduces the viscosity and $\mu N/P$. The resultant reduction in the coefficient of friction reduces the friction work and permits the bearing oil temperature to return to its former value.   To the left of point A an increase in oil temperature leads to an *increase* in f and a further increase in oil temperature until bearing failure results.   It is therefore necessary to keep $\mu N/P$ greater than A for safety, yet not too high or excessive friction loss will result.   It is evident that the proper choice of oil viscosity is most important.

In similar engines running at the same piston speed, the bearing load P due to inertia and gas-pressure forces will be the same (see Chap. 8). Since piston speed $s = 2 \times$ stroke $\times N$, then if l represents the scale or size of the engine, $l \propto$ stroke and $s \propto lN$.   At constant piston speed, therefore, $N \propto 1/l$.   To keep $\mu N/P$ the same, it is therefore necessary to increase the viscosity of the oil with the size of the engine (make $\mu \propto l$). When this is done, f will be the same and it can be shown that under these conditions fmep will be the same for all engines of the series.   Brake horsepower and friction horsepower will then be proportional to l^2.

Important Properties of Oil

Viscosity.   As discussed above, an oil must have sufficient viscosity to prevent seizure at the highest loads and lowest speeds likely to be encountered in practice.   Excessive viscosity, on the other hand, results in high friction losses and interferes with the proper flow of oil through the piping.   The usual test for viscosity is made by measuring the time required for 60 ml of oil to pass through a standard orifice at a standard temperature.   Oils are classified as to viscosity by means of "SAE number."   Oils having the same SAE number have approximately the same viscosity at the same temperature.

Viscosity Index.   It is advantageous to have an oil whose viscosity is not greatly affected by temperature, so that lubrication will be satisfactory in cold weather or during warm-up as well as at normal operating temperature.   Viscosity index is a number which indicates the quality of the oil in this respect.   To determine the viscosity index, the oil is cooled from 210 to 100°F, and the change in viscosity is measured.   The change is compared with that which a good paraffin-base oil and a poor naphthenic-base oil would have had.   If the viscosity change was as small as the paraffin oil, the oil under test would be rated 100 viscosity index. If its viscosity changed as much as the naphthenic oil, its viscosity index would be zero. Certain oils containing additives and some synthetic oils have been produced with viscosity-index values above 100.

Pour point. Some oils tend to form a crystalline network which prevents flow at low temperature. The temperature at which this phenomenon occurs is called the pour point. In order to ensure a flow of oil to the oil-pump inlet at low temperatures, an oil of low pour point should be used. Special processing and chemical additives are used to obtain lower pour points. If the congealed oil is stirred mechanically, it will flow, showing that the pour point and the viscosity are different characteristics.

Stability. Some oils tend to break down chemically at high temperature to form gummy deposits, sticking piston rings and coating surfaces. Some oils form sludge in the presence of water or other products of combustion. Sludge changes the viscosity of the oil and tends to clog the oil passages. Stability may be improved by refining methods. Ventilation of the crankcase is often helpful.

Oiliness. Some oils and oil additives have the property of clinging to a metal surface by molecular attraction. This means that a thin layer of lubricant will be present even under extreme conditions. Oiliness will help to protect surfaces during starting, before the normal flow of oil is established, or during temporary loss of oil-pump pressure. "Oily" oils show relatively low values of f to the left of point A in Fig. 49.

SUGGESTION FOR FURTHER READING

Hersey, M. D.: "Theory of Lubrication," Wiley, New York, 1938.

PROBLEMS

General

1. The following data were taken on an eight-cylinder engine with total displacement of 221 in.^{3}, by motoring and firing at 2,000 rpm:

hp required to motor engine with pistons removed = 1.5
hp required to motor engine with pistons in place but cylinder head removed = 11.5
hp required to motor with engine completely assembled = 16.0
ihp = 108 by indicator
bhp = 90 by power measurement
Pumping hp = 2.5 by indicator

Show all calculations.

(*a*) What is firing mechanical fhp?

(*b*) What is motoring mechanical fhp?

(*c*) What is your best estimate of firing piston fhp?

(*d*) How much is the difference between firing and motoring pumping fhp? Explain.

2. An eight-cylinder engine when tested at a specified speed at 550 lb/hr air rate and 44 lb/hr fuel rate yields 85 bhp. When the ignition to one of the cylinders is cut off, the engine is found to deliver 70 bhp. Assuming perfect distribution of air and fuel, estimate the fhp of this engine under the stated conditions.

3. At 1,000 rpm an engine has ihp of 50 and fhp of 15. Of the latter, 9 fhp can be considered due to coulomb friction and 6 fhp due to viscous friction. If the imep is held constant by varying the throttle position and the rpm is increased to 2,000 by reducing the load on the engine shaft,

(a) Calculate the new fhp.

(b) Calculate the new bhp.

Ignore the effect of inertia forces.

4. An engine has a bsfc of 0.70 at 2,000 fpm piston speed. The fhp = 30; the bhp = 90. If the friction varies as the upper automotive curve of Fig. 46, what is the bsfc when the piston speed is reduced to 1,000 fpm and the bhp is reduced to 50? Assume fuel-air ratio and η_i do not change.

Lubrication

5. A bearing lightly loaded enough so that the simple relationships apply has $f = 0.006$ and absorbs 0.3 hp. If the load, rpm, and viscosity remain constant, what would be the new value of f and the new horsepower absorbed if the bearing area is reduced to one-half its original value by:

(a) Reducing the diameter of the bearing (constant clearance)?

(b) Reducing the axial length of the bearing?

(c) Using a smaller geometrically similar bearing?

6. A bearing, 2 in. in diameter and 2 in. long, carries a load of 4,000 lb when running at 3,000 rpm, with an oil viscosity of 20 centipoises. A geometrically similar bearing of 1 in. diameter operates at the same lubricant viscosity at 4,000 rpm.

(a) Based on experience with the larger bearing, what load will it carry safely?

(b) The friction torque of the large bearing is 8 in.-lb. Estimate the friction torque of the small bearing.

7. A full journal bearing 2 in. in diameter and 3 in. in length carries an average load of 16,000 lb. At 4,000 rpm, the minimum oil viscosity for safe operation is 10 centipoises. The corresponding power loss is 1.1 hp. Another full journal bearing 2.5 in. in diameter and 4 in. in length (same D/c and bearing material as the first bearing) has to carry an average load of 30,000 lb at 3,000 rpm. Using *only* the information furnished, calculate for the new bearing:

(a) The minimum oil viscosity required to give safe operation.

(b) The corresponding power loss.

8. Show that the power to overcome bearing friction in geometrically similar engines running at the same piston speed is proportional to the square of a characteristic length l, if the ratio of viscosity to characteristic length is the same for all engines.

9. An engine with a bore of 4 in. and stroke of 5 in. develops 500 ihp and has a power loss in its bearings of 2.2 hp. This amounts to a bearing fmep of 3.1 psi. A geometrically similar engine with 6 in. bore operates at the same piston speed and same imep as the above engine. Oil of the same working viscosity is used in both engines. Assuming simple bearing theory to apply,

(a) What horsepower will be lost in the bearings of the similar engine?

(b) What will be the bearing fmep?

(c) Comment on the conditions under which the bearings of the second engine are operating. Explain.

CHAPTER 7

DETONATION

The Importance of Detonation

By increasing the compression ratio of an engine, the efficiency can theoretically be improved indefinitely. From a practical standpoint, there are two important limitations to the process:

1. The maximum pressure of the cycle rises rapidly with compression ratio (see Fig. 31), so that the increased structural weight required to resist this pressure finally overcomes the advantages of the increased efficiency.

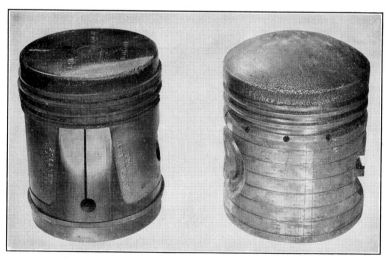

Fig. 50. Pistons showing typical detonation damage.

2. At high compression ratios the combustion process takes place in an abnormal manner, resulting in excessive noise and rapid deterioration of certain parts of the engine. This abnormal combustion is called *detonation*. Typical detonation damage to a piston is shown in Fig. 50. It is obvious from this that severe detonation must be avoided.

By increasing the inlet pressure (supercharging), the power of a given engine can theoretically be increased indefinitely. Again, from a practical point of view, there are several limitations to this process:

1. High inlet pressures produce high charge densities in the cylinder and increase the quantity of heat rejected to the cylinder walls to the point where (although the efficiency of the engine is not particularly affected) the engine's cooling system is unable to carry the extra heat away and the engine overheats and destroys itself.

2. High inlet pressures result in high maximum pressures in the cylinder, which necessitate increased structural weight.

3. High inlet pressures result in destructive detonation.

Often the point of detonation is reached before cooling or structural difficulties are encountered. Detonation may therefore impose a *limit* on the allowable compression ratio and hence on the efficiency obtainable with an actual engine, or detonation may impose a *limit* on the amount of supercharging possible with a given engine and hence on the amount of power output obtainable from the engine.

There are many methods besides decreasing the compression ratio or the amount of supercharge which will reduce detonation to the point where the destructive effects are eliminated. Unfortunately most of these methods also result in a loss of efficiency, a loss of power, or both.

Because of the losses associated with detonation-control methods, engines are often operated very close to the detonation point. With such borderline control, small changes in engine-operating conditions or slight malfunctioning of the engine may produce a state of dangerous detonation.

An understanding of the detonation process is obviously essential in order that detonation be immediately recognized and control measures applied which will result in the smallest possible loss in efficiency or power.

Theory of Detonation

There is much still to be learned about detonation, and it is outside the scope of this text to discuss the considerable amount of work being done in this field. The somewhat simplified theory of detonation presented here is adequate for the practicing engineer and will explain satisfactorily nearly all the phenomena encountered in actual engine practice.

The detonation process. After ignition of the charge has taken place near top center, the flame front travels progressively across the combustion space and the cylinder pressure rises as more and more of the fuel is burned. The peak pressure normally occurs when the flame reaches the far side of the cylinder and passes through the last part of the charge. At any given instant during the burning process, the pressure can be assumed the same in both the burned and unburned portions of the cylinder charge since pressures in a closed space equalize at the speed of sound.

If the history of the very last part of the charge to burn is examined in detail, it will be seen that at the time the flame front is about to reach it, it has already been subjected to rapid compression by the piston during the compression stroke, followed by further rapid compression from the general pressure rise accompanying the burning process. The cylinder pressure (and therefore the pressure in the last part of the charge) will have almost reached p_3, the maximum pressure of the cycle, since almost all the charge has been burned.

As the last part of the charge is compressed rapidly and therefore practically adiabatically by the burning of the first part of the charge, its temperature will rise according to the adiabatic relationship, until it exceeds the self-ignition temperature of the fuel-air mixture present.

Spark plug only

Spark plug and hot spot

B.T.C.   20°   10°   T.C.
Spark plug and hot spot, preignition

FIG. 51. High-speed Schlieren photographs of burning started by spark plug and by hot spot. Spark plug at top; engine speed, 500 rpm; compression ratio, 7.0; engine-jacket temperature, 250°F; fuel, toluene. (*From NACA Tech. Rept. 710 by R. C. Spencer.*)

The temperature of all portions of the last part of the charge will be substantially the same. If the fuel-air ratio is also fairly uniform throughout the unburned charge, spontaneous ignition of *all* portions of this last part of the charge may occur almost *simultaneously*.

High-speed motion pictures of normal and detonating combustion are shown in Figs. 51 and 52. Notice that normal burning is smooth and progressive, while in detonating combustion the burning of the last part of the charge appears to be instantaneous and without a flame front. This is to be expected from the theory.

Returning to the history of the last part of the charge to burn, it is seen that this portion of the charge is compressed to a very high pressure (practically the peak pressure of the normal cycle) *before it ignites*. Burning then usually takes place so rapidly that the surrounding burned gases, because of their inertia, do not move appreciably during the process. That is, the last part of the charge burns at approximately *constant volume* from an initial pressure of p_3. The final pressure in this part of the cylinder will therefore be extremely high—perhaps as much as 2,000 or 3,000 psia. Since the pressure in the other parts of the cylinder is only p_3 (usually less than 1,000 psia), a pressure wave immediately starts from the detonating region, crosses the combustion space, and is reflected back and forth several times by the cylinder walls. The characteristic knock or "ping" of detonation is caused by the pressure wave periodically hitting the cylinder walls. Figure 53 shows diagrammatically a combustion space in which the burning process ends in

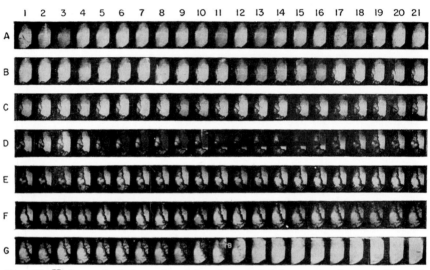

Fig. 52. High-speed photographs of burning started by spark plugs at side and bottom; 40,000 pictures per second. Detonation occurs in frame G-11. (*From NACA Tech. Rept.* 785 *by C. D. Miller and W. O. Logan.*)

detonation. Pressures representative of an unsupercharged cycle are indicated. Figure 54 is a *p-v* diagram of a constant-volume cycle. On the same diagram is shown the *p-v* history, under detonating conditions, of the last part of the charge to burn. The specific volume of this detonating portion of the charge during the time of flame travel is seen to be much lower than the average for the cylinder as a whole.

In the light of the above theory, detonation will be defined as the compression ignition and almost instantaneous burning of the last part of the charge, caused by the general rise in cylinder pressure associated with the burning of the first part of the charge.

The delay period. Experiments have been made in which a fuel-air mixture was rapidly compressed to high pressures and temperatures in a special apparatus. It was found that even when these mixtures were compressed and held at temperatures far above their self-ignition tem-

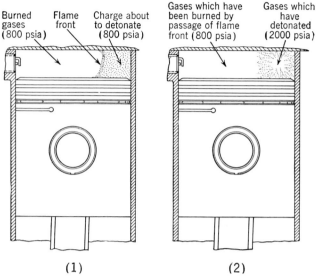

FIG. 53. Diagrams of combustion space just before and just after detonation of last part of charge.

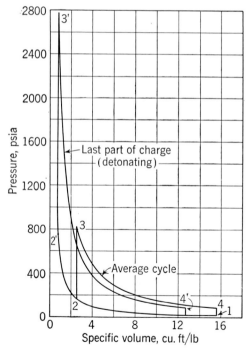

FIG. 54. Pressure-volume diagram of a constant-volume fuel-air cycle with last part of charge detonating. $p_e = p_i = 14.7$ psia, $F = 0.0782$, $r = 6$, $f = 0.04$, $T_i = 520°$R.

peratures, a short period of time, called the delay period, would elapse before ignition occured. From these results it is therefore not surprising that in an engine cylinder detonation does not necessarily occur each time the last part of the charge is compressed above its self-ignition temperature by the burning of the first part of the charge.

If the delay period is sufficiently long, the flame front may pass through the last part of the charge and burn it in the normal manner during the delay. In this case detonation will not occur. When the delay period is short enough so that it comes to an end before the flame front has passed through the entire charge, then, in the case of most fuels, that part of the charge which is still unburned ignites spontaneously and burns in almost zero time. This is detonation as defined above.

It is apparent that detonation can be reduced by increasing the length of the delay period, or by reducing the time required for the normal flame front to cross the combustion space and reach the last part of the charge. The time required for flame travel obviously depends upon flame speed and the distance the flame is required to travel to reach the far side of the combustion space. The factors affecting flame speed are discussed in Chapter 5.

Experiments have shown that the delay period is shortened by anything which increases the temperature or pressure of the last part of the charge to burn. The delay period is also influenced by the fuel-air ratio and varies with the type of fuel used.

Results of Detonation

Knocking sound. As mentioned above, a pressure wave, starting at the point of detonation, vibrates back and forth across the cylinder. The pitch of this sound depends upon the size and shape of the combustion space and the velocity of the wave, which is propagated at the speed of sound in the cylinder gases. Detonation can seldom be heard in aircraft engines because of the high noise level of exhaust and propeller, but the sound of detonation is very objectionable in automobile engines.

High local heat rejection. Detonation may cause severe damage at a point in the cylinder opposite the spark plug. This is where the last part of the charge would naturally be located. From Fig. 54 it is seen that, until pressure equalization takes place, the pressures and gas densities in this spot are extremely high. Because of the high local pressure, the hot gases are probably forced past the piston rings at this point. The combination of high density and rapid flow of hot gases would cause a high rate of heat transfer from the cylinder gases to the piston and rings. These parts are often found melted away locally after an engine has been subjected to severe detonation (see Fig. 50).

The detonation wave crossing and recrossing the cylinder causes a flow of gases in and out of the spark-plug cavity. This relative motion between the hot gases and the spark-plug parts greatly increases the amount of heat picked up by the spark plug. Overheating of the spark plug may have two consequences. The electrical and thermal characteristics of the plug may be so altered as to make it useless. In addition, the plug electrodes may become incandescent and ignite the fresh mixture long before ignition is supposed to occur.

Preignition. Ignition of the mixture by some hot surface within the combustion space (usually before the normal ignition spark occurs) is called preignition. As seen above, overheating of the spark-plug electrodes due to the effects of detonation can lead to preignition. The effect of preignition is exactly the same as if a very advanced spark timing were being used. As shown in Fig. 35, the time losses are greatly increased, and the efficiency and power are correspondingly reduced. With severe preignition the engine power may drop to zero.

Carbon in the exhaust. When detonation occurs in an engine equipped with short exhaust stacks, puffs of gray smoke can usually be seen if a light background is present. At night these puffs are seen as bright yellow flashes, in contrast to the normal exhaust flame, which is light blue. It is thought that the combustion taking place in the detonating part of the charge is chemically somewhat different from normal burning, and free carbon is one of the products. Free carbon is not produced in normal combustion unless the mixture is excessively rich.

High rate of pressure rise. With all the last part of the charge burning simultaneously, there will naturally be an extremely rapid development of pressure on this side of the cylinder. A sudden application of load of this sort may produce high stresses and local mechanical damage.

Power output and efficiency. Contrary to popular belief, detonation when unaccompanied by preignition does not affect engine power output or efficiency to any extent. If an engine operating with best-power spark advance is made to detonate by changing the antiknock quality of the fuel, a 1 or 2 per cent drop in power and efficiency may be noted. Since detonation results in a more rapid burning of part of the charge, a more retarded spark would be optimum for this condition. It has been demonstrated that an engine with a slightly retarded spark will develop *more* power when it is made to detonate by the introduction of very small quantities of knock-inducing chemical.

Effect of Engine Variables on Detonation

Effect of inlet pressure. An increase in inlet pressure increases flame speed, which would reduce the tendency to detonate; however, an increase in inlet pressure increases p_3, the maximum pressure of the cycle, and thus the pressures to which the last part of the charge is subjected.

The high pressures decrease the delay period, which increases the tendency of the charge to detonate. In cases of this kind it has been found that the effect of the engine variable on the delay period always predominates. Increasing the inlet pressure, therefore, increases the tendency to detonate because of its effect on the length of the delay period.

Effect of inlet temperature. An increase in inlet temperature reduces the flame speed somewhat and increases the temperature of the last part of the charge to burn, which shortens the delay period and greatly increases the tendency to detonate.

Effect of compression ratio. An increase in compression ratio results in higher cylinder pressures (p_2 and p_3). Since the last part of the charge to burn will be subjected to these pressures before the normal flame reaches it, the delay period will be shortened and the tendency to detonate will increase.

Effect of spark advance. An increase in spark advance increases the peak pressure of the cycle and therefore increases the pressure (and temperature) to which the last part of the charge is subjected. This shortens the delay period and increases the tendency to knock.

Effect of fuel-air ratio. The length of the delay period for ordinary fuels is minimum at a fuel-air ratio of about 0.08 and increases as the mixture is made richer or leaner than this. The flame speed, on the other hand, is maximum at a fuel-air ratio of about 0.08 (best power). These two effects counteract each other, but experiments show that if other engine variables are held constant, the short delay at 0.08 fuel-air ratio is the predominating factor. Thus at constant inlet pressure the maximum tendency to knock occurs at about best-power fuel-air ratio.

Effect of engine rpm. An increase in engine rpm increases the turbulence within the cylinder and therefore increases the flame speed. The length of the delay period is not greatly affected by engine speed, although the more rapid compression of the charge occurring at high speed undoubtedly shortens the delay slightly. Most fuels, therefore, show a decided tendency to detonate less at high speeds since the normal flame front reaches and burns the last part of the charge more quickly under these conditions. There are some fuels which detonate more readily at high speeds. The reason for this behavior has not been fully established.

The effect of cylinder size. As explained in Chap. 8, large engines of necessity operate at low rpm, while small engines operate at high rpm. Thus the piston speed, turbulence, and flame speeds are found to be about the same in similar engines, regardless of size. The time required for the flame to travel across the combustion space would therefore be greater in the large engines. With approximately the same temperatures and pressures in the cylinder, the delay period would be relatively unaffected by size.   The larger cylinders will therefore be more likely to detonate, as more time is available for completion of the delay-period reactions.

Combustion-chamber design.   Proper design of the combustion space is quite helpful in reducing detonation.   The normal flame can be made to reach the last part of the charge more quickly by reducing the distance it must travel.   This can be done by designing a compact combustion

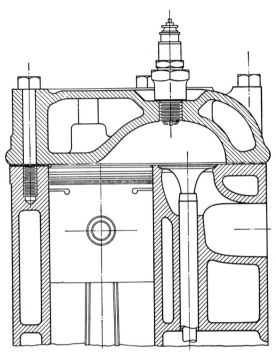

Fig. 55. The Ricardo-type cylinder head for L-head engines.   (*From "The High Speed Internal Combustion Engine" by Ricardo and Glyde, Blackie.*)

space, by locating the spark plug in the center of the chamber, or by using more than one spark plug.   Spark plugs should be so placed that the last part of the charge will not be located near hot engine parts such as exhaust valves.   The heat picked up from such parts will seriously shorten the delay period.

The normal flame can also be made to reach the last part of the charge more quickly, by increasing the turbulence within the cylinder.   A very successful means of accomplishing this is shown in Fig. 55.   At the end of the compression stroke, in the Ricardo head, the mixture is forced out from above the piston into the combustion space.   The turbulence produced from this jet of mixture, combined with the general compactness of the combustion space, greatly reduces the burning time.

Type of fuel. The tendency of a fuel to detonate depends upon its self-ignition temperature, the length of its delay period for a given set of conditions, and (since detonation requires an instantaneous burning of the last part of the charge) how rapidly the last part of the charge burns after compression ignition takes place. Benzene (C_6H_6) is an example of a fuel which does not readily detonate. Experiments indicate that under ordinary conditions the combustion of benzene at the end of the delay period is relatively slow, so that no violent pressure wave is produced and the usual effects of detonation are absent. The addition of small amounts of lead tetraethyl appears to increase the delay period of most fuels, thereby reducing their tendency to detonate. Addition of nitrates or nitrites has the opposite effect.

Effect of water. Detonation may be considerably reduced by adding water to the inlet air or injecting water into the cylinder before ignition takes place. It is probable that water acts to increase the length of the delay period by chemical means as well as by reducing temperatures within the cylinder.

Detonation Rating of Fuels

Because detonation is a complex phenomenon which is not fully understood, present methods of rating fuels for their relative ability to resist detonation are somewhat rough and unsatisfactory. Fuel A, which detonates slightly less than fuel B in engine X, may detonate more than fuel B in engine X if the test conditions are changed. Fuel A may also detonate more than fuel B in engine Y of different design, although the operating conditions are otherwise the same.

Because fuel-rating methods are varied and continually changing, only the most common method will be discussed here, and then only in general terms.

Octane number. In rating fuels a standard single-cylinder engine called the CFR (Coordinating Fuel Research) engine is used. In this engine the compression ratio is mechanically adjustable by movement of the cylinder in and out of the crankcase. The fuel to be rated is run at a standard speed with certain standard inlet conditions, and the detonation intensity is controlled by adjusting the compression ratio.

In testing a fuel for detonation rating, the fuel is compared in the CFR engine with various mixtures of standard fuels, until a mixture is found which has the same tendency to detonate as the fuel being tested.

One of the primary standard fuels is normal heptane.

$$\begin{array}{ccccccc}
\text{H} & \text{H} & \text{H} & \text{H} & \text{H} & \text{H} & \text{H} \\
| & | & | & | & | & | & | \\
\text{H---C---C---C---C---C---C---C---H} \\
| & | & | & | & | & | & | \\
\text{H} & \text{H} & \text{H} & \text{H} & \text{H} & \text{H} & \text{H}
\end{array}$$

Straight-chain hydrocarbons of this sort detonate easily. Normal heptane detonates more readily than any fuel ordinarily used in spark-ignition engines and is arbitrarily assigned an octane number of zero. The other primary standard fuel is isooctane (2,2,4-trimethylpentane).

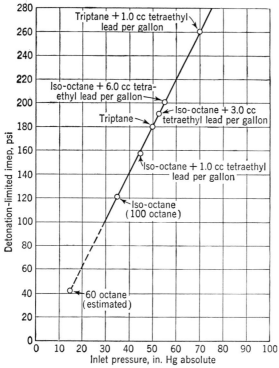

FIG. 56. Effect of different fuels on detonation. General Motors single-cylinder supercharged engine. $r = 6.5$, $F = 0.072$ to 0.074, 900 rpm, 28° spark advance, jacket temperature = 200°F, inlet temperature = 250°F. (*Kettering, J. SAE, vol.* 53, *no.* 6, *June*, 1945.)

$$\begin{array}{ccccc}
H & CH_3 & H & H & H \\
| & | & | & | & | \\
H-C-&C-&C-&C-&C-H \\
| & | & | & | & | \\
H & CH_3 & H & CH_3 & H
\end{array}$$

This fuel is quite resistant to detonation and has been arbitrarily assigned an octane number of 100.

A fuel which has the same tendency to detonate in the CFR engine as a mixture of 65 per cent isooctane and 35 per cent heptane, by volume, is rated as 65 octane number.

The *octane number* of a fuel may therefore be defined as the percentage by volume of isooctane in a mixture of isooctane and normal heptane which has the same tendency to detonate as the fuel in question.

If a fuel of high octane number is used in an engine designed to operate without detonation on low-octane fuel, no improvement in efficiency or power will be noted. The advantage of a high-octane fuel is that, by its use, the *limit* which detonation imposes on power output or efficiency is raised. An engine using high-octane gasoline can be operated at a high compression ratio and therefore with high efficiency without detonation; or the engine can be supercharged to high output without detonation; or optimum spark advance may be employed, raising both power and efficiency, where formerly a retarded spark was required for detonation control. Figure 56 shows the manifold pressures and resulting meps obtainable without detonation when a particular engine is operated with fuels of higher and higher octane number.

Normal combustion characteristics such as the rate of flame travel, fuel-air ratio for best power, heating value of the fuel, etc., will be the same for chemically similar fuels regardless of the octane number of the fuel.

Detonation Control

In automobile engines the compression ratio is usually made high enough for reasons of efficiency so that detonation takes place at low engine speed and high manifold pressure (full throttle). The ignition is automatically retarded under these conditions to prevent detonation. At high engine speeds and partly opened throttle (cruising), the automatic mechanism returns the ignition to optimum timing. This control reduces full-throttle power somewhat, particularly at low speeds. As fuels of higher octane number become available, higher compression ratios will be possible, giving better mileage; or less ignition retard will be necessary, giving better low-speed power and acceleration.

In aircraft engines, because of the type of ignition system used, it is difficult to change the ignition timing. Because of this it is more common to use a rich fuel-air ratio to suppress detonation at high manifold pressures (take-off, climb, or for maximum airplane speed). The effect on maximum power is slight (see Fig. 39); and although the efficiency is greatly reduced, the full-power operating condition is usually of short duration, so that the extra amount of fuel used is small.

As mentioned previously, detonation is sometimes suppressed in high-output engines by injecting water into the inlet manifold or into the cylinder. With a given fuel and air input, considerable water can be injected before the power or efficiency are noticeably affected. In practice, suppression is secured by first increasing the fuel-air ratio to about 0.10 and injecting water at about half the fuel rate (see Fig. 57).

The use of extra fuel and extra water has the added effect of reducing the flame temperature. This makes it easier to cool the engine.

The necessity for detonation control often leads to design compromise. For example, for the same intensity of detonation, higher meps can be obtained by reducing the compression ratio and increasing the manifold pressure. This means reduced efficiency, however.

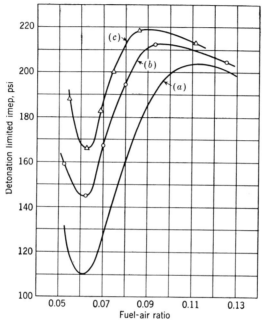

Fig. 57. Effect of water injection on detonation. CFR engine. (a) No water. (b) Water = 0.25 fuel. (c) Water = 0.50 fuel. (*Rowe and Ladd, J. SAE, vol.* 54, *no.* 1, *January,* 1946.)

For high efficiency a high compression ratio is required, but then the manifold pressure and mep which can be obtained without detonation will be reduced.

Figure 58 shows the highest meps which may be obtained without detonation in a supercharged engine with a normal fuel at various values of inlet-air temperature and fuel-air ratio. In every case the manifold pressure is adjusted until incipient detonation is encountered. Note the importance of maintaining low inlet temperatures. The effect of enriching the mixture is seen to be great at first but of less value at very rich mixtures. Mean effective pressures higher than the surface of this figure may be obtained merely by increasing the manifold pressure, but the resulting detonation will probably ruin the engine. The meps permissible without detonation (the surface of the figure) may be raised, for example, by using a better fuel, lowering the compression ratio, or injecting water.

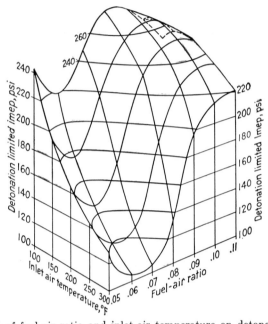

FIG. 58. Effect of fuel-air ratio and inlet-air temperature on detonation. (*Droege-mueller, Hersey, and Kuhrt, J. SAE, December, 1944.*)

Recognition of Detonation

It is necessary to recognize the presence of detonation and apply control measures before damage is done. In engines with muffled exhaust the sound of detonation may be heard. With loud exhaust or propeller noises it is often impossible to hear detonation.

On page 103 mention was made of the effect of detonation on the heat rejected to the spark plug. The temperature of the spark-plug gasket as measured by a thermocouple embedded in it is commonly used as an indication of detonation. A sudden or abnormal temperature rise under steady operating conditions is probably the result of detonation.

Since spark-plug-gasket temperatures may be affected by changes in fuel-air ratio, engine speed, manifold pressure, cooling-air flow, etc., a more satisfactory method has been developed. This consists of an electrical pickup mounted on the cylinder head. This unit is sensitive to the vibration caused by the detonation wave striking the cylinder head. The output of the cylinder unit is amplified and made to flash a warning signal. Eventually units of this sort will probably be used to apply detonation-control measures automatically.

In engine-testing work, when short exhaust stacks are used, it is often possible to detect detonation by the presence of intermittent puffs of gray smoke in the exhaust, which appear as bright yellow flashes when the test cell is darkened. This method is not satisfactory where extreme accuracy is required.

Preignition

Ignition of the charge by some hot surface within the engine can result in extremely large losses in efficiency if this ignition occurs earlier than the normal spark-plug discharge. The effect is obviously the same as a very advanced ignition timing; and the additional negative work done by the piston during the compression stroke, on the already burning gases, produces higher peak pressures and temperatures in the cylinder. Even if surface ignition occurs in some part of the cylinder remote from the spark plug *after* normal ignition has taken place at the plug, the two flame fronts so formed may burn the mixture so quickly that too much pressure rise will occur before top center.

The above effects are called "preignition" even though they may sometimes occur after the normal spark. Since the effect of preignition is similar to an advanced spark, it is to be expected that preignition will lead to detonation by increasing the peak cylinder pressure, and therefore the pressure and temperature of the last part of the charge. On page 103 it was shown that detonation could lead to preignition. A vicious circle is thus probable, with one leading to the other until damage is done or all power is lost.

Sources of preignition. Quite high surface temperatures are necessary to produce preignition. One of the most common sources is carbon deposits in the cylinder. The low heat conductivity of these deposits causes the inner surfaces to attain a high temperature. Under some conditions continuous smoldering undoubtedly takes place in the deposits and ignites the mixture. An improperly selected spark plug whose electrodes operate too hot is a frequent cause of preignition. Violent detonation will usually overheat the electrodes of the coolest-running spark plugs.

Highly supercharged engines are more prone to preignition because more heat is rejected to the combustion-chamber walls (see Chap. 12). Fortunately the high-octane fuels used in supercharged engines appear to be more resistant to preignition than low-octane fuels.

Preignition damage. In engines of high output, continued early ignition with the resulting higher cylinder-gas temperatures sometimes results in excessive heating of piston heads. The high cylinder pressures may force the hotter gases past the piston rings, producing local melting of the piston. In engines operated at lower manifold pressures, or in more conservatively designed engines, operated at lower meps, it is doubtful that preignition, unaccompanied by detonation, causes much damage. The loss of power and efficiency which accompanies pre-ignition is, however, very serious.

Tests for preignition. The standard test for preignition is to shut off the ignition. If the engine still fires, it is assumed that preignition was taking place when the ignition was on. Experience shows that this assumption is not always valid. Sudden loss of power with no evidence of mechanical malfunctioning is fairly good evidence of preignition. The best proof of preignition is the appearance of an indicator card taken with a high-speed indicator of the balanced-pressure type.

SUGGESTION FOR FURTHER READING

Leary, W. A., and E. S. Taylor: The Significance of the Time Concept in Engine Detonation, *NACA Wartime Rept.* W-32, 1943.

PROBLEMS

1. (*a*) With similar engines all operating at the same piston speed, what is the effect of engine size on the spark advance required for best power? Explain completely but briefly.

(*b*) With similar engines operating at the same piston speed, what is the effect of engine size on the tendency of the engine to detonate? Explain completely but briefly.

2. (*a*) Draw a complete p-V diagram of an engine cycle in which preignition occurs $90°$ before top center and is followed by instantaneous combustion.

(*b*) Indicate in the table below the effect of preignition on the quantities listed.

	Increased	Decreased	Unchanged
p_3			
T_3			
T_4			
mep			
η			

3. An aircraft engine is equipped with a controllable-pitch propeller, so that any reasonable combination of rpm and manifold pressure is possible. The compression ratio = 6.5. At a fuel-air ratio of 0.08, an absolute manifold pressure of 45 in. Hg, and 2,700 rpm, the ihp = 1,400, and the isfc = 0.50. Moderate detonation is encountered under these conditions, and it is permissible to eliminate it by changing one of the normal operating variables at a time. Which one of the above would you vary, and in what direction, to:

(*a*) Reduce detonation without loss of power or indicated efficiency?

(b) Reduce detonation without much loss in indicated efficiency but at the expense of considerable loss in power?

(c) Reduce detonation without much loss in power but at the expense of considerable loss in indicated efficiency?

(d) Reduce detonation but with equal per cent loss in power and indicated efficiency?

4. (a) The following geometrically similar engines are supercharged to keep p_1 and T_1 the same in all the engines. They all use same fuel and same fuel-air ratio.

Engine	Stroke, in.	rpm
A	2	1,000
B	4	3,000
C	6	2,000

Assuming flame speed is proportional to inlet velocity, which engine would be least likely to detonate? Explain carefully the reason for your choice.

5. A spark-ignition engine is operating with very slight detonation. The engine speed is increased by 20 per cent, and the throttle is readjusted to permit 20 per cent more combustible mixture to enter the engine per unit of time. No other adjustments are made. Discuss the effect of the above changes on the detonation of this engine.

6. By supercharging it is possible to increase the air capacity of an engine from 1,200 to 1,550 lb/hr. Under these conditions the compression ratio must be lowered from 7.5 to 6 in order to avoid detonation. Calculate from your knowledge of the fuel-air cycle:

(a) The ratio of indicated thermal efficiency supercharged to indicated thermal efficiency unsupercharged.

(b) The ratio of ihp supercharged to ihp unsupercharged.

CHAPTER 8

AIR CAPACITY

In the previous chapters we have studied engine efficiency and the various factors which affect it. By the use of fuel-air-cycle computations and a consideration of the actual combustion process, it is possible to make a close estimate of the indicated thermal efficiency of an actual engine operating at any fuel-air ratio or compression ratio.

The *power* output of an engine depends not only upon the efficiency of the engine but also upon the chemical energy input per unit of time. If the energy input to the engine can also be closely estimated for any operating condition, then the power output of the engine will be known.

No fuel can be burned in an engine cylinder unless air is present. Therefore, the limitation on the amount of fuel which can be usefully introduced and burned per minute is the amount of air which the engine will draw into its cylinders per minute.

The quantity of air an engine will draw in per minute (*i.e.*, the *air capacity*) is practically unaffected by the presence or absence of fuel in the air. The reason for this is that although the fuel vapor increases the mixture volume by about 2 per cent, the evaporation of this fuel in the inlet manifold lowers the temperature of the mixture so that it occupies approximately the same volume as the air alone would have occupied if fuel had not been added. In other words, an engine made to rotate at constant speed will draw in approximately the same amount of air per minute, whether fuel is introduced into the air stream or not.

In terms of the air capacity $w_a/\min$, the input in pounds of *fuel* per minute will be $(w_a/\min)F$, and, using the symbols of Chap. 2, the chemical energy input in Btu per minute will be $(w_a/\min)Fe_c$, and the ihp output will be, from (34),

$$\text{ihp} = (w_a/\min)(Fe_c\eta_i)\frac{778}{33,000} \qquad (34a)$$

With optimum ignition timing, the indicated thermal efficiency of a given engine is affected almost exclusively by changes in fuel-air ratio, so that at *constant* fuel-air ratio the value of the parenthesis $(Fe_c\eta_i)$ will be constant. At values of F between about 0.075 and 0.085, the efficiency falls off with increased fuel-air ratio in such a way as to make the product $(Fe_c\eta_i)$ also approximately constant over this range.

It is therefore seen that for any constant value of F or for values of F varying between 0.075 and 0.085, the ihp will be proportional to w_a/min. For example, if w_a/min be increased 20 per cent by increasing the inlet pressure (throttle) or by increasing the number of suction strokes (engine rpm) or by cooling the inlet air, the engine power will in each case be increased 20 per cent. Figure 59 shows the effect of w_a/min on the ihp of a typical engine.

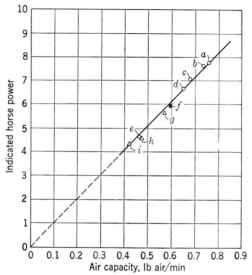

Fig. 59. Effect of air capacity on ihp of a four-stroke engine. (*Sloan Laboratory.*) CFR engine, $3\frac{1}{4} \times 4\frac{1}{2}$, $r = 7$, $F = 0.075$, best-power spark advance, $p_{ex} = 30$ in. Hg. Other conditions as follows:

Point	rpm	p_i, in. Hg	T_i, °F	Point	rpm	p_i, in. Hg	T_i, °F
a	1,600	29.2	100	f	1,200	29.1	160
b	1,600	28.9	100	g	1,200	26.4	100
c	1,400	29.2	100	h	1,000	24.6	100
d	1,200	29.1	100	i	1,200	20.0	100
e	800	29.5	100				

A well-adjusted engine of normal compression ratio operating between 0.075 and 0.085 fuel-air ratio will have a value of $(Fe_c\eta_i)$ of about 400 Btu/lb air. This figure will be useful as a rough check on the amount of air required for a given power output. For more accurate work, the value of η_i should be estimated for the particular compression ratio and fuel-air ratio being used.

Estimation of Air Capacity

Considering the engine as an air pump, it is evident that the volume of air which will be drawn in per minute will be approximately equal to the number of suction strokes per minute times V_d.   In a four-stroke engine this would be (rpm/2) $\times$ No. cyls $\times$ V_d, since each cylinder has a suction stroke every two crankshaft revolutions.

The mass of air per minute will be approximated by multiplying the above by the inlet-air density.   The "inlet" may be chosen wherever it is convenient.   In unsupercharged engines this is usually taken in the room or at the carburetor inlet.   In supercharged or throttled engines, the inlet density is usually calculated for conditions in the inlet manifold. Because the effect of the fuel is negligible, it is assumed in the calculations that only air is present.   The "ideal" air capacity will then be

$$\frac{\text{rpm}}{2} \times \text{No. cyls.} \times V_d \gamma_i \tag{60}$$

where γ_i is inlet-air density.

As all these quantities are easily measured, the ideal air capacity is easy to calculate.

In an actual engine, the entering air may pick up heat from hot inlet valves or other engine parts, throttling may occur in the inlet system, or other effects may be present to make the density of the air entering the cylinder different from the density of the air at the inlet.   Thus the actual air capacity may be considerably different from the ideal.

The ratio of actual air capacity to ideal air capacity is commonly known as the "volumetric efficiency," although it is not an efficiency in the usual sense.   Using the symbol η_v for this quantity,

$$\eta_v = \frac{w_a/\text{min}}{(\text{rpm}/2) \times \text{No. cyls.} \times V_d \gamma_i} \tag{61}$$

so that

$$w_a/\text{min} = \frac{\text{rpm}}{2} \times \text{No. cyls.} \times V_d \gamma_i \eta_v \tag{61a}$$

If we define γ_{cyl} as

$$\frac{\text{Mass of air entering cylinder per suction stroke}}{V_d}$$

then

$$\gamma_{\text{cyl}} = \frac{w_a/\text{min}}{(\text{rpm}/2) \times \text{No. cyls.} \times V_d}$$

and from (61),

$$\eta_v = \frac{\gamma_{\text{cyl}}}{\gamma_i} \tag{62}$$

Volumetric Efficiency

If the volumetric efficiency can be estimated, the engine air capacity and ihp may be calculated from expressions (61a) and (34a), as the other quantities are known or may be closely estimated.

Static and dynamic effects. If an engine ran slowly enough so that there was no pressure loss in the inlet system; with inlet- and exhaust-manifold pressures equal, valves opening and closing at top and bottom center, and inlet-air temperature high enough so that no temperature rise would take place on the way into the cylinders, then γ_{cyl} would equal γ_i and η_v would be 100 per cent.

The effects on η_v of varying the inlet-air temperature or of varying the ratio of inlet-manifold pressure to exhaust-manifold pressure are called *static* effects and are assumed for simplicity to be independent of engine speed. At normal engine speeds, the inertia and fluid friction of the gases in the inlet and exhaust manifolds, in conjunction with the particular valve timing being used, lead to inequalities of pressure throughout the system which also affect the volumetric efficiency. These are called *dynamic* effects and are assumed to be independent of the static effects. The assumption that static and dynamic effects are independent of each other may be shown by tests to be accurate enough for most performance calculations. A more rigorous treatment would undoubtedly prove too complicated for practical application.

Effect of inlet-air temperature. η_v is the ratio of air mass actually drawn in to air mass which would have been drawn in, if each displacement volume had been filled at inlet density. If the air density is reduced by heat pickup anywhere between the inlet and the cylinder, the air actually drawn in will be less and the volumetric efficiency will be lowered.

Now if the temperature of the inlet air is *increased*, this will reduce the temperature difference between the incoming air and the hot engine parts, so that less heat will be picked up by the air on the way into the cylinder; and the air-density loss between inlet and cylinder will be less than before. In this case, the air mass actually drawn in will be nearer to the ideal. That is, the volumetric efficiency will be increased. Using expression (62), at moderate inlet-air temperature, due to heat pickup, γ_{cyl} will tend to be less than γ_i. If the inlet-air temperature were *increased* sufficiently, heat could actually be lost by the air on the way into the cylinder, tending to make γ_{cyl} greater than γ_i and increasing the volumetric efficiency.

Note from expression (61a) that air capacity depends upon the product of γ_i and η_v. When inlet-air temperature is increased, η_v does not increase enough to compensate for the reduction in γ_i; and the air capacity itself will be reduced.

Figure 60 is a typical curve of η_v vs. inlet-air temperature for an engine operating at some constant rpm and constant inlet and exhaust pressures. The absolute values of η_v indicated by this curve are of course dependent upon the engine design and the particular rpm, p_i, and p_{ex} being used.

However, for a change in inlet temperature from T_{i_1} to T_{i_2}, the ratio η_{v_2}/η_{v_1} for this engine may be closely calculated from this curve for *any* rpm or inlet or exhaust pressure. Of course, engines of different designs have slightly different-shaped curves of η_v vs. T_i; but experience has shown that the empirical relationship

$$\frac{\eta_{v_2}}{\eta_{v_1}} = \sqrt{\frac{T_{i_2}}{T_{i_1}}} \tag{63}$$

where T_i = inlet-air temperature in degrees Rankine, is fairly accurate for a wide variety of engines. We shall therefore use this expression for estimating changes in η_v due to variations in inlet-air temperature.

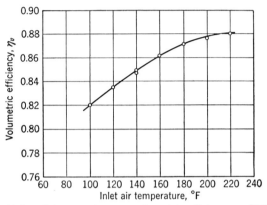

FIG. 60. Effect of inlet-air temperature on volumetric efficiency. CFR engine, $3\frac{1}{4} \times 4\frac{1}{2}$, $r = 7$, $p_i = 29$ in. Hg, $p_{ex} = 30.2$ in. Hg, $F = 0.07$, 1,000 rpm, best-power spark advance, constant jacket temperature. (*Malcolm and Pereira, MIT SM thesis,* 1944.)

Effect of inlet and exhaust pressure. Assuming we have a slow-moving engine with no heat pickup by the inlet air, valve events at top and bottom center, and inlet and exhaust pressures equal, we should expect to take in a volume of air equal to V_d with density equal to γ_i on each suction stroke (that is, $\eta_v = 1$). If p_{ex} differs from p_i, however, the following process takes place, as shown in Fig. 61:

At the end of the exhaust stroke, the exhaust valve closes, trapping residual gas in the clearance space above the piston at exhaust-pipe pressure p_{ex}. When the inlet valve opens, this residual gas will be either compressed or expanded to inlet pressure p_i depending upon whether p_i is greater or less than p_{ex}. Thus fresh charge will flow *into* this cylinder before the intake stroke is started if $p_i > p_{ex}$, or, on the other hand, if $p_i < p_{ex}$, residual gas will flow into the inlet manifold so that part of the intake stroke will have to be used in returning this gas to the cylinder before fresh charge will enter the cylinder. From the above, it is seen that if p_i is greater or less than p_{ex}, the volume drawn into the cylinder will be greater or less than V_d.

By assuming the residual gas which originally occupied the clearance volume V_{cl} to be compressed or expanded isentropically to inlet pressure, an expression for the effect of the ratio p_{ex}/p_i on the volumetric efficiency may be obtained.

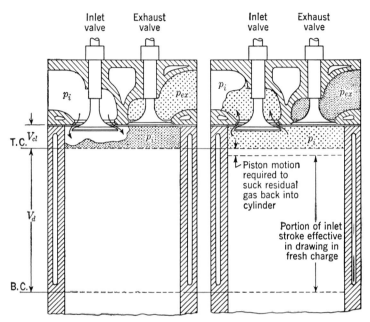

(a) $p_i > p_{ex}$; Residual gas which occupied clearance volume, V_{cl}, at p_{ex} is compressed to p_i by incoming fresh charge before inlet stroke starts

(b) $p_i < p_{ex}$; Residual gas which occupied V_{cl} at p_{ex} expands to p_i and fills a portion of inlet port before inlet stroke draws it into cylinder again

FIG. 61. Diagrams showing effect of inlet and exhaust pressure on residual gas in clearance volume at the beginning of inlet stroke.

If the volume occupied by the residual gas at inlet pressure is V_{cl}', then

$$p_{ex}(V_{cl})^k = p_i(V_{cl}')^k \qquad (64)$$

where k is the ratio of specific heats for the residual gas (a figure of 1.35 for k is sufficiently close), so that

$$V_{cl}' = V_{cl}\left(\frac{p_{ex}}{p_i}\right)^{1/k} \qquad (64a)$$

Let ΔV = change in volume of the residual gas in going from p_{ex} to $p_i = V_{cl} - V_{cl}'$. If ΔV is positive, it represents the extra volume of fresh charge which enters the engine before the intake stroke starts.   If ΔV is negative, it represents the volume of residual gas which flows back into the inlet manifold before the inlet stroke starts.   From (64a),

$$\Delta V = V_{cl} - V_{cl}\left(\frac{p_{ex}}{p_i}\right)^{1/k}$$

$$= V_{cl}\left[1 - \left(\frac{p_{ex}}{p_i}\right)^{1/k}\right] \tag{65}$$

But

$$\frac{V_{cl}}{V_d} = \frac{1}{r-1}$$

from the definition of r; so

$$\Delta V = V_d\frac{1}{r-1}\left[1 - \left(\frac{p_{ex}}{p_i}\right)^{1/k}\right] \tag{66}$$

The total volume V_0 which will enter the cylinder will be $V_d + \Delta V$, or

$$V_0 = V_d + V_d\frac{1}{r-1}\left[1 - \left(\frac{p_{ex}}{p_i}\right)^{1/k}\right] \tag{67}$$

If $p_{ex} = p_i$, the volume entering the cylinder would be V_d; therefore,

$$\frac{\eta_v \text{ for the given ratio } p_{ex}/p_i}{\eta_v \text{ for } p_i = p_{ex}} = \frac{V_0}{V_d}$$

From (67)

$$\frac{V_0}{V_d} = 1 + \frac{1}{r-1}\left[1 - \left(\frac{p_{ex}}{p_i}\right)^{1/k}\right] \tag{68}$$

Multiplying (68) by $(r-1)/(r-1)$,

$$\frac{V_0}{V_d} = \frac{r - 1 + 1[1 - (p_{ex}/p_i)^{1/k}]}{r-1}$$

$$= \frac{r - (p_{ex}/p_i)^{1/k}}{r-1} \tag{69}$$

When p_{ex}/p_i is changed from one value (1) to another value (2), applying (69),

$$\frac{\eta_v \text{ for cond. (2)}}{\eta_v \text{ for } p_{ex} = p_i} = \frac{\dfrac{r - [p_{ex}/p_i]_2^{1/k}}{r-1}}{\dfrac{r - [p_{ex}/p_i]_1^{1/k}}{r-1}}$$

or

$$\frac{\eta_{v2}}{\eta_{v1}} = \frac{r - \left(\dfrac{p_{ex}}{p_i}\right)_2^{1/k}}{r - \left(\dfrac{p_{ex}}{p_i}\right)_1^{1/k}} \tag{70}$$

Expression (70) is quite useful for predicting the effects of inlet- and exhaust-pressure changes on η_v. Keep in mind when calculating air capacity that changes in inlet pressure affect γ_i as well as η_v.

If an engine has considerable valve overlap, *i.e.*, if the inlet and exhaust valves are both open at the same time near top center, the residual gas will not be compressed or expanded but may be pushed out the exhaust by the incoming charge when $p_i > p_{ex}$ or exhaust gases may flow back into the cylinder through the exhaust valve if $p_i < p_{ex}$. This will make the effect of changes in the p_{ex}/p_i ratio somewhat greater than indicated by expression (70).

Typical curves of η_v vs. (p_{ex}/p_i) are shown in Fig. 62.

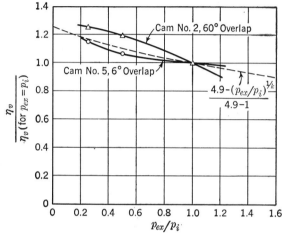

FIG. 62. Effect of p_{ex}/p_i on volumetric efficiency. CFR engine, $3\frac{1}{4} \times 4\frac{1}{2}$, $r = 4.9$, $F = 0.078$, $T_i = 120°F$, 500 rpm, best-power spark advance. Inlet-valve diameter = 1.05 in., lift = 0.262 in. Cam No. 2, I.O. 30°BTC, I.C. 60°ABC, E.O. 60°BBC, E.C. 30°ATC. Cam No. 5, I.O. 3°BTC, I.C. 60°ABC, E.O. 60°BBC, E.C. 3°ATC. (*Sloan Laboratory.*)

Effect of inertia and fluid friction. When a gas flows through a system of pipes, valves, and chambers such as an engine-inlet system, several types of forces may come into play. The relative importance of the various types of forces depends, among other things, upon the gas velocity and the size and shape of the passages.

Forces due to gas viscosity. Gases have viscosity or resistance to shear (see Chap. 6) because molecules in the slow-moving layers of gas cross over into adjacent layers of more rapidly moving gas, and vice versa. When a laminar type of flow exists, this action tends to slow down the faster layers and speed up the slower layers by momentum transfer. In engine-inlet systems the viscous forces are negligible because the turbulence present breaks up the layers of gas.

Forces due to inertia and elasticity of the gases.   When gases pass at high speed through curved or irregular-shaped passages such as the inlet system of an engine, they are subjected to rapid changes in velocity and direction.   These accelerations acting on the mass of the gas give rise to large inertia forces.   The compression and expansion of the flowing gases produce large elastic forces.   It has been found that under these conditions the type of flow and the losses in the inlet system will be determined by the ratio of the inertia forces to the elastic forces.   For flow passages of geometrically similar design such as the inlet systems of

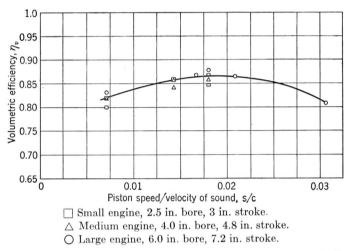

□ Small engine, 2.5 in. bore, 3 in. stroke.
△ Medium engine, 4.0 in. bore, 4.8 in. stroke.
○ Large engine, 6.0 in. bore, 7.2 in. stroke.

Fig. 63. Effect of piston speed on volumetric efficiency of three geometrically similar engines.   (*Sloan Laboratory.*)   Bore 2.5, 4.0, and 6.0 in., $r = 5.7$, $p_i = 28$ in. Hg abs, $p_{ex} = 32$ in. Hg abs.   Best-power fuel-air ratio and spark advance, $T_i = 150°F$, jacket temperature = 150°F.

geometrically similar[1] engines of various sizes, the ratio of inertia to elastic forces will be the same when the value of the quantity u/c is the same.   In this expression, which is known as the Mach number, u is the gas velocity at any given corresponding point in the systems and c is the velocity of sound in the gases.

In Chap. 5, it was shown that velocities in the inlet system are related to piston speed, so that instead of using the value of u at some particular point in the inlet system, it is more convenient to use the ratio s/c as the engine-inlet Mach number.   Since s/c controls the type of flow in the inlet system, it follows that when geometrically similar

---

[1] Two engines are geometrically similar if every linear dimension of one engine is K times that of the corresponding part of the other engine (they are exact scale models of each other).   Thus the length of any particular part may be chosen to represent the size of the engine.   This length is called the characteristic length.

engines are operated at the same static conditions (T_i, p_i, p_{ex}), all the engines, regardless of size, will have the *same curve of* η_v *vs.* s/c. Figure 63 is a typical curve of η_v vs. s/c for a family of various-sized geometrically similar engines.

Changes in the geometry of the inlet system, such as length of inlet manifold, size of inlet valve, or inlet-valve timing, will change the shape of this curve. The exact shape of the curve of η_v vs. s/c cannot be predicted for a new design but must be determined by testing one engine of the family. For a given engine design, each value of s/c results in a single definite value of η_v. It is therefore said that η_v is a "function of s/c," or $\eta_v = f(s/c)$.

Effect of piston speed and engine size on air capacity. Air capacity

$$w_a/\text{min} = \frac{\text{rpm}}{2} \times \text{No. cyls.} \times V_d \gamma_i \eta_v \qquad (61a)$$

Applying this expression to similar engines, we note that $V_d \propto l^3$ and $\eta_v = f(s/c)$. If the static conditions are constant, γ_i is constant and c is also constant since the speed of sound in air depends only on the square root of the air temperature. Then

$$w_a/\text{min} \propto \text{rpm} \times \text{No. cyls.} \times l^3 \times f(s) \qquad (71)$$

From page 74,

$$\text{Piston speed } s = 2 \times \text{rpm} \times \text{stroke} \propto \text{rpm} \times l$$

where l = the characteristic length (see footnote, page 122). Substituting in expression (71),

$$w_a/\text{min.} \propto \text{No. cyls.} \times l^2 \times s \times f(s)$$

or

$$w_a/\text{min} \propto \text{No. cyls.} \times l^2 \, s\eta_v \qquad (72)$$

In comparing the air capacity of different-sized similar engines by expression (72), the square of any corresponding dimension such as (bore)^2 may be used for l^2, or any corresponding areas such as A_p or A_v may be used.

From (72) the air capacity per cylinder per square inch of piston area is proportional to $s\eta_v$. The curve of $s\eta_v$ for a group of similar engines is obtained by taking the curve of η_v vs. s for the group and multiplying it by its own abscissa as in Fig. 64.

It is seen that at the lower piston speeds where η_v is nearly constant, $s\eta_v$, or the air capacity, increases rapidly; but at high piston speeds a point may be reached where η_v is falling off as rapidly as s is increasing. This point will represent the *piston speed* for maximum air capacity and is the *same* for all engines of a similar group, *regardless of size*.

An engine may be mechanically overstressed, owing to the inertia of its moving parts, at a speed lower than that required for maximum air capacity. Inertia forces are proportional to the mass times the acceleration according to Newton's law. In geometrically similar engines, the mass of corresponding parts is proportional to ρl^3. The acceleration of corresponding parts at the same crank angle, due to the rotation of the crankshaft, camshaft, etc., is proportional to $r\omega^2$. In this expression $r \propto l$, and $\omega^2 \propto (\text{rpm})^2$. The inertia forces F will be proportional to

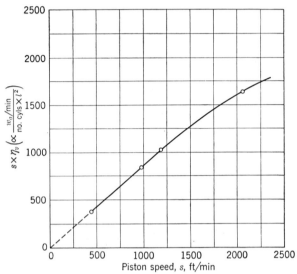

Fig. 64. Effect of piston speed on air capacity of the engines of Fig. 63, plotted as $s\eta_v$ vs. piston speed from the same data.

$\rho l^3 l \times (\text{rpm})^2$. These forces act upon corresponding areas proportional to l^2. The inertia stresses will therefore be

$$\frac{\text{Inertia forces}}{\text{Area}} \propto \frac{\rho l^4 (\text{rpm})^2}{l^2}$$

In similar engines made of the same materials $\rho = \text{constant}$. Thus the inertia stresses will be proportional to $(l \times \text{rpm})^2$. But $l \times \text{rpm} \propto$ piston speed so that inertia stresses $\propto (s)^2$.

From this it is seen that all engines of a similar group will reach the maximum allowable inertia stresses at the *same piston speed*.

Therefore, whether due to consideration of maximum air capacity or limiting inertia stresses, *geometrically similar* engines all tend to be run at the *same piston speed*. Under these conditions the engines will all have the same η_v and the same $s\eta_v$, and their maximum air capacity will be proportional to $l^2 \times$ No. cyls. From this it is seen that an engine of t $\cdots$ ce the characteristic length l having a V_d of $(2)^3$, or 8 times as much, will develop only $(2)^2$, or 4, times as much power when both engines are run at the same piston speed. This may perhaps be more clearly seen when it is realized that the larger engine is running at only half the rpm of the smaller one and so is using its large displacement volume only half as often. Engines should therefore be rated in hp/(No. cyls. $\times l^2$), which might be expressed as

$$\frac{\text{hp/cyl.}}{(\text{Bore})^2} \quad \text{or} \quad \frac{\text{hp/cyl.}}{(V_d)^{2/3}}$$

It is incorrect to rate engines in horsepower per cubic inch of total displacement as is commonly done. Small engines always have more horsepower per cubic inch of displacement since they run at higher rpm and use their displacement volume more often.

Combined Static and Dynamic Effects

The over-all volumetric efficiency is the result of the combined effects of all static and dynamic factors. To clarify this point, assume that all static effects take place in the first compartment in the diagram of Fig. 65

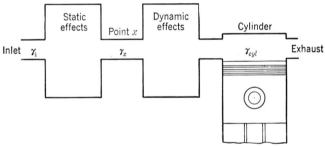

FIG. 65. Diagram showing static and dynamic effects on density of inlet charge as though taking place separately.

and all dynamic effects take place in the second compartment. The effect of the static factors is to change the air density from γ_i to γ_x so $\eta_{v\,\text{static}} = \gamma_x/\gamma_i$. The effect of the dynamic factors is to change the air density from γ_x to γ_{cyl} so $\eta_{v\,\text{dynamic}} = \gamma_{\text{cyl}}/\gamma_x$.

From expression (62),

$$\eta_{v\,\text{over-all}} = \frac{\gamma_{\text{cyl}}}{\gamma_i}$$

$$\eta_{v\,\text{static}} \times \eta_{v\,\text{dynamic}} = \frac{\gamma_x}{\gamma_i}\frac{\gamma_{\text{cyl}}}{\gamma_x} = \frac{\gamma_{\text{cyl}}}{\gamma_i}$$

or

$$\eta_{v\,\text{over-all}} = \eta_{v\,\text{static}} \times \eta_{v\,\text{dynamic}} \tag{73}$$

Similarly the combined static effect is obtained by multiplying the two static effects together.

For a change from one set of operating conditions (1) to another (2) we have from (73)

$$\left(\frac{\eta_{v_2}}{\eta_{v_1}}\right)_{\text{over-all}} = \left(\frac{\eta_{v_2}}{\eta_{v_1}}\right)_{\text{static}} \left(\frac{\eta_{v_2}}{\eta_{v_1}}\right)_{\text{dynamic}} \qquad (74)$$

and from (63) and (70)

$$\left(\frac{\eta_{v_2}}{\eta_{v_1}}\right)_{\text{over-all}} = \sqrt{\frac{T_{i_2}}{T_{i_1}}} \times \frac{r - [p_{ex}/p_i]_2^{1/k}}{r - [p_{ex}/p_i]_1^{1/k}} \left(\frac{\eta_{v_2}}{\eta_{v_1}}\right)_{\text{dynamic}} \qquad (75)$$

To find $(\eta_{v_2}/\eta_{v_1})_{\text{dynamic}}$, obtain from the particular engine or family of similar engines a curve of $\eta_{v\,\text{over-all}}$ vs. s/c similar to Fig. 63 with *any* constant set of static conditions.

For this curve $(\eta_{v_2}/\eta_{v_1})_{\text{static}} = 1$ because the static conditions were not changed while the curve was being run. Therefore from (74) $(\eta_{v_2}/\eta_{v_1})_{\text{over-all}} = (\eta_{v_2}/\eta_{v_1})_{\text{dynamic}}$, and for a change in piston speed the ratio of $(\eta_{v_2}/\eta_{v_1})_{\text{dynamic}}$ can be measured directly from the curve. From expression (34a) for a change in operating conditions

$$\frac{\text{ihp}_2}{\text{ihp}_1} = \frac{(w_a/\text{min})_2}{(w_a/\text{min})_1} \frac{(Fe_c\eta_i)_2}{(Fe_c\eta_i)_1}$$

and from (61a) and (72)

$$\frac{\text{ihp}_2}{\text{ihp}_1} = \frac{\gamma_{i_2}}{\gamma_{i_1}} \frac{(\text{No. cyls.})_2}{(\text{No. cyls.})_1} \left(\frac{l_2}{l_1}\right)^2 \left(\frac{s_2}{s_1}\right) \sqrt{\frac{T_{i_2}}{T_{i_1}}}$$
$$\frac{r - [p_{ex}/p_i]_2^{1/k}}{r - [p_{ex}/p_i]_1^{1/k}} \left(\frac{\eta_{v_2}}{\eta_{v_1}}\right)_{\text{dynamic}} \left[\frac{(Fe_c\eta_i)_2}{(Fe_c\eta_i)_1}\right] \qquad (76)$$

From (43),

$$\text{mep} = \frac{\text{work/cycle}}{V_d} \qquad \text{in.-lb/in.}^3$$

Work per cycle, in.-lb

$$= V_d\gamma_i\eta_v(Fe_c\eta_i)J \times 12$$

In this expression V_d is in cubic feet. If V_d in cubic inches is used, we must divide by 1,728 in.³/ft³. Therefore,

$$\text{imep} = \gamma_i\eta_v(Fe_c\eta_i)\frac{J}{144} \qquad (77)$$

and

$$\frac{(\text{imep})_2}{(\text{imep})_1} = \frac{\gamma_{i_2}}{\gamma_{i_1}} \sqrt{\frac{T_{i_2}}{T_{i_1}}} \times \frac{r - [p_{ex}/p_i]_2^{1/k}}{r - [p_{ex}/p_i]_1^{1/k}} \left(\frac{\eta_{v_2}}{\eta_{v_1}}\right)_{\text{dynamic}} \left[\frac{(Fe_c\eta_i)_2}{(Fe_c\eta_i)_1}\right] \qquad (78)$$

Note that the imep depends only upon how well each cylinder is filled ($\gamma_i \eta_v$), while power depends in addition upon the number of cylinders and size l and piston speed s.

SUGGESTIONS FOR FURTHER READING

Livengood, J. C., and J. D. Stanitz: The Effect of Inlet-valve Design, Size, and Lift on the Air Capacity and Output of a Four-Stroke Engine, *NACA T.N.* 915, 1943.

Livengood, J. C., and J. V. D. Eppes: Effect of Changing the Stroke on Air Capacity, Power Output, and Detonation of a Single-cylinder Engine, *NACA A.R.R.* 4E24, February, 1945.

Livengood, J. C., A. R. Rogowski, and C. F. Taylor: The Volumetric Efficiency of Four-stroke Engines, *SAE Trans.*, vol. 6, no. 4, 1952.

PROBLEMS

1. A spark-ignition engine with $r = 7$ and $p_{ex} = p_i$ has imep $= 124$. The ihp $= 410$. $\eta_v = 0.80$. Assuming a constant rpm and fuel-air ratio, calculate ihp and η_v:

(a) If inlet temperature only is raised 12 per cent.

(b) If inlet pressure only is raised 12 per cent.

(c) If exhaust pressure is raised 12 per cent.

(d) Calculate imep and ihp if engine rpm only is raised 12 per cent (assume η_v remains constant).

2. At constant fuel-air ratio and compression ratio what change in engine-operating conditions could result in the following:

(a) Increase in η_v but a decrease in imep?

(b) Decrease in imep but an increase in ihp?

(c) Increase in imep with no change in η_v?

3. An engine which normally develops 120 ihp and uses 760 lb air/hr is tested at the usual fuel-air ratio and rpm and is found to develop only 105 ihp and use 700 lb air/hr.

(a) What two things in general would you say were wrong with the engine?

(b) How much power would you get if you fixed one of the difficulties *only?*

(c) How much power would you get if you fixed *only* the other difficulty?

4. With standard atmospheric (14.7 psia, 60°F) conditions at inlet and exhaust, an engine gives ihp $= 100$, bhp $= 80$, and bsfc $= 0.55$ lb/bhp-hr. The compression ratio is 7.0.

(a) A supercharger is now added to the engine, which raises the inlet pressure to 20 psia and inlet temperature to 110°F, under otherwise identical conditions. Estimate the ihp of the modified engine.

(b) Estimate the bhp and bsfc of the modified engine if the power to drive the supercharger is 5.5 hp. Assume that the fhp of the engine remains virtually constant.

5. (a) A multicylinder engine with a stroke of 4.5 in. and bore of 4 in. has a curve of volumetric efficiency vs. piston speed the same as that shown in Fig. 63. If this engine has an ihp of 400 at 2,700 rpm, what ihp will a similar engine of 5.35 in. bore develop at 2,700 rpm?

(b) Calculate the ratio of inertia stresses of the large engine to inertia stresses of the small engine under these conditions.

6. A two-cylinder engine has a total displacement of 300 in.³, runs at 2,300 rpm, and develops 120 ihp.

(a) What will be the total displacement of a similar engine with six cylinders which will deliver the same ihp?

(b) At what rpm will it operate?

7. Complete this chart of *similar* cylinders operating at the same piston speed:

Bore, in.	ihp	r.p.m.	η_v	imep
2	——	5,000	——	127
4	34	——	——	——
6	——	——	0.80	——

8. An engine with 6 in. stroke operating at sea level has $\eta_i = 0.30$, $F = 0.08$, heating value of fuel $= 18,500$ Btu/lb, η_v vs. s the same as Fig. 63.

(a) What will be imep at 1,000 rpm?

(b) What will be imep at 2,000 rpm?

(c) If fmep $= 25$ psi at 2,000 rpm, what will bsfc be?

(d) What will imep become at 1,000 rpm if air temperature rises to 130°F?

9. With $p_{ex} = p_i = 14.7$ psia and $T_i = 520°$R, an engine has a curve of η_v vs. piston speed as shown in Fig. 63 and develops 100 ihp at 1,000 fpm piston speed. Calculate η_v and ihp for this engine at 2,000 fpm piston speed if $p_i = 29.4$ psia, $T_i = 640°$R, $p_{ex} = 14.7$ psia. Assume that $r = 7$.

CHAPTER 9

FUEL-AIR-RATIO REQUIREMENTS

Unfortunately there is no single fuel-air ratio which is optimum for all conditions of operation. The fuel-air ratio for maximum power is not the same as the fuel-air ratio for maximum economy, and the fuel-air ratio for maximum economy varies with the per cent of maximum power being developed. The fuel-air ratio requirements for starting, warm-up, and acceleration are also different from those for steady operation.

The carburetor must be designed and adjusted to supply somewhere near the proper mixture under all conditions of operation; otherwise high fuel consumption, loss of power, or other difficulties will result.

Steady-running Requirements

Mixture requirements for maximum power. Figure 39 shows a curve of imep for an engine running at full-throttle opening. The maximum mep occurs at a fuel-air ratio of about 0.08. As explained in Chap. 5, the maximum quantity of fuel is burned and maximum energy is released when a little more than the chemically correct amount of fuel is introduced. When a slight excess of fuel is introduced so that all the oxygen present in the cylinder is used up by the time combustion has ceased, further addition of fuel will do no good because there is no oxygen with which it can combine; and, in fact, the combustion of a large excess of fuel with the *same* amount of oxygen results in a *smaller* amount of energy released.

The effect of closing the throttle (lowering the manifold pressure) is to reduce the indicated power and imep by reducing both γ_i and η_v. This lowers the entire imep curve as shown in Fig. 66. Lower manifold pressure also reduces the flame speed, increasing the time losses. This lowers η_i, which further reduces the imep.

At full throttle and with a best-power mixture, the flame speed is high, and the time losses are very small, since the piston is near top center and moves very little during the burning process. Closing the throttle reduces the flame speed and adds an increment to the crank angle turned during the burning. The piston motion corresponding to this additional crank angle is still quite small, however, so that at $F = 0.08$ the effect of throttling on time losses is almost negligible. When the full-throttle fuel-air mixture is very rich or very lean, the flame speed is low enough so that the piston may be quite far from top center by the time burning is completed. In this case the increase in crank angle required for burning the mixture at part throttle will result in a much larger piston motion. In general, then, throttling increases the time losses when they are already large and has little effect when the time losses are small. The effect of part-throttle time losses may be seen in Fig. 66, where the imep curve for the throttled condition indicates a greater proportionate power loss at very rich or very lean mixture than does the full-throttle curve.

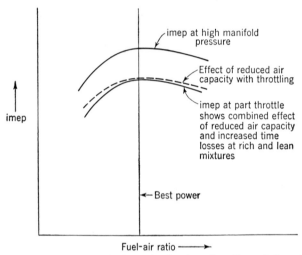

FIG. 66. Diagram of imep vs. fuel-air ratio showing the effect of throttling on imep at constant rpm.

From the above it is seen that, for any given throttle setting, the imep will be maximum at a fuel-air ratio of about 0.08.

$$\text{Mechanical efficiency } \eta_{\text{mech}} = 1 - \frac{\text{fmep}}{\text{imep}} \qquad (54a)$$

Since fmep changes more slowly than imep when the imep is varied, η_{mech} is maximum at high imep.

From expression (53), bmep = imep $\times \eta_{\text{mech}}$; so for any throttle setting or manifold pressure, the bmep will also be maximum at approximately $F = 0.08$, because at this fuel-air ratio both imep and η_{mech} are maximum. Experimental imep and bmep curves are shown in Fig. 67.

Mixture requirements for minimum specific fuel consumption. Figure 39 shows a curve of indicated thermal efficiency for an engine operating at full throttle. The maximum efficiency occurs at a fuel-air ratio of about 0.06. As explained previously, the maximum occurs at a point slightly leaner than the chemically correct fuel-air ratio because excess air ensures complete combustion of the fuel when mixing is not perfect; and the lower maximum temperatures associated with the lean mixture favorably affect the chemical equilibrium and specific heat of the gases. If the mixture is made too lean, however, the flame speed is reduced so

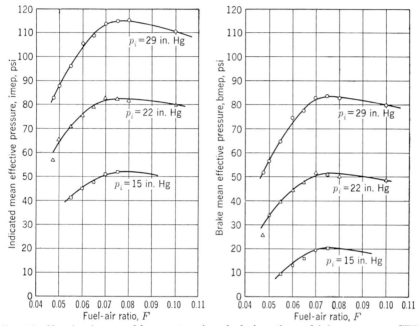

FIG. 67. Showing imep and bmep at various fuel-air ratios and inlet pressures; CFR engine, $3\frac{1}{4} \times 4\frac{1}{2}$, $r = 6$, 1,200 rpm, $p_{ex} = 30$ in. Hg, $T_i = 120°F$, best-power spark advance. (*Sloan Laboratory.*)

much that the large time losses overcome the above-mentioned beneficial effects and the efficiency falls off.

$$\text{isfc} = \frac{2{,}545}{e_c \eta_i} \qquad (36a)$$

The isfc corresponding to the η_i of Fig. 39 is shown in Fig. 68a. The only important effect of throttling on isfc or efficiency is the change in time losses. As discussed above, the time losses are only very slightly affected at $F = 0.08$; but as the mixture is made richer or leaner, the effect of throttling on time losses becomes much larger. Therefore we see that the curves of isfc for part-throttle operation are very close to the full-throttle curve at $F = 0.08$ and draw away from it at leaner and richer mixtures.

On the lean side, the effect is much as though the isfc curve were rotated clockwise about the $F = 0.08$ point. This action shifts the point of minimum isfc (maximum η_i) slightly to the right, or to a richer fuel-air ratio. The point of minimum isfc, or best indicated economy, is thus seen to occur at progressively richer fuel-air ratios as the manifold pressure is reduced (throttle closed).

Since bsfc $=$ isfc$/\eta_{\text{mech}}$ and since η_{mech} is a maximum at maximum imep, then for *any* isfc curve at *any* given throttle setting the corresponding bsfc curve will be closest at $F = 0.08$ and will draw away, especially at

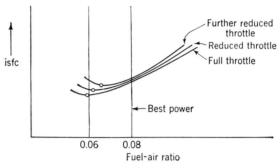

Fɪɢ. 68*a*. Diagram showing effect of throttling on isfc of an engine operating at various fuel-air ratios and constant rpm.

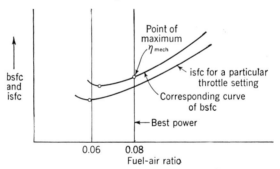

Fɪɢ. 68*b*. Diagram showing isfc and the corresponding bsfc of an engine operating with fixed-throttle setting at various fuel-air ratios and constant rpm.

lean mixtures, where the imep falls off rapidly. The effect of η_{mech} on the location of the minimum bsfc is similar to the effect of throttling on the location of the minimum isfc. Therefore the point of minimum bsfc will occur at slightly richer fuel-air ratios than the corresponding minimum isfc (see Fig. 68*b*). Experimental isfc and bsfc curves are shown in Fig. 69.

It is seen from these curves that, because of the low mechanical efficiency existing at low mep, the bsfc is very high under throttled conditions. This is reasonable because at part throttle most of the fuel energy is being used to overcome friction and only a little is left to pro-

duce useful work.   At full throttle a much larger quantity of fuel energy
enters the engine, approximately the same amount of fuel as before is
used to overcome friction, and most of the fuel energy is left to produce
useful work.

Mixture requirements for various outputs.   At any given rpm, the
curves of bmep and bsfc for various throttle settings will be similar in
shape to Figs. 67 and 69.   At higher rpm, the bsfc curves will be higher
because of the increase in fmep with speed.   The bmep curves will be
lower because the fmep increases with engine speed, while the imep drops

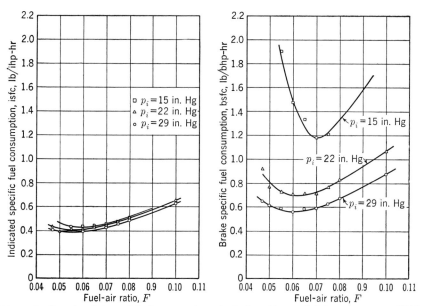

Fig. 69. Showing isfc and bsfc at various fuel-air ratios and inlet pressures; CFR
engine operating under same conditions as in Fig. 67.

off because of the usual drop in η_v at high speeds.   The general shape
and location of maximum imep and minimum isfc will be much the same.

Curves similar to the above are shown in Fig. 70.   Here we see that
there is only one fuel-air ratio and throttle position which will result in
maximum power.   That is point A at $F = 0.08$ and full throttle.   If it is
desired to reduce power to, say 80 per cent of maximum, it might be done
by throttling at $F = 0.08$ to point B.   This will result in an increase in
bsfc from A to B on the lower set of bsfc curves.   The increase is due to
lower mechanical efficiency.   A more economical method would have
been to maintain full throttle and lean out the mixture to point C.
This gives lower bsfc because the lean mixture improves the indicated
thermal efficiency more than enough to compensate for the reduced

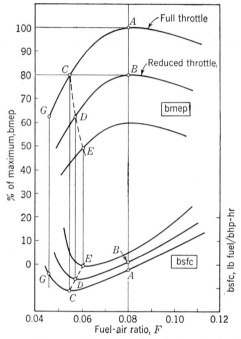

FIG. 70. Typical curves of bmep and corresponding bsfc vs. fuel-air ratio for an engine operating at different throttle positions.

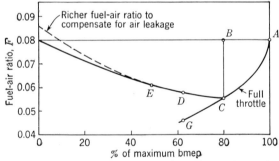

FIG. 71. Optimum fuel-air ratio vs. per cent of maximum bmep for the engine of Figs. 67 and 69.

mechanical efficiency. If still less power were desired, further leaning out at full throttle to point G would be undesirable, as the time losses would be very great at such lean mixtures, and misfiring would also be likely to occur. It would be better in this case to keep the fuel-air ratio adjusted close to the minimums of the various bsfc curves moving from point C to point D and on to point E, etc.

This path, if plotted as optimum fuel-air ratio vs. per cent of maximum bmep, would appear as in Fig. 71.   The points A, B, C, etc., are also shown on this curve.   From A to C the throttle is wide open, and the mixture is reduced from maximum power to maximum economy.   From C to E the fuel-air ratio becomes progressively richer, as explained above. This curve must be automatically approximated by the carburetor over a range of throttle positions and engine speeds.

When the engine is idling very little fuel is used, so that the question of economy is not important.   Since the manifold is at a high vacuum during idling, considerable air may leak in at the various joints and through the inlet-valve guides.   To compensate for this air dilution, the carburetor usually supplies a slightly richer mixture for idling than the extension of the best economy curve would indicate.

Transient Requirements

Volatility tests.   A typical gasoline fuel is a mixture of many hydrocarbons.   Some of them have high vapor pressures and low boiling points.   These are called the "light ends."   Some of them are less volatile and are called the "heavy ends."   One test of gasoline volatility, known as the ASTM distillation, consists in heating 100 ml of gasoline in a flask, passing the vapor through a condenser, and collecting the condensate.   The temperature of the vapor in the flask when the first drop of condensate appears is called the "initial point."   The temperature of the vapor in the flask when 10 ml of condensate has collected is called the "10 per cent point," and the temperature of the vapor when the liquid in the flask disappears is called the "end point."   Another test for volatility is to measure the vapor pressure of the gasoline at 100°F. This is known as the Reid vapor pressure.   Both tests are conducted in a closely prescribed manner using special apparatus.   Figure 72 shows ASTM distillation curves for an automobile and an aviation fuel.

Starting and warm-up requirements.   When a cold engine is turned over during starting, much of the heavy ends supplied by the carburetor remains a liquid or recondenses on the cylinder walls and piston head. Although the fuel-air ratio at the carburetor may be well within the normal combustion limits of gasoline-air mixtures, the ratio of *evaporated* fuel to air in the cylinder may be far too lean to ignite and burn.   It may then be necessary to supply temporarily as much as 5 or 10 times the normal amount of gasoline at the carburetor to obtain enough evaporated light ends to run on, until the manifold and cylinder parts become warm. A low 10 per cent point temperature on the ASTM distillation curve is an indication that large amounts of light ends are present in the gasoline. Such a fuel should show superior cold-weather starting characteristics.

As the engine warms up, the fuel-air ratio supplied at the carburetor must be reduced to keep the evaporated fuel-air ratio from becoming too rich. This adjustment is sometimes made manually and sometimes automatically by means of a thermostatic control. The time required to warm up the engine completely, so that the normal steady-running carburetor adjustment may be resumed, has been found to correlate roughly with the temperature of the central portion of the ASTM curve.

While high volatility is advantageous for starting and warm-up, fuels having low 10 per cent points and high Reid vapor pressures tend to form vapor bubbles in the carburetor and fuel lines if the temperatures in the vicinity of the engine are too high. These vapor bubbles interfere with

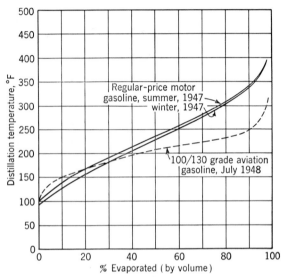

FIG. 72. ASME distillation curves of automobile and aviation gasolines. ("*National Motor-gasoline Survey,*" *Winter,* 1947–1948, *and* "*Survey of Commercial Aviation Gasoline Characteristics,*" *November,* 1948, *U.S. Department of the Interior, R.I.* 4354 *and R.I.* 4435.)

the supply and metering of the fuel and may disturb the fuel-air ratio so seriously as to cause the engine to stop.

A high 90 per cent point temperature is an indication that considerable heavy ends are present. While heavy ends help to reduce the vapor pressure, they tend to cause carbon deposits in the cylinder; and in condensing on the cylinder walls, they dilute and remove the lubricating-oil film. Eventually they may find their way past the piston rings into the crankcase and dilute the engine oil.

It is clear that gasoline must be carefully made to fit the engine and the engine-operating conditions. The refiners vary the ASTM curve and the Reid vapor pressure to suit the type of engine, the geographical location, and the season.

Acceleration requirement. Under steady-running conditions, there is always a fairly large amount of liquid fuel moving along the manifold walls. The air and evaporated fuel take much less time than the liquid streams and large droplets to get from the carburetor to the cylinders. Of course, under equilibrium conditions, the same amount of fuel and air per minute enters the engine as leaves the carburetor. When a sudden increase in power is required and the throttle is suddenly opened, all the additional air and the *evaporated* part of the additional fuel supplied by the carburetor reach the cylinders almost immediately. The unevaporated part of the additional fuel supplied by the carburetor may not reach the cylinders for several seconds after the throttle is opened. The cylinders will therefore temporarily receive only part of the extra fuel which leaves the carburetor. This temporary lean mixture prevents the engine from developing full power just at the time when it is most desired. In some instances it is possible to stall the engine from this cause, simply by opening the throttle suddenly. To avoid this trouble, it is common practice to design the carburetor so that a large amount of fuel will be injected into the inlet manifold if the throttle is suddenly opened. Part of this accelerating charge, as it is called, will be sufficiently atomized or evaporated to be carried into the cylinder with the additional air. Warming the inlet manifold and using volatile fuel will benefit this condition by reducing the amount of unevaporated fuel in the manifold.

Distribution

During warm-up or when fuel of low volatility is used, considerable liquid fuel will be present in the manifold. Even under the best conditions, the manifold will contain a certain amount of liquid and large fuel droplets which do not evaporate until reaching the cylinder. It is common practice to feed two cylinders from a single elbow in the inlet manifold. Unless great care is used in the manifold design, liquid fuel will be thrown to the outside of the elbow, making the fuel-air ratio greater in the cylinder nearest the outside. This effect is illustrated in Fig. 73.

Poor distribution of fuel to the cylinders of a multicylinder engine always results in a loss in power and efficiency and makes the carburetor adjustment much more difficult.

Effect of distribution on power. If Fig. 74 represents the bmep of an engine with perfect distribution, plotted against fuel-air ratio supplied by the carburetor, then each cylinder will have the same fuel-air ratio and will be operating at the same point on the curve. If maximum power is desired, the carburetor is adjusted to $F = 0.08$ and all cylinders will receive a fuel-air ratio of 0.08. If the distribution is poor and the carburetor is still set to supply a 0.08 mixture, some of the cylinders (B', C', D') will be richer than 0.08 and will therefore develop less power. Some (A') will be leaner than 0.08 and will also develop less power. It is particularly disadvantageous to have one cylinder much leaner than the others. As shown in Fig. 74, this cylinder (A) will develop much less

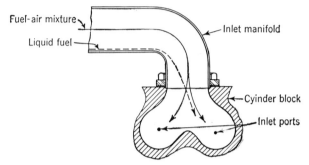

Fig. 73. Liquid fuel flowing along the wall of the inlet manifold may be thrown to the outer side as it turns in manifold elbow, causing the outer cylinder to receive a richer mixture than the inner cylinder.

power, and the carburetor will have to be set rich to bring it up on the flat part of the curve. The other cylinders will then be excessively rich and will waste a great deal of fuel. When a rich mixture is required to control detonation, if one cylinder is running lean then all the other

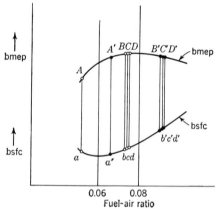

Fig. 74. Effect of poor mixture distribution on bmep and bsfc of a multicylinder engine.

cylinders must be excessively enriched to avoid detonation in the lean cylinder.

Effect of distribution on brake specific fuel consumption. With one cylinder running lean, it was seen above that all the other cylinders would operate at high bsfc if the carburetor were adjusted to increase the power output of the lean cylinder. Thus the bsfc for maximum output would be seriously affected.

For maximum economy with perfect distribution, all cylinders would be operated at about $F = 0.06$. With poor distribution, it will be impossible for all cylinders to operate at minimum bsfc at the same time, and some cylinders will always be wasting fuel. Thus the minimum bsfc for the engine will be increased. With one lean cylinder, it may be impossible to adjust the carburetor to permit the other cylinders (b, c, d) to operate at $F = 0.06$ because, in that case, the lean cylinder (a) may be too lean to fire, or at least the lean cylinder will be operating excessively lean with large time losses and high bsfc.

Methods of improving distribution. For good distribution it is important to evaporate as much of the fuel as possible in the manifold. Distribution is aided by using volatile fuel and warming the manifold walls. Too much manifold heat is undesirable, as it reduces the air capacity and increases the possibility of detonation. Good atomization of the fuel at the carburetor is beneficial. Distribution is usually better at part throttle because violent mixing of fuel and air takes place as the mixture passes the partly opened throttle. A smaller inlet-manifold cross section with consequently increased velocities should help to carry along the larger fuel droplets. Higher engine speeds will have the same effect. The point where fuel is introduced must be chosen with attention to the air-flow conditions in the manifold. Unequal distribution of fuel across the inlet-manifold cross section at the carburetor may persist throughout the length of the manifold. This effect is usually studied experimentally. Centrifugal separation of fuel droplets can be minimized by avoiding sudden changes in direction and sharp corners in the manifold.

SUGGESTIONS FOR FURTHER READING

Berry, O. C., and C. S. Keggerreis: The Carburetion of Gasoline, *Purdue Univ. Eng. Expt. Sta. Bull.* 5, 1920.
Sparrow, S. W.: The Arithmetic of Distribution in a Multi-cylinder Engine, *NACA T.N.* 162, 1923.

PROBLEMS

1. A supercharged engine has a cruising (part throttle) bsfc of 0.43 at 2,000 rpm and 0.06 fuel-air ratio. Its mechanical efficiency is 89 per cent, and its bmep is 180 psi. Assuming the fmep remains constant,

(*a*) What will the mechanical efficiency be at full throttle, $F = 0.09$, bmep = 240 psi?

(*b*) What will the full-throttle bsfc be if enriching from 0.06 to 0.09 fuel-air ratio reduces indicated thermal efficiency from 32 to 24 per cent?

2. Assume a fuel has been found which burns very rapidly at any fuel-air ratio. Plot a curve of isfc vs. F for an engine using this fuel. On the same sheet plot for comparison a curve of isfc vs. F for the same engine using a normal fuel. Explain briefly.

3. Plot a curve of bsfc vs. fuel-air ratio for an engine at full throttle having:

(*a*) No time loss, but with friction loss present.

(*b*) No time loss and no friction loss.

Indicate the position of the chemically correct fuel-air ratio.

4. When tested separately, each cylinder of a two-cylinder engine gives the performance shown in Fig. 39. When assembled as a two-cylinder engine, one cylinder receives a 25 per cent leaner mixture than the other, although the quantity of air received by each is the same. Calculate the imep and isfc of the engine when the fuel-air ratio supplied by the carburetor is 0.065.

5. (*a*) Each cylinder of a two-cylinder engine has the characteristics of Fig. 39, when operated at full throttle at an inlet temperature of 100°F. Owing to poor distribution one cylinder has an F of 0.060; the other has an F of 0.076. If the fmep is 20 psi, what is the bsfc of this engine?

(*b*) By increasing the inlet temperature to 300°F, it is possible to obtain *perfect* distribution, but the increase in inlet temperature reduces the imep of the engine to 86 per cent of its previous value. Assuming the same fmep, and F at the carburetor as in (*a*), calculate the resulting bsfc.

6. Figure 37 shows about 1% O_2 and 1% CO in the exhaust gases of an engine at $F = 0.067$. Explain clearly but briefly the effect of poorer mixing of fuel and air on these two percentages.

CHAPTER 10

CARBURETORS

Purpose. The function of the carburetor is to supply fuel in such quantities as to meet the mixture requirements of the engine at all times.

Main Metering System

The main metering system of the conventional carburetor consists of a mechanism which supplies a nearly constant, basic fuel-air ratio over a wide range of speeds and loads. This mixture corresponds approximately to best economy at full throttle, *i.e.*, about the minimum useful fuel-air ratio the engine will require. To obtain the richer mixtures necessary for full-power and for part-throttle operation, supplementary devices are employed in the carburetor.

The main metering system usually consists of one or more venturis through which the engine air passes. The pressure drop produced in the venturi throats by the air flow is used directly or indirectly to control the rate of fuel flow through one or more fuel orifices. The fuel is then mixed with the incoming air in the form of small droplets by means of a nozzle.

Orifice or venturi with incompressible fluid. Although the air is expanded and compressed as it flows through the carburetor venturi, for the sake of simplicity it will be considered incompressible, as is the fuel, and suitable corrections will be made later.

Assuming a frictionless flow of air through a venturi with no heat transfer and negligible difference in height between entrance and throat, expression (28) may be applied between the entrance (1) and throat (2) (see Fig. 75a). The entire expression need not be used because, with no heat transfer, $Q = 0$; with no external work being done, $W = 0$; $Z_2 - Z_1$ is assumed negligible; and without friction or compression, $E_2 = E_1$. Therefore,

$$\frac{wu_2^2}{2gJ} - \frac{wu_1^2}{2gJ} = \frac{p_1 V_1}{J} - \frac{p_2 V_2}{J} \qquad (79)$$

From (5), $\gamma = w/V$; dividing (79) by w, and substituting,

$$\frac{u_2^2 - u_1^2}{2gJ} = \frac{p_1 - p_2}{\gamma_a J}, \qquad (80)$$

141

or

$$u_2{}^2 - u_1{}^2 = \frac{2g}{\gamma_a}(p_1 - p_2) \qquad (80a)$$

If A is the cross-sectional area at any point and γ_a is constant, the same weight of air $(A\gamma_a u)$ passes 1 as passes 2, so that

$$A_1\gamma_a u_1 = A_2\gamma_a u_2, \text{ or } A_1 u_1 = A_2 u_2, \text{ or } u_1 = (A_2/A_1)u_2. \qquad (81)$$

Substituting (81) in (80a),

$$u_2{}^2\left[1 - \left(\frac{A_2}{A_1}\right)^2\right] = \frac{2g}{\gamma_a}(p_1 - p_2),$$

and

$$u_2 = \sqrt{\frac{2g\dfrac{\Delta p_a}{\gamma_a}}{1 - (A_2/A_1)^2}} \qquad (82)$$

where $\Delta p_a = (p_1 - p_2)$.

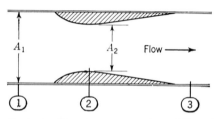

Fig. 75a. Venturi with entrance area A_1 and throat area A_2.

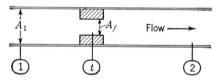

Fig. 75b. Fuel-metering orifice with orifice area A_f.

The factor $\sqrt{1 - (A_2/A_1)^2}$ is a correction for the approach velocity u_1. If A_1 is large compared with A_2, u_1 will be negligible and (82) will reduce to

$$u_2 = \sqrt{2g\frac{\Delta p_a}{\gamma_a}} \qquad (83)$$

The flow in pounds per second $(w_a/\text{sec}) = A_2\gamma_a u_2$. Substituting in (82)

$$w_a/\text{sec} = A_2\sqrt{\frac{2g\gamma_a \Delta p_a}{1 - (A_2/A_1)^2}} \qquad (84)$$

In any actual venturi the contraction of the stream may prevent it from completely utilizing the area A_2, while friction will cause an increase in E_2 (heating of the fluid) which from expression (28) will result in a lower value for u_2. These effects may be provided for in any given orifice by the use of a coefficient of discharge C_a defined as

$$\frac{\text{lb/sec, actual flow}}{\text{lb/sec, theoretical flow}}$$

Including the coefficient of discharge, expression (84) may be rewritten as

$$w_a/\text{sec} = A_2 C_a \sqrt{\frac{2g\gamma_a \, \Delta p_a}{1 - (A_2/A_1)^2}} \qquad (84a)$$

If the approach-velocity factor is combined with C_a into a single coefficient, this is called K_a, the flow coefficient. In this case,

$$w_a/\text{sec} = A_2 K_a \sqrt{2g\gamma_a \, \Delta p_a} \qquad (84b)$$

The fuel is metered in the carburetor by flowing through one or more orifices (see Fig. 75b). The same theory applies to the fuel flow, and the same sort of expression as (84b) is obtained, with Δp being the pressure drop between the orifice inlet and orifice throat. The pressure drop between orifice inlet and orifice *outlet* ($p_1 - p_2$) is called Δp_f and may be used instead of $p_1 - p_t$ in the expression for fuel flow by changing the flow coefficient K_f. When this is done,

$$w_f/\text{sec} = A_f K_f \sqrt{2g\gamma_f \, \Delta p_f} \qquad (85)$$

The fuel-air ratio supplied by the carburetor is therefore, from (84b) and (85),

$$F = \frac{w_f/\text{sec}}{w_a/\text{sec}} = \frac{A_f K_f}{A_2 K_a} \sqrt{\frac{\gamma_f}{\gamma_a}} \sqrt{\frac{\Delta p_f}{\Delta p_a}} \qquad (86)$$

The simple carburetor. Figure 76 is a diagram of the main metering system of a simple carburetor. The fuel is pumped or flows by gravity into the float chamber. When the fuel reaches the proper height in the chamber, the float rises sufficiently to cut off the flow. The level of the fuel is thus kept constant in the float chamber. The fuel flows out of the float chamber through a metering orifice into the nozzle, which opens into the venturi throat. When no air is flowing through the venturi, the air pressure on the fuel surface at the top of the nozzle in the venturi throat is the same as the air pressure on the fuel surface in the float chamber and no fuel will flow.

When the engine is running, air will flow through the venturi, making p_2 less than p_1, that is, a pressure drop $\Delta p_a = p_1 - p_2$ will exist between the entrance of the venturi and the throat.   The air pressure on the fuel surface in the float chamber is p_1.   The pressure on the fuel at the entrance to the fuel orifice will be equal to the air pressure on the float-chamber fuel surface plus the pressure due to the depth of the fuel.   This is $p_1 + \gamma_f h$, where h is the depth of the fuel orifice below the surface.   If the top of the nozzle is level with the fuel surface in the float chamber, the

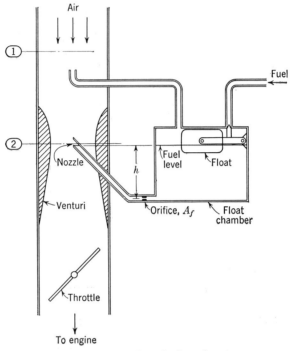

FIG. 76. Simple downdraft carburetor.

pressure on the fuel at the outlet of the fuel orifice will be $p_2 + \gamma_f h$ so that Δp_f across the fuel orifice will be

$$(p_1 + \gamma_f h) - (p_2 + \gamma_f h) = p_1 - p_2 = \Delta p_a$$

With Δp_f in this case equal to Δp_a, the fuel-air ratio for this main metering system will be, from (86),

$$F = \frac{A_f K_f}{A_2 K_a} \sqrt{\frac{\gamma_f}{\gamma_a}} \tag{87}$$

Effect of nozzle lip.   It is not practical to have the top of the nozzle at the same level as the float-chamber fuel, for unless the carburetor is level, fuel may run out the nozzle when the engine is not operating, wasting fuel and creating a fire hazard.   In actual carburetors the top of the fuel nozzle is always made slightly higher than the float-chamber fuel level (see Fig. 77). If x is the effective height of the nozzle above the fuel level in the float chamber,

$$\Delta p_f = (p_1 + \gamma_f h) - [p_2 + \gamma_f(h + x)]$$

and

$$\Delta p_f = \Delta p_a - \gamma_f x \tag{88}$$

Enough air must pass through the venturi to make $\Delta p_a = \gamma_f x$ before the fuel is raised to the top of the nozzle. When $\Delta p_a > \gamma_f x$, fuel flow will

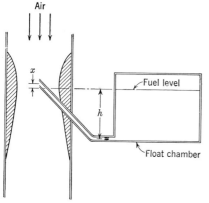

Fig. 77. Nozzle with a lip of effective height x above fuel level.

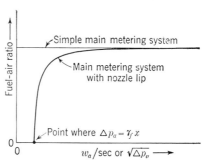

Fig. 78. Effect of nozzle lip on fuel-air ratio in a main metering system.

start, as Δp_f will then be positive. The fuel-air ratio for a carburetor with a lip of this sort will be, from (86) and (88),

$$F = \frac{A_f K_f}{A_2 K_a} \sqrt{\frac{\gamma_f}{\gamma_a}} \sqrt{\frac{\Delta p_a - \gamma_f x}{\Delta p_a}} = \frac{A_f K_f}{A_2 K_a} \sqrt{\frac{\gamma_f}{\gamma_a}} \sqrt{1 - \frac{\gamma_f x}{\Delta p_a}} \tag{89}$$

At low air flows where Δp_a is less than $\gamma_f x$, there will be no fuel flow. At intermediate air flows, F will be less than given by expression (87) for the simple metering system; but at high air flows, where Δp_a is large compared with $\gamma_f x$, the fraction $\gamma_f x/\Delta p_a$ becomes negligible, and the fuel-air ratio approaches that for the simple carburetor. Curves of fuel-air ratio vs. air flow for these two metering systems are shown in Fig. 78.

In many carburetors a vent line is run from the top of the float chamber to the entrance to the carburetor. This is to make sure that p_1 pressure is acting on the fuel surface in the float chamber.[1]

Effect of altitude. A carburetor properly adjusted at sea level will

---

[1] A vent tube such as that shown in Fig. 76 will pick up total pressure at point 1. This is the pressure which would have existed at 1 if A_1 were infinitely large. In this case, therefore, the approach factor is unity and may be neglected.

supply too rich a mixture at high altitude.   This is due to the fact that the air density γ_a decreases with altitude.   Expression (87) shows that with a simple metering system $F \propto 1/\sqrt{\gamma_a}$ as the altitude changes.   At 15,000 ft altitude $\gamma_a = 0.0481$ so that

$$\frac{F_{15,000}}{F_{sl}} = \sqrt{\frac{0.0765}{0.0481}} = 1.26$$

Such a large change in F is not permissible, so that carburetors for use above about 5,000 ft are equipped with automatic altitude compensation.

If the carburetor nozzle has a lip, then expression (89) applies and it is necessary to know Δp_a to calculate F. To find Δp_a, estimate the air capacity by the methods of Chap. 8, and solve for Δp_a in expression (84b).

Effect of compressibility.   Since p_2 is less than p_1 and the air flowing through the venturi is not incompressible, the density of the air in the throat will be less than the density of the air at the entrance.   This change in density will have the effect of increasing u_2 but of reducing w_a/sec.   Expression (84b) is therefore not exact.   The exact expression for w_a/sec is

$$w_a/\text{sec} = A_2 K_a \sqrt{2g\gamma_a \Delta p_a}\ \Phi_1 \tag{90}$$

where γ_a = density of air at entrance to carburetor air passage

$\quad\Phi_1$ = compressibility factor

It can be shown that the compressibility factor

$$\Phi_1 = \left(\frac{p_2}{p_1}\right)^{1/k} \sqrt{\frac{k}{k-1}\frac{\left[1 - \left(\dfrac{p_2}{p_1}\right)^{(k-1)/k}\right]}{1 - (p_2/p_1)}}$$

For a given value of k, the value of Φ_1 depends therefore upon the value of p_2/p_1, or $\Delta p_a/p_1$. Φ_1 for air is plotted against $\Delta p_a/p_1$ in Fig. 79.   At low flows, when $p_2 \approx p_1$ and the air is not subject to much expansion in the venturi throat, Φ_1 approaches one, and expression (90) becomes the same as (84b).

Critical flow.   If the downstream pressure p_3 in the venturi is reduced, with a constant upstream pressure p_1, the w_a/sec will increase until $\Delta p_a/p_1$ reaches a value of 0.472.   When this value is reached, the velocity at the throat will be sonic.   Any further reduction in p_3 will have no effect on p_2, on $\Delta p_a/p_1$, or on w_a/sec.   This is called the critical flow for the venturi.   At critical flow $\Phi_1 = 0.705$.

The value of the critical flow for a given venturi can be found by rewriting expression (90) as

$$w_a/\text{sec} = A_2 K_a \sqrt{2g\gamma_a p_1}\sqrt{\frac{\Delta p_a}{p_1}}\ \Phi_1 \tag{90a}$$

Substituting the critical values of $\Delta p_a/p_1$ and Φ_i,

$$\text{Critical } w_a/\text{sec} = A_2 K_a \sqrt{2g\gamma_a p_1} \times \sqrt{0.472} \times 0.705 \qquad (91)$$

This is the maximum amount of air which will flow through the venturi at γ_a entrance density and p_1 entrance pressure.

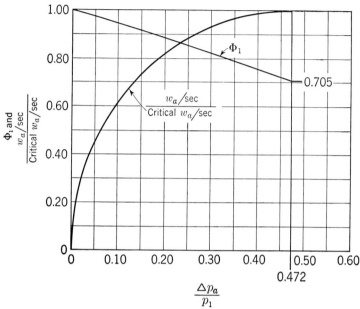

FIG. 79. Compressibility factor Φ_1 and ratio of w_a/sec to critical w_a/sec vs. $\Delta p_a/p_1$.

At any other value of w_a/sec,

$$\frac{w_a/\text{sec}}{\text{Critical } w_a/\text{sec}} = \frac{A_2 K_a \sqrt{2g\gamma_a p_1} \times \sqrt{\Delta p_a/p_1} \times \Phi_1}{A_2 K_a \sqrt{2g\gamma_a p_1} \times \sqrt{0.472} \times 0.705}$$

$$= \sqrt{\frac{(\Delta p_a/p_1)}{0.472}} \times \frac{\Phi_1}{0.705} \qquad (92)$$

Expression (92) shows that the fraction of critical flow existing and the values of $\Delta p_a/p_1$ and Φ_1 depend upon each other. Therefore $(w_a/\text{sec})/(\text{critical } w_a/\text{sec})$ can be plotted against $\Delta p_a/p_1$ as in Fig. 79.

Using Fig. 79 and expression (90a), w_a/sec can be found for any value of $\Delta p_a/p_1$. Also the value of $\Delta p_a/p_1$ can be found for any value of w_a/sec by first calculating critical w_a/sec from (91) and using Fig. 79.

Example. (*a*) What is the maximum possible flow through a 2-in.-diameter venturi with $K_a = 0.9$ and standard sea-level conditions?

(*b*) What flow will take place when $\Delta p_a = 2$ psi?

(*c*) What will be the value of Δp_a at $w_a = 0.850$ lb/sec?

Solution. (a) Using (91) with $\gamma_a = 0.0765$ lb/ft^3 and $p_1 = 14.7$ psia,

$$w_a/\text{sec} = \frac{\pi \times (2)^2}{4 \times 144} \times 0.9 \sqrt{2 \times 32.2 \times 0.0765 \times 14.7 \times 144} \times \sqrt{0.472} \times 0.705$$

$$= 0.970 \text{ lb/sec}$$

(b)
$$\frac{\Delta p_a}{p_1} = \frac{2}{14.7} = 0.136$$

From Fig. 79

$$\frac{w_a}{w_{a_{\text{crit}}}} = 0.70$$

$$w_a = 0.70 \times 0.970 = 0.679 \text{ lb/sec}$$

(c)
$$\frac{w_a}{w_{a_{\text{crit}}}} = \frac{0.850}{0.970} = 0.875$$

From Fig. 79

$$\frac{\Delta p_a}{p_1} = 0.24$$

$$\Delta p_a = 0.24 \times 14.7 = 3.53 \text{ psi}$$

Effect of compressibility on fuel-air ratio. The exact expression for fuel-air ratio is found by substituting (90) for (84b) in expression (86).

$$F = \frac{A_f K_f}{A_2 K_a} \sqrt{\frac{\gamma_f}{\gamma_a}} \sqrt{\frac{\Delta p_f}{\Delta p_a}} \times \frac{1}{\Phi_1} \tag{93}$$

or by substituting in expression (89),

$$F = \frac{A_f K_f}{A_2 K_a} \sqrt{\frac{\gamma_f}{\gamma_a}} \sqrt{1 - \frac{\gamma_f x}{\Delta p_a}} \times \frac{1}{\Phi_1} \tag{94}$$

If the flow coefficients are assumed constant and if the altitude is constant and x is negligible, it is seen that $F \propto 1/\Phi_1$. This quantity varies from 1.00 to $1/0.705$ as the air flow goes from zero to the critical value. Therefore the fuel-air ratio is subject to a possible enrichment of $1/0.705 = 1.42$, or 42 per cent. This enrichment is avoided by making the venturi large enough so that the maximum air capacity of the engine will represent only a small fraction of the critical flow. In aircraft engines which have the supercharger between the carburetor and the engine, special difficulties with compressibility are encountered. From expression (91) it is seen that critical flow occurs at lower air quantities at high altitude since $\sqrt{\gamma_a p_1}$ is smaller. In maintaining the same air flow at altitude as at sea level by means of the supercharger, the carburetor is working at a higher per cent of critical flow and therefore a lower value of Φ_1. This reduction in Φ_1 results in enrichment which is in addition to the effect of reduced γ_a discussed on page 146. To avoid the use of an excessively large carburetor for high-altitude work, the supercharging is often divided into two stages, with the carburetor installed after the first stage. In this way the "altitude" at the carburetor will be reduced.

Mixture Control

The main metering system of a carburetor is usually designed to supply a fuel-air ratio of about 0.06 at the higher air flows. This fuel-air ratio represents approximately maximum economy at *full throttle*, the lowest fuel-air ratio on the mixture-requirement curve of Fig. 71. It is therefore necessary to provide means for varying the mixture to obtain maximum power when required and best economy at part throttle and to meet various transient conditions which will be discussed later.

The metering pin. One method of changing the fuel-air ratio is to provide a tapered pin which is arranged to be moved in and out of the

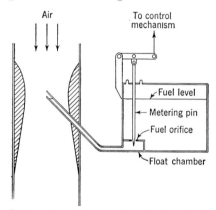

Fig. 80. Carburetor with metering pin in main fuel orifice.

main fuel orifice or in and out of an auxiliary fuel orifice. Motion of this pin may be produced manually or by means of some automatic mechanism. The motion of the metering pin will change the value of $A_f K_f$ in expression (93). A metering-pin mixture control is shown in Fig. 80.

Back-suction control. A method for changing the fuel-air ratio which is widely used in the larger carburetors, probably because it is easily adaptable to automatic control, is the back-suction control. A diagram of this system is shown in Fig. 81. A relatively large vent line connects the carburetor entrance (point 1) with the top of the float chamber. Another line, containing a very small orifice, connects the top of the float chamber with the venturi throat (point 2). During operation there will be a very slight air flow through these two lines from point 1 to point 2. A sliding valve is placed in the large vent line. This is the control element. When the valve is wide open, the vent line is unrestricted, the pressure in the float chamber is essentially equal to p_1, and the fuel orifice operates with $\Delta p_f \approx (p_1 - p_2)$. If the slide valve is closed, the float chamber communicates only with the venturi throat and the pressure on the fuel surface will be p_2. Then Δp_f will be zero, and no fuel will flow. By adjusting the control valve, the relative pressure drop at the valve and at the small orifice may be varied, and any pressure between p_1 and p_2 may be obtained in the float chamber. With back-suction control, Δp_f will no longer be $\Delta p_a - \gamma_f x$ [Eq. (88)] but will be

$$\Delta p_f = (p_c - p_2) - \gamma_f x \qquad (95)$$

where p_c is float-chamber pressure.

Mixture control for altitude compensation. On page 146 it was pointed out that as the altitude is increased, the fuel-air ratio becomes richer in

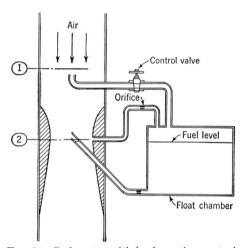

Fig. 81. Carburetor with back-suction control.

proportion to $1/\sqrt{\gamma_a}$. In aircraft carburetors the metering pin or back-suction-control valve is usually actuated by a sealed metal bellows which is placed in the entrance to the carburetor. The bellows is filled with nitrogen, which quickly assumes the same pressure and temperature as that of the entering air; *i.e.*, the expansion of the nitrogen and the motion of the bellows will depend upon γ_a. By suitable design, the value of $A_f K_f$ or of p_c can be made to change to compensate for all changes in $1/\sqrt{\gamma_a}$. There will still be some disturbance of the fuel-air ratio at altitude due to changes in Φ_1 as the ratio of air flow to critical air flow is changed.

Mixture control for maximum power. In the discussion of Chap. 9 it was shown to be uneconomical to reduce engine power from maximum by closing the throttle. If maximum power is no longer desired, the output is best reduced by leaning out the mixture until the maximum-economy fuel-air ratio is obtained at full throttle. For still less power the throttle is gradually closed, and the fuel-air ratio is kept at best economy along the curve of Fig. 71.

The device which changes the mixture from maximum power to maximum economy when maximum power is no longer required is called the *economizer system*. The economizer mixture control is usually of the metering-pin type. The pin is fully withdrawn from the fuel orifice only when maximum power is required. In automobiles the economizer metering pin may be linked to the throttle so that when the throttle is almost fully open the metering pin is withdrawn. This

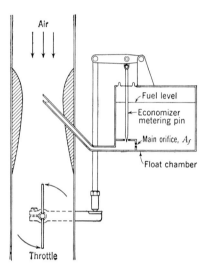

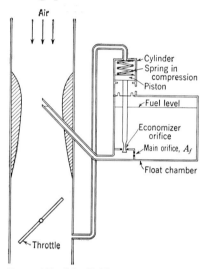

Fig. 82a. Throttle-operated economizer in a carburetor.

Fig. 82b. Manifold-pressure-operated economizer in a carburetor.

ensures maximum-power mixture whenever the throttle is wide-open. Sometimes the economizer system is depended upon to give additional enrichment for detonation control at high outputs. Enrichment for detonation control may be desired *before* the throttle is wide-open in the case of an engine climbing a steep hill or accelerating, because the lower engine speed is conducive to detonation. Level-road operation at the same throttle setting as above may cause no detonation because of the higher engine speed. Since enrichment is not always desired at the same throttle setting, the economizer in some automobile carburetors is actuated by the manifold pressure. When the throttle is opened, the manifold pressure rises. The change in manifold pressure acting on a piston withdraws the metering pin. The manifold pressure at full-throttle high engine speed is less than at full-throttle low engine speed, because of friction in the manifold. Thus if the economizer is set to enrich at full-throttle high speed, it will enrich at less than full throttle at low speed. This may be an advantage if detonation is present since, at the same manifold pressure, detonation may be present at low engine speed but not at high engine speed. Examples of both types of economizer are shown in Fig. 82 *a* and *b*.

In constant-speed engines, the economizer is sometimes operated by the air-metering element so that enrichment occurs near maximum air capacity. This would be unsatisfactory in variable-speed engines, for if the economizer were set to operate near full throttle at high speed, it would fail to operate at full-throttle low speed because the low-speed air capacity would not be high enough.

Idle cutoff. An idling automobile engine is stopped by merely turning off the ignition. In high-performance engines, particularly the air-cooled type, the engine may be quite warm when idling owing to the low velocity of the air over the cooling surfaces. When the ignition is turned off and the engine slows down almost to a stop, preignition sometimes takes place in one or two cylinders. Because of the low rpm, the inertia of the flywheel or propeller is not sufficient to carry the piston over top center, and the engine "kicks back" and turns backward a revolution or so. The reversal of direction imposes undesirable stresses on such parts as supercharger gear trains and is therefore avoided when possible.

In stopping an engine of this type, the throttle is opened slightly to increase the idling rpm. With the ignition still on, the mixture control is moved to the idle-cutoff position. This operates a valve which completely closes all fuel orifices. The engine may fire a few times as it uses the fuel still in the inlet manifold, but by the time the engine speed has dropped enough so that a "kickback" is possible, the fuel-air ratio will be too lean to fire and the engine will stop smoothly. The ignition is then shut off.

Idling system. In Fig. 78 it was shown that the main metering system not only failed to enrich the mixture at low air flows to keep the fuel-air ratio at best economy according to the optimum curve of Fig. 71 but also supplied no fuel at all at idling. The idling or low-speed fuel-metering system is provided to compensate for this defect in the main metering system.

In a conventional idling system such as is shown in Fig. 83, a small fuel line is run from the float chamber to a point a little on the engine side of the throttle. This line usually contains a fixed fuel orifice. As the throttle is closed, the manifold suction increases, drawing more fuel through the idle metering orifice and discharging it from openings *b* and *c*. (The air bleed *a* is to prevent siphoning of fuel from the float chamber when the manifold pressure is high.) With the air flow decreasing and the fuel flow from the idling system increasing, it is possible to obtain too rich a mixture from the idling system at nearly closed throttle. The small opening b discharges fuel until the edge of the throttle plate moves past it. When this occurs, the air pressure on opening b will become much higher than the air pressure on opening c. Air will enter b and reduce the suction on the idling system. This action keeps the idling fuel-air ratio from becoming too rich. The needle valve in opening c is for manually adjusting the idling mixture.

Most idle systems are very difficult to analyze, and the final design is the result of much experimentation. The sum of the idling-system, economizer-system, and main-metering-system fuel flow should approximate Fig. 71.

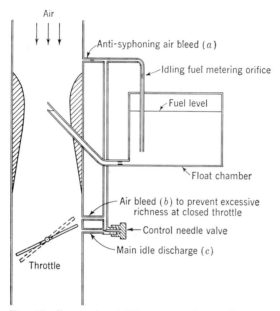

Fig. 83. Conventional idling system in a carburetor.

Accelerating pump. As mentioned in Chap. 9, it is necessary to supply a temporarily rich mixture to the manifold when the throttle is suddenly opened, because the additional air supply reaches the engine quickly, while part of the additional fuel may not reach the engine for several seconds after the throttle is opened.

Figure 84 shows one type of accelerating pump. The pump consists of a piston connected to the piston rod through a spring. The piston operates in a cylinder, which receives its fuel from the float chamber and has an outlet into the inlet manifold. The piston rod is connected so that opening the throttle moves the piston into the cylinder. When the throttle is moved slowly, the fuel in the pump cylinder can flow back into the float chamber through small passages. When the throttle is suddenly opened, the piston rod moves down, compressing the spring. The spring then forces the piston down, and the fuel in the pump cylinder is injected into the manifold air stream during the period of temporary leanness.

Choke valve.   To provide the rich mixtures required for cold starting and warm-up, automobile carburetors are supplied with a butterfly valve situated between the entrance to the carburetor (point 1) and the venturi

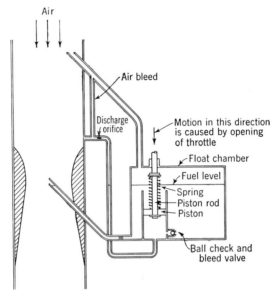

Fig. 84. Accelerating-pump mechanism in a carburetor.

throat (point 2).   Figure 85 shows a typical choke valve.   By partly closing the choke, a larger pressure drop can be produced between 1 and 2 than would normally result from the amount of air flowing through the venturi.   This strong suction at the venturi throat will draw large quantities of fuel from the nozzle and supply enough light ends in the cylinders to bring the ratio of evaporated fuel to air within the combustible limits.   Choke valves are sometimes made with a spring-loaded by-pass so that high pressure drops and excessive choking will not result after the engine has started and has attained a higher rpm.   Since the amount of choking required depends upon the temperature of the engine parts, the choke is often automatically controlled by means of a thermostat.

Priming.   The choking process requires several revolutions of the engine to fill the manifold and cylinders with rich mixture and is therefore best suited to engines having electric starters.   In the past, aircraft engines have been started by manually turning the propeller or by the use of inertia starters which store up enough energy in a flywheel to turn the engine through only a few revolutions. To supply a rich mixture for starting aircraft engines without preliminary turning, it has been the practice to use a manually operated priming pump which pumps liquid fuel through a special system of small pipes, into the inlet ports of several cylinders. With this system, one or two cylinders will be ready to fire on the first revolution of the engine.

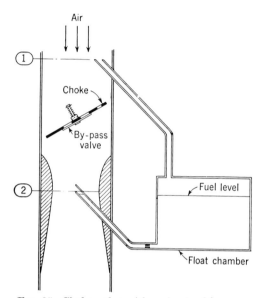

FIG. 85. Choke valve with spring-load by-pass.

The Injection Carburetor

It is sometimes inconvenient to introduce the fuel into the air stream at the venturi throat. The evaporation of the fuel may lower the mixture temperature enough to freeze the moisture in the air. When this happens, ice may collect on the throttle, reducing the air capacity of the engine to a dangerous extent, or may form in the venturi, changing its shape and metering characteristics. It is therefore advantageous to introduce the fuel at some other point in the inlet system where the temperature or movement of the parts will prevent ice formation. Favorite locations are after the throttle and at the supercharger impeller hub. Distribution may also be improved when it is possible to locate the fuel nozzle advantageously with regard to the air flow in the inlet system.

Principles. The injection carburetor operates on the same principle as the conventional float-type carburetor, but the fuel flow is controlled *indirectly* by the venturi pressure drop. The fuel nozzle may be located wherever desired with this carburetor, and the pressure available at the nozzle for atomization of the fuel can be comparatively high.   The float chamber, which is not suitable for flight acrobatics because it must remain level to function properly, is eliminated.   Figure 86 is a diagram of an injection-type carburetor.   The air flow to the engine is controlled by the throttle in the usual way.   As the air flows through the venturi, the usual pressure drop Δp_a is produced.   The throat pressure p_2 is led to chamber B, while the total entrance pressure p_1 is picked up by means

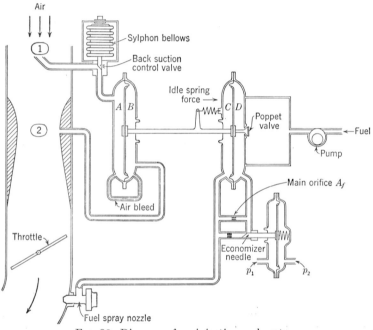

FIG. 86. Diagram of an injection carburetor.

of impact tubes and carried to chamber A.   The diaphragm separating these two chambers thus has a pressure difference acting on it of Δp_a. This pressure acting on the diaphragm area produces a force which tends to move the rod connecting the air-chamber diaphragm with the diaphragm between fuel chambers C and D.   An extension of this rod operates a poppet valve, permitting fuel at fuel-pump pressure to enter chamber D.   This fuel flows through the various fuel-metering orifices to the fuel nozzle.   Chamber C is connected to the nozzle side of the fuel orifices.   As the fuel poppet valve opens owing to the Δp_a across the air diaphragm, increasing amounts of fuel flow through the fuel orifices and out the nozzle.   The rising pressure drop Δp_f across the fuel orifices due to the increasing fuel flow is communicated to chambers C and D.   When

Δp_f becomes equal to Δp_a, the force acting on the fuel diaphragm will be equal and opposite to the force acting on the air diaphragm and the poppet will not open any farther. The operation of the carburetor is insensitive to the exact pressure required to operate the spray nozzle or the exact value of the fuel-pump pressure, except that the fuel-pump pressure must be considerably higher than that required to open the nozzle. For example, let us suppose that $\Delta p_a = 3$ psi, the pressure required to operate the nozzle is 5 psi, and the fuel pump pressure is 15 psi. With $\Delta p_a = 3$ psi the poppet will open until enough fuel flows through the fuel orifices to produce $\Delta p_f = 3$ psi; then the pressure in chamber C will be nozzle pressure $= 5$ psi, and the pressure in chamber D will be nozzle pressure $+ \Delta p_f = 5 + 3 = 8$ psi. The poppet will be in such a position as to give a drop from 15 to 8 psi. If the pump pressure rises to 17 psi, more fuel will flow through the poppet and through the orifices. This will make the pressure in chamber D greater than 8 psi and Δp_f greater than Δp_a; and the rod will be forced to the left, closing the poppet until the pressure in chamber D is restored to 8 psi.

Idling. For idling, and to enrich the mixture for best economy at lower air flows, a small spring is used which applies a slight force on the fuel diaphragm, tending to hold the poppet valve open. With the idle spring acting,

$$\Delta p_f = \Delta p_a + \Delta p_i \tag{96}$$

where Δp_i is the idle-spring force per square inch of diaphragm area. Substituting (96) in expression (93),

$$F = \frac{A_f K_f}{A_2 K_a} \sqrt{\frac{\gamma_f}{\gamma_a}} \sqrt{1 + \frac{\Delta p_i}{\Delta p_a}} \times \frac{1}{\Phi_1} \tag{97}$$

Since Δp_i is a constant, F will *increase* as the throttle is closed and Δp_a becomes smaller. The effect of the idling spring is the same as a *negative* nozzle lip on a float-type carburetor. To prevent excessively high fuel-air ratios at very low air flows, a linkage to the throttle is provided which reduces A_f as the throttle is closed.

Altitude compensation. Altitude compensation is achieved by the use of back-suction control. A density-controlled valve is placed in the line between the carburetor entrance (p_1 pressure) and chamber A. A very small air bleed connects chambers A and B. At low altitude where the air density is high, the automatic valve is open, chamber A is at p_1 pressure, and $p_A - p_B = p_1 - p_2 = \Delta p_a$. At altitude where γ_a is low and the fuel-air ratio tends to increase [see expression (93)], the automatic valve is partly closed. As a small air flow exists through the air bleed from point 1 to point 2, the drop in pressure through the automatic valve makes $p_A < p_1$ so that $p_A - p_B < \Delta p_a$. Owing to the construction of the carburetor $\Delta p_f = p_D - p_C = p_A - p_B$. Therefore with the automatic valve operating, $\Delta p_f < \Delta p_a$, and the fuel-air ratio is reduced to the correct value.

Economizer system. Enrichment to give best power and detonation control is produced in this carburetor by an economizer needle which is automatically withdrawn from a fuel orifice when a certain value of air flow is reached. The Δp_a caused by the venturi air flow is made to act upon a special diaphragm connected to the economizer needle. The needle is held in the orifice by a spring. At the proper air flow, Δp_a is sufficient to overcome the spring force, and the needle is withdrawn. This type of economizer is satisfactory only for constant-speed engines.

SUGGESTION FOR FURTHER READING

Thorner, R. H.: "Aircraft Carburetion," Wiley, New York, 1946.

PROBLEMS

1. A carburetor has a pressure drop in the venturi of $\Delta p_a = 3$ in. Hg.   Assume x and approach velocity are negligible.   Write down the sea-level values of:

(a) $\dfrac{\Delta p_a}{p_1}$.

(b) Φ_1.

(c) $\dfrac{F}{F \text{ at very low flow}}$.

(d) $\dfrac{w_a/\text{sec}}{\text{Critical } w_a/\text{sec}}$.

2. (a) A carburetor with a 2-in.-diameter venturi throat operates with 4 in. Hg pressure drop between the atmosphere and the venturi throat at full throttle at sea level   What per cent of critical flow will this be (neglect approach velocity)?

(b) Assume that the engine is to be operated at 12,000 ft altitude, $p = 9.35$ psia, $T = 476°R$, with a supercharger between carburetor and engine supplying the same quantity of air per minute as was used at sea level. What throat diameter would have to be used to keep the same per cent of critical flow as occurred with the 2-in.-diameter throat at sea level?

(c) What would the value of Φ_1 be under both these conditions?

3. (a) A carburetor with 1½-in.-diameter venturi throat is operating at low values of $\Delta p_a/p_1$. If the discharge coefficient for the venturi is 0.9, x is negligible, and $K_f = 0.7$, what diameter should the fuel orifice be to give $F = 0.08$ at sea level?

(b) What F would this carburetor give at 20,000 ft altitude? ($p = 6.76$ psia, $T = 447°R$.)

4. A carburetor with a 1-in.-diameter venturi, approach factor $= 1$, x negligible gives an enrichment due to compressibility (Φ_1) of 20 per cent at sea level. How large a venturi diameter would be necessary to limit this enrichment to 10 per cent with the same air flow? What would the value of Δp_a be for each venturi under the above conditions?

5. A carburetor main metering system (x is negligible) has a critical flow at sea level ($T = 520°R$, $p = 14.7$ psia) of 100 lb air/min. Under these conditions, $F = 0.087$.

(a) Calculate Δp_a for these conditions.

(b) Calculate F for this carburetor at low flow.

(c) Calculate critical air flow at 15,000 ft altitude ($p = 8.3$ psia, $T = 465°$R).

(d) Calculate Δp_a at 15,000 ft at critical flow.

(e) Calculate F at 15,000 ft at low flow.

(f) Calculate F at 15,000 ft at critical flow.

6. A carburetor has a 1.5-in. venturi-throat diameter. $K_a = 0.85$. x is negligible. Approach factor $= 1$.

(a) Calculate Δp_a at sea level when air flow is 0.20 lb/sec.

(b) If the carburetor is adjusted to give $F = 0.07$ at very low air flow, what is the value of F at 0.20 lb/sec air flow?

7. An automobile carburetor having its float chamber vented to the atmosphere is tested in the factory without an air cleaner. At an air rate of 500 lb/hr and at sea-level conditions, the main metering system of this carburetor is found to yield a fuel-air ratio of 0.065. The venturi-throat pressure is 12.0 psia.

This carburetor is now installed in an automobile, and an air cleaner is placed on the inlet to the carburetor. With the engine operating at 500 lb/hr air consumption and at sea-level conditions, there is found to be a pressure drop through the air filter of 0.5 psi. Assuming $x = 0$ and orifice coefficients constant, calculate:

(a) The venturi-throat pressure with cleaner.

(b) Fuel-air ratio with cleaner.

Assume that the flow through the carburetor is incompressible ($\Phi_1 = 1$).

8. The injection carburetor shown in the accompanying figure is in operation at sea level with 53 per cent of critical air flow through the venturi.

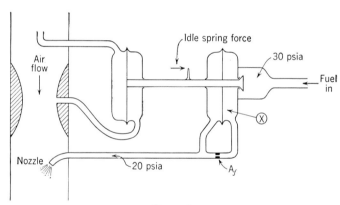

PROB. 8.

$K_a = 0.9$

$K_f = 0.6$

$A_2 = 4$ in.²

$A_f = 0.016$ in.²

Equivalent area of each diaphragm $= 9$ in.²

Idling spring force $= 1$ lb

Fuel-pump pressure $= 30$ psia

Pressure behind spray nozzle $= 20$ psia

Fuel density $= 45$ lb/ft³

(a) What is the absolute pressure at point x in the accompanying diagram, in pounds per square inch?

(b) What fuel-air ratio will the carburetor supply under these conditions?

9. The main metering system given in the figure uses a sharp-edged orifice in place of a venturi, as shown. The pressure drop across this orifice is used to suck fuel from the nozzle. Discuss this construction. What sort of curve of F vs. w_a/sec will it give? What are its advantages and disadvantages?

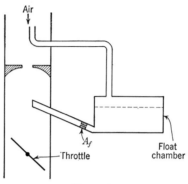

PROB. 9.

10. A downdraft carburetor with an air cleaner is shown in cross section in the sketch.

Venturi diameter $= 2$ in., $K_a = 0.92$
$K_f = 0.60$, x is negligible
$F = 0.080$, $\Delta p_f = 3$ in. Hg
At entrance to air cleaner $p = 14.7$ psia, $T = 520°$R

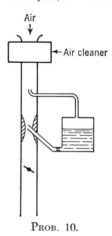

PROB. 10.

Under these conditions there is a 2-psi drop in pressure through the air cleaner (no change in temperature). Calculate the fuel-air ratio if the air cleaner is removed. (Assume $\Phi_1 = 1$.)

11. A carburetor is providing a 12:1 air-fuel ratio. A 16-in. H_2O differential is causing the fuel to flow through the fuel jet of the single-jet carburetor. An air cleaner is added that decreases the pressure at the entrance to the venturi by 9 in. H_2O. Approximately how much will this change the air-fuel ratio:

(a) With float chamber vented to the atmosphere?

(b) With float chamber internally vented?

Assume $\Phi_1 = 1$.

12. A carburetor operating at one-half of full-throttle air capacity supplies a fuel-air ratio of 0.075. Sixty per cent of the fuel evaporates in the manifold; the rest flows along the walls as a liquid. The throttle is suddenly opened wide. Assuming that the carburetor still supplies a fuel-air ratio of 0.075 and that 60 per cent of the fuel supplied still evaporates, what will be the fuel-air ratio in the cylinder immediately after opening the throttle?

13. (a) A carburetor has a venturi of 4.72 in. diameter throat. $K_a = 0.98$, $x = 0$, approach factor $= 1$. What metering suction will be available when 5,600 lb air/hr is entering the carburetor at sea-level conditions?

(b) What diameter fuel orifice ($K_f = 0.60$) must be used to obtain a fuel-air ratio of 0.065 for this condition? (Fuel weighs 45 lb/ft³.)

14. An aircraft engine, rated at 2,000 hp for take-off, uses 7 lb of air/hp-hr at this condition. What diameter single venturi should be used in order to obtain a metering pressure drop (difference between total pressure ahead of the venturi and static pressure in the venturi throat) of 3.5 in. Hg at standard sea-level carburetor-inlet conditions? ($K_a = 0.98$.)

15. A carburetor venturi has a 1.5-in. throat diameter, $K_a = 0.85$. x is negligible. Approach factor $= 1$. What should the diameter of fuel orifice be, to give $F = 0.08$ at sea level, when $\Delta p_a = 3$ in. Hg? Assume $K_f = 0.5$. (Gasoline weighs 44 lb/ft³.)

16. The venturi of a simple carburetor has a throat diameter of 3 in. and a K_a of 0.95. The fuel orifice has a diameter of 0.2 and a K_f of 0.68. $x = 0.2$ in. Approach factor $= 1$.

(a) Compute the air rate required to start the fuel flow, at sea level.

(b) Compute the fuel-air ratio at sea level, at an air flow of half the critical value.

17. A carburetor has a venturi-throat diameter of 1.5 in. $K_a = 0.85$ at sea level. $\gamma_a = 0.0765$ lb/ft³. $x = \frac{1}{2}$ in. $K_f = 0.60$. $\gamma_f = 44$ lb/ft³. At an air flow of 0.30 lb/sec how large a fuel-orifice diameter will be required to give $F = 0.07$? What will be F at 0.1 lb/sec? At what w_a/sec will $F = 0$? (Assume $\Phi_1 = 1$.)

CHAPTER 11

SPARK IGNITION

The operator of a spark-ignition engine expects the ignition system to fire thousands of consecutive cylinders full of fuel-air mixture without a "miss," although the manifold pressure may vary from 5 to 40 psia, the fuel-air ratio may vary from 0.06 to 0.12, and the rpm from 400 to 4,000. In addition, the ignition must occur at the proper crank angle so that the time losses are held at a minimum. If detonation is encountered, ignition timing may also be modified for detonation control.

Requirements for Ignition

Although the exact mechanism of the ignition process is not well known, several important requirements can be mentioned.

Voltage. There must be sufficient voltage at the spark-plug electrodes so that a spark discharge will take place. The voltage required to jump

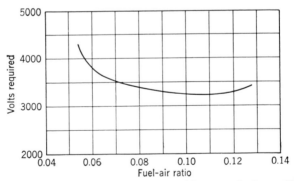

FIG. 87. Effect of fuel-air ratio on voltage required for a spark plug. (*Rabezzana and Randolph, Automotive Inds., Jan.* 18, 1930.)

the spark-plug gap varies with the length of the gap and with conditions inside the cylinder. Variation in fuel-air ratio affects the required voltage, as shown in Fig. 87. Cylinders with excessively lean mixtures near the spark plug will require higher voltages. Such a condition may exist if the distribution is poor or if the cylinder charge is not homogeneous. The ignition coil must therefore deliver excess voltage to ensure a spark when the engine is cold and fuel vaporization is poor.

162

The voltage requirements of a spark gap increase with the density of the gas between the electrodes. For this reason, engines require higher voltage at the spark plugs when they are operating at high manifold pressures or high compression ratios or when the ignition is timed to occur closer to top center.

It is of course possible to design the ignition system to produce a voltage far above normal requirements. Usually only a moderate excess in voltage is provided, because very high ignition voltage would necessitate great care and expense in insulating the high-tension leads to the spark plugs and other parts of the distributing system. There would also be greater erosion of the spark-plug electrodes and more possibility of spark-plug-insulation failure.

Volume occupied by the spark. The fact that a spark discharge occurs each time does not ensure ignition of the cylinder charge. It appears from experience that it is necessary to affect some minimum number of molecules with the spark, in order to initiate a self-sustaining flame front. The minimum number of molecules probably depends upon the fuel-air ratio, amount of residual gas, temperature, and other engine-operating conditions.

This effect may be noticed if a very small gap is used between the spark-plug electrodes. The engine will fire regularly at high manifold pressures because the density of the charge is high and there are sufficient charge molecules in the gap at the time of spark discharge. When the manifold pressure is reduced, reducing the number of molecules in the gap, firing becomes irregular, even though the voltage requirement is less. If the electrode gap is now increased, so that a larger charge volume will be affected by the spark, the engine will again fire regularly. When a reasonably homogeneous combustible mixture is present, and there is sufficient voltage to ensure a discharge, across a gap sufficiently long to include the proper number of molecules, regular firing will follow. Any increase in spark intensity over that required for regular firing will have no effect whatever on engine performance.

Preignition

Preignition has been defined in Chap. 7 as ignition of the charge by some hot surface within the cylinder. The action of the hot spot is similar to that of a spark plug, in that a flame front starts from this point and travels across the combustion space in the normal manner. The disadvantage of preignition is that it is not under the control of the operator and the timing of the combustion will be adversely affected. Whether the preignition flame front starts before the flame front from the spark plug or during the burning process, the charge will be burned too soon and the result will be the same as though the normal spark had been timed too early.   Preignition can therefore cause detonation, high peak pressures, or increased time losses with the resulting loss in efficiency and high exhaust temperatures.   Violent preignition may cause considerable damage in high-output engines and may reduce the power of an engine to zero through time losses or even by igniting the fresh charge before the inlet valves close.

The surface temperature necessary to produce preignition varies with the fuel, the material of the surface, and engine-operating conditions. Surface temperatures of approximately 2000°F are usually required to produce preignition.   Overheated engine deposits, spark-plug electrodes, and spark-plug insulation are common sources of preignition.

Ignition Timing

The effect of ignition timing on time losses was discussed in Chap. 5. For minimum time losses ignition should take place so that the burning process is completed 10 to 15° after top center.   The crank angle at which ignition should occur will therefore depend upon the flame speed, the distance the flame has to travel, and the engine speed.   These factors have been discussed in Chap. 5, where the effect of engine-operating conditions on flame speed was fully covered.   Obviously any change which increases the number of crankshaft degrees required for the burning process will require an earlier ignition for minimum time losses.

Spark Plugs

A spark plug consists of an outer casing, which may be screwed into the combustion space.   Within the casing is an insulated electrode sealed to prevent leakage of cylinder gases.   This electrode carries the ignition current to the spark-plug gap, where the spark jumps to a second electrode, which is fastened to the grounded part of the casing.   Figure 88 shows a cross section of a typical spark plug.

If the insulation or electrodes of a spark plug operate too cool, deposits will form on them which may be electrically conducting, short-circuiting the plug so that no spark occurs.   If the insulation or electrodes operate too hot, the insulation may be damaged or preignition may occur before the passage of the normal spark.   The operating temperature of the plug depends upon the area of insulation and electrode exposed to the hot gases and the length of the heat path from electrode points and insulation back to the cooled part of the cylinder wall into which the plug is screwed. A plug with a short, stubby center electrode and insulator will run cooler than one with a long, thin exposed center electrode.   The former is called a "cold" plug, the latter a "hot" plug.   As more heat is picked up by a plug when exposed to the cylinder gases at high mep and high rpm, a cold plug must be used to avoid preignition in engines of high output. Such a plug would tend to foul up with deposits at low mep and low rpm or when cooling is excessive. Plugs are carefully chosen to operate at proper temperature in a given engine at normal operating conditions. A well-designed plug will perform satisfactorily over a fairly

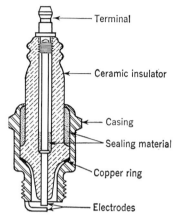

FIG. 88. Cross section of a typical spark plug (Champion).

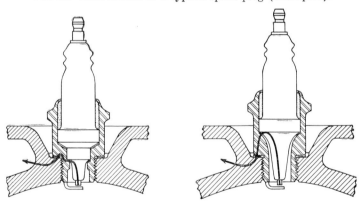

"Cold" spark plug   "Hot" spark plug

FIG. 89. Cross sections of "cold" and "hot" spark plugs. Arrows represent principal paths of heat conduction from insulated electrode to cooling medium.

wide range of engine speeds and loads. Examples of hot and cold plugs are shown in Fig. 89.

Insulation material. The most common material for spark-plug insulators is porcelain. This material is relatively inexpensive and plentiful and easy to manufacture. The composition may be varied to suit particular conditions. Ceramic material is brittle and easily damaged and may combine with lead to form slag under severe conditions. Mica is also used for spark-plug insulators.   High-grade mica is expensive and difficult to obtain.   This material is used in laminations and is less subject to mechanical damage than ceramic materials.   Mica is physically changed by severe overheating so that a mica plug once overheated is unsuitable for further use.

Standard Battery Ignition System

A diagram of a standard ignition system is shown in Fig. 90.   When the switch is closed, current from the battery flows through the primary winding of the ignition coil through a set of contacts, called breaker points, to the engine frame and back to the battery.   This current, flowing through the coil primary, which is wound on a soft iron core,

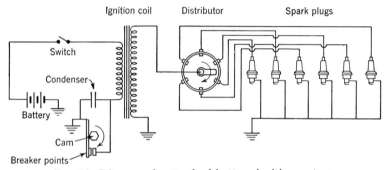

FIG. 90. Diagram of a standard battery ignition system.

produces a magnetic field in the core.   A cam, driven by the engine shaft, is arranged to open the breaker points whenever an ignition discharge is required.   When the breaker points open, the current which had been flowing through the points now flows into the condenser, which is connected across the points.   As the condenser becomes charged, the primary current falls and the magnetic field collapses.   The collapse of the field induces a voltage in the primary winding, which charges the condenser to a voltage much higher than battery voltage.   The condenser then discharges into the battery, reversing the direction of both the primary current and the magnetic field.   The rapid collapse and reversal of the magnetic field in the core induce a very high voltage in the secondary winding of the ignition coil.   The secondary winding consists of a large number of turns of very fine wire wound on the same core with the primary.   The high secondary voltage is led to the proper spark plug by means of a rotating switch called the distributor, which is located in the secondary, or high-tension, circuit of the ignition system.

If a condenser were not used in the primary circuit, the high primary voltage caused by the collapse of the magnetic field around the primary winding would cause an arc across the breaker points. The arc would burn and destroy the points and would also prevent the rapid drop in primary current and magnetic field which is necessary for the production of the high secondary voltage.

Note that the spark timing is controlled by the crank angle at which the breaker points open, while the distributor merely determines the firing sequence of the spark plugs. Changes in ignition timing may be affected by rotating the plate which holds the breaker points, relative to the cam. Later ignition will result if the plate is displaced in the direction in which the camshaft rotates.

In automotive practice the position of the breaker-point plate is controlled by the inlet-manifold pressure acting upon a diaphragm. As the throttle is opened, the diaphragm rotates the plate, retarding the spark just enough to prevent detonation at each manifold pressure.

The ignition timing may also be varied by changing the angular relation between the breaker cam and the shaft which drives it. In automobile engines the relative cam position is varied by means of centrifugal weights and a mechanical linkage. At increased engine speeds, where the tendency to detonate is reduced, the centrifugal mechanism advances the ignition timing as close to optimum as detonation will permit.

As fuels vary in octane number and as the effect of engine speed and manifold pressure on the tendency to detonate varies among fuels of the same octane number, the automatic spark-advance mechanism gives only approximately the proper ignition timing and should be readjusted occasionally to compensate for changes in engine condition and fuel quality.

Magneto Ignition System

The magneto ignition system is similar in principle to the battery system except that the magnetic field in the core of the primary and secondary windings is produced by a rotating permanent magnet. As the magnet turns, the field produced varies from a positive maximum to a negative maximum and back again. As this magnetic field falls from a positive maximum value, a voltage and current are induced in the primary winding. This primary current produces a magnetic field of its own which keeps the total magnetic field surrounding the primary and secondary windings approximately constant. When the permanent magnet has turned far enough so that *its* contribution to the total field is strongly negative, the breaker points are opened and the magnetic field about the secondary winding suddenly goes from a high positive value to a high negative value. This induces a high voltage in the secondary winding which is led to the proper spark plug by the distributor.

The magneto is an efficient, reliable, self-contained unit which is often preferred for aircraft engines because storage batteries are heavy and troublesome. Special starting means are required, however, as the magneto will not furnish enough voltage for ignition at low speeds. Variation in ignition timing is more difficult with the magneto since the breaker points must be opened when the rotating magnets are in the most favorable position. It is possible to change the engine crank angle at which the magneto points open without disturbing the relationship between point opening and magnet position by designing the attachment pad so that the entire magneto body may be rotated a few degrees about its own shaft. Obviously this method is not as satisfactory as rotating a timer cam plate.

CHAPTER 12

HEAT REJECTION AND COOLING

Since the cylinder-gas temperatures in internal-combustion engines often reach 5000°R, it is necessary to provide cooling for the walls of the combustion space. The temperature of the inside surface of the cylinder walls is usually kept below 400°F to prevent deterioration of the oil film. Chemical and physical changes in the oil resulting from high temperature may cause wear and sticking of the piston rings, scoring of the cylinder walls, or seizure of the piston. It has been shown experimentally that most of the heat which enters the piston head flows out through the piston rings into the cylinder wall. Excessive cylinder-wall temperatures will therefore increase the operating temperature of the piston head. The strength of the piston may be seriously reduced by high temperature, particularly if the piston is made of aluminum alloy; and failure of the piston head may result. The temperature of the cylinder head must also be kept below 450°F or so. The effect of temperature on the strength of an aluminum-alloy cylinder head is similar to the effect on the piston. In addition, the spark plugs and valves are kept cool by their contact with the cooled cylinder head. An overheated cylinder head may lead to overheated spark-plug electrodes, causing preignition. The exhaust valve may become hot enough to cause preignition or to soften and fail structurally. Preignition results in a loss in efficiency and higher cylinder-gas temperatures, so that if high cylinder-head temperatures should cause preignition, the presence of preignition would serve to increase the cylinder-head temperatures still more, until engine failure or complete loss of power resulted. As the last part of the charge to burn is in contact with the walls of the combustion space during the burning period, a high cylinder-wall or cylinder-head temperature will reduce the delay period and cause detonation.

Wherever a moving gas comes in contact with a wall, there exists a relatively stagnant gas layer which acts as a thermal insulator. The thickness and conductivity of this layer depend upon the Reynolds number of the gas flow; $i.e.$, the value of $\rho u l/\mu$ existing in the gas. The resistance of this layer to heat flow is quite high, so that when moderate quantities of heat are drawn from the cylinder gases through the gas layer and through the cylinder walls into the cooling air or into the

169

cylinder water jackets, a large temperature drop is produced in the stagnant layer. The cylinder-gas temperature may therefore be 5000°R, while the inner cylinder-wall surface may be only 700 or 800°R (see Fig. 91). If no cooling were provided, there would of course be no heat flow and no resulting temperature drop in the stagnant layer, so that the whole cylinder wall would soon reach the "average" temperature of the cylinder gases.

It has been shown in Chap. 5 that the heat lost by the cylinder gases during combustion and expansion, although representing about 8 per cent of the energy of the fuel, does not greatly affect the efficiency of the engine cycle. In addition, some heat, which would otherwise be thrown away in the exhaust gases, is transferred to the exhaust ports during the blowdown process and finds its way into the engine-cooling system. In all, at full throttle approximately 15 per cent of the energy of the fuel appears in the cooling system. As the engine converts about 30 per cent of the fuel energy into work, the cooling system must carry away and dispose of an amount of heat equivalent to about half the work output of the engine.

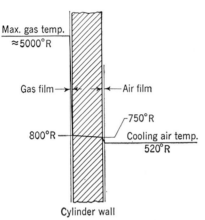

Fig. 91. Order of magnitude of temperatures across an air-cooled cylinder wall.

As engine-operating conditions are varied, the temperature of the cylinder gases and the thickness and conductivity of the stagnant gas layer will change. In order to keep the temperature of the inner surface of the combustion chamber constant, it will therefore be necessary to draw out of the cylinder larger or smaller quantities of heat per unit of time. The effect of engine-operating conditions on the amount of heat which the engine-cooling system must handle will be considered below.

Heat-transfer Theory

Calculation of heat-transfer data indicates that the cylinder gases are poor radiators in spite of their high temperature so that almost all the heat transfer to the cylinder walls is by convection. The process is probably very similar to that occurring when a hot gas flows through a pipe. An analysis based on this assumption has been made by Taylor and Taylor[1] and is repeated here in modified form. The results of

[1] C. F. Taylor and E. S. Taylor, "The Internal Combustion Engine," International Textbook, Scranton, Pa., 1948.

many heat-rejection tests on internal-combustion engines indicate that this method is most useful and reliable.

For gases in pipes McAdams and others have shown by dimensional analysis and experiment that

$$\frac{ql}{k} = \text{const} \times \left(\frac{\rho u l}{\mu}\right)^n \left(\frac{C_p \mu}{k}\right)^m \tag{98}$$

where q = coefficient of heat transfer, Btu/(time $\times$ area $\times$ temp diff.)
   l = characteristic length or size
   k = thermal conductivity of the gases, Btu/(time $\times$ area $\times$ temp gradient)
   ρ = mass density
   u = velocity of gases
   μ = viscosity of gases
n, m = exponents

The term $\rho u l/\mu$ is recognized as a Reynolds number for the cylinder-gas motion. The term $C_p \mu/k$ is called Prandtl's number and is almost constant for gases. It may therefore be lumped into the constant in expression (98) so that

$$\frac{ql}{k} = \text{const} \times \left(\frac{\rho u l}{\mu}\right)^n \tag{98a}$$

Since Prandtl's number is constant, $k \propto \mu C_p$, and substituting in (98a),

$$\frac{ql}{\mu C_p} = \text{const} \times \left(\frac{\rho u l}{\mu}\right)^n \tag{98b}$$

$$q = \text{const} \times C_p \, (\rho u)^n \left(\frac{l}{\mu}\right)^{n-1} \tag{98c}$$

Let Q = Btu/time; then

$$Q = q \, \Delta T \times \text{area} \propto q \, \Delta T \, l^2 \tag{99}$$

where ΔT is the temperature difference between gas and wall. Substituting from (98c),

$$Q = \text{const} \times \Delta T \, C_p(\rho u)^n (l)^{n+1} (\mu)^{1-n} \tag{100}$$

Heat transfer in the engine. When expression (100) is applied to the engine, the symbols are interpreted as follows:

Q = Btu/min leaving through the walls of the combustion chamber. This is the average rate of heat flow which must be dissipated by the cooling system.

ΔT = the temperature difference between the cylinder gases and the inner surfaces of the combustion chamber walls. The cylinder-gas temperature varies widely during the cycle, but the engine behaves as though some constant gas temperature existed in the chamber. The "average" ΔT of a running engine is affected by fuel-air ratio, which controls the gas temperature; and cooling-jacket or fin temperature, which controls the temperature of the combustion-chamber walls. At constant fuel-air ratio the average gas temperature will be constant; and as cooling is usually varied to keep the inner-cylinder-wall temperature approximately constant, ΔT will also tend to be constant.

The specific heat of the cylinder gases C_p increases with gas temperature. At constant fuel-air ratio the average gas temperature, and therefore C_p, will be constant.

The cylinder-gas density ρ corresponds closely to γ_{cyl} of Chap. 8 and is therefore proportional to $\gamma_i \eta_v$ by expression (62). At constant fuel-air ratio, $\rho \propto$ imep by expression (77). Of course, ρ varies with piston position during the cycle, but an "average" value applies.

The symbol u stands for the velocity of the cylinder gases relative to the cylinder walls. Although this quantity varies during the cycle and is different in different parts of the combustion space, it is assumed for a given engine that the average gas velocity at any given point in the cylinder and in the cycle is proportional to the original velocity through the inlet valve. The inlet velocity was found in Chap. 8 to be approximately proportional to the piston speed. Piston speed is therefore substituted for u for engine application.

Any length in the combustion chamber may be chosen for l. Usually the cylinder bore is most convenient. Note that the term l^{n+1} includes the area exposed to the hot gases (which is proportional to l^2) and the Reynolds-number term l^{n-1}.

The viscosity of the cylinder gases μ increases with temperature. At constant fuel-air ratio, the average value of μ will be constant.

The value of the constant in expression (100) depends upon the geometry of the combustion chamber, the extent of carbon deposits, and other details of engine design. It is seldom possible to assign a value to the constant, nor is it ordinarily necessary to do so. If the amount of heat rejected or the radiator size required is known for a given set of operating conditions in the engine or in a similar engine, expression (100) can be used to estimate the heat rejection for other operating conditions. If no initial data are available, it may be assumed that, at full throttle and best power fuel-air ratio, Q is approximately equivalent to 50 per cent of the ihp.

The value of the exponent n is about 0.8 for gases moving in pipes. Experiments show that n is closer to 0.6 or 0.7 in engine cylinders.

Effect of Operating Conditions

Effect of fuel-air ratio. A change in fuel-air ratio will change the temperature of the cylinder gases and affect the flame speed. The maximum gas temperature will occur at a fuel-air ratio of about 0.075. At this fuel-air ratio, therefore, ΔT will be a maximum. The maximum heat rejection usually occurs at fuel-air ratios slightly leaner than this value. The reason is thought to be that at leaner fuel-air ratios the flame

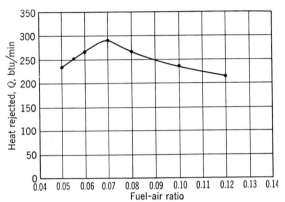

FIG. 92. Effect of fuel-air ratio on heat rejected to coolant in a liquid-cooled engine. CFR engine, $3\frac{1}{4} \times 4\frac{1}{2}$, $r = 6$, 1,200 rpm, $p_i = 29$ in. Hg, $p_{ex} = 30$ in. Hg, $T_i = 120°F$. Air consumption $= 0.0115$ lb/sec, best-power spark advance. (*Sloan Laboratory.*)

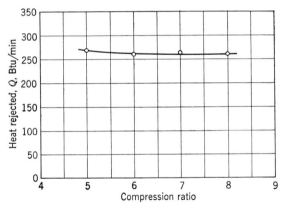

FIG. 93. Effect of compression ratio on heat rejected to coolant in a liquid-cooled engine. CFR engine, $3\frac{1}{4} \times 4\frac{1}{2}$, 1,200 rpm, $p_i = 28.9$ in. Hg, $p_{ex} = 29.9$ in. Hg, $T_i = 120°F$, $F = 0.075$, best-power spark advance. (*Sloan Laboratory.*)

speed is lower and the piston will have exposed a larger cylinder-wall area by the time burning is over. The effect of fuel-air ratio on heat rejection is shown in Fig. 92.

Effect of compression ratio. An increase in compression ratio causes a slight increase in gas temperature at top center; but because of the greater expansion of the gases, there will be a considerable reduction in gas temperature near bottom center where a large cylinder-wall area is exposed.   The exhaust-gas temperature will also be much lower so that the heat rejected during blowdown will be less.   Figure 93 shows the effect of compression ratio on heat rejection.

Effect of spark advance.   A spark advance earlier than optimum will result in time losses on the compression stroke.   This extra work done on the gases by the piston will cause the gas temperatures to be higher during combustion, expansion, and blowdown and thereby increase the heat rejection.   A spark advance later than optimum will result in the maximum temperature of the cycle occurring considerably after top center, with consequently more cylinder-wall area exposed.   The effective expansion of the gases is reduced, so that the gas temperature during expansion and blowdown will be higher and more heat will be rejected to the cooling system.

Effect of preignition and detonation.   The effect of preignition on heat rejection is the same as an early ignition timing.

Although detonation causes large changes in *local* heat-transfer conditions, the over-all effect on heat transfer of detonation unaccompanied by preignition appears to be negligible.

Effect of engine output.   At constant fuel-air ratio the indicated thermal efficiency of an engine is essentially constant.   In this case, ihp $\propto w_a/\text{min}$, or, from expression (72), ihp $\propto$ No. cyls. $\times l^2 s \eta_v$.   If γ_i is variable, the expression for ihp becomes

$$\text{ihp} \propto \text{No. cyls.} \times l^2 s \gamma_i \eta_v \tag{101}$$

From (77) at constant fuel-air ratio, imep $\propto \gamma_i \eta_v$ so that

$$\text{ihp} \propto \text{No. cyls.} \times l^2 s \times \text{imep} \tag{102}$$

In an engine at constant fuel-air ratio ΔT, C_p and μ are practically constant.   Assuming this condition and substituting $\gamma_i \eta_v \propto$ imep for ρ, and s for u, in expression (100),

$$Q \propto \text{No. cyls.} \times l^{n+1}(\text{imep} \times s)^n \tag{103}$$

Dividing (103) by (102),

$$\frac{\text{Heat loss/min}}{\text{Power output}} = \frac{Q}{\text{ihp}} \propto (l \times \text{imep} \times s)^{n-1} \tag{104}$$

Since n is less than unity, we see from (104) that less heat will be lost for the same ihp in large engines or in engines operated at high meps or high piston speeds.

For a *given* engine in which the number of cylinders and l are constant, ihp $\propto s \times$ imep, and $Q \propto (\text{imep} \times s)^n$, or the heat rejected per minute

$$Q \propto (\text{ihp})^n \tag{105}$$

For a group of similar engines operating at the same inlet conditions and piston speed, imep $\times$ s will be constant, and

$$Q \propto l^{n+1} \times \text{No. cyls.} \tag{106}$$
$$\text{ihp} \propto l^2 \times \text{No. cyls.}$$

so that

$$\frac{Q}{\text{ihp}} \propto l^{n-1} \tag{107}$$

The total combustion-chamber area of a group of similar engines will also be proportional to $l^2 \times$ No. cyls., so that the heat rejected per square inch of wall surface will be

$$\frac{Q}{l^2 \times \text{No. cyls.}} \propto l^{n-1} \tag{108}$$

Large engines therefore lose less heat per unit of cylinder-wall area.

If similar engines are being operated at different inlet conditions and piston speeds, the heat loss per square inch of wall surface will be found by dividing (103) by $l^2 \times$ No. cyls.,

$$\frac{Q}{l^2 \times \text{No. cyls.}} \propto l^{n-1}(\text{imep} \times s)^n \tag{109}$$

Effect of cylinder-wall temperature. The effect of cylinder-wall temperature on heat rejection is simply a matter of the effect on ΔT. Because the "average" cylinder-gas temperature is fairly high (of the order of 1500°R), moderate changes in combustion-chamber-wall temperatures will have only a slight effect on ΔT. The cylinder-wall temperature is usually controlled to rather close limits. Cylinder temperature of liquid-cooled engines is limited by the boiling point of the coolant used. The stability of the cylinder-wall oil film or the strength requirements of the cylinder structure limit the cylinder temperature in air-cooled engines. On the other hand, temperatures are kept as high as practicable since lowering the cylinder-wall temperatures means increased viscous piston friction in all engines, increased cooling drag in the case of aircraft, and increased radiator size in liquid-cooled engines in order to dissipate the heat at lower coolant temperatures.

Temperature Gradients in Engine Parts

For a constant temperature difference between the cylinder gases and the combustion-chamber walls, the average rate of heat flow out of the cylinder gases into each unit of wall area exposed to the gases is controlled by the factors of expression (109).

This rate of heat flow produces a temperature gradient in the parts through which the flow occurs.   The relationship between the heat flow in Btu per square inch per minute and the temperature gradient is given by the standard conduction formula

$$\frac{Q}{\text{Area}} = \frac{k\,\Delta T'}{d} \tag{110}$$

where k = thermal conductivity of part
$\Delta T'$ = temperature drop along heat-flow path in the part
d = length of heat-flow path in the part
In similar engines $d \propto l$, and substituting for Q/area the right side of expression (109) in (110),

$$\Delta T' \propto \frac{l^{n-1}(\text{imep} \times s)^n l}{k}$$

$$\Delta T' \propto \frac{(l \times \text{imep} \times s)^n}{k} \tag{111}$$

Large engines or engines run at high mep or piston speed will therefore require lower coolant or fin temperatures to keep the inner-combustion-chamber-surface temperatures at the proper values.

Cooling

All engines are cooled by air passing over some sort of heat-exchanging surface.   In "air-cooled" engines, this surface consists of fins cast or machined on the outside of the cylinders.   In "liquid-cooled" engines the heat flows first into a liquid medium such as water or water-ethylene glycol mixture.   This medium is circulated through a heat exchanger called a radiator.   The radiator is built with fins through which the cooling air circulates.

Power required to cool.   There are certain general principles which apply in all cases of engine cooling.   These principles will be brought out in the following analysis.   In order to simplify the treatment, a given engine is assumed to operate at constant fuel-air ratio, and the changes in fin or coolant temperature are assumed small enough so that ΔT, the temperature difference between cylinder gas and wall, may be considered constant.   The density and temperature of the cooling air are assumed to be unaffected by its flow through the engine or radiator fins.

From expression (83) the velocity of the cooling-air flow will be

$$u_a \propto \sqrt{\frac{\Delta p_a}{\gamma_a}} \tag{112}$$

where Δp_a is the pressure drop through the fins.   The flow in pounds per second through the fins will be

$$w_a = A_e u_a \gamma_a \tag{113}$$

where A_e is the flow area between the fins.

The flow work required to push 1 lb of air into the fins is $p_1 v$, where p_1 is the pressure before the fins and v is the specific volume of the air. The flow work regained as the air leaves the fins is $p_2 v$. The work required to force the air through the cooling system will be the difference.

$$\frac{\text{Work}}{\text{lb}} \left(\frac{\text{ft-lb}}{\text{lb}} \right) = \Delta p_a v = \frac{\Delta p_a}{\gamma_a} \tag{114}$$

The power required for cooling (hp_c) will be work/lb $\times$ lb/sec. Combining (113) and (114),

$$\text{hp}_c \propto A_e u_a \Delta p_a \tag{115}$$

hp_c must be supplied by a fan or by the motion of the vehicle carrying the fins or radiator.

But from (112) $\Delta p_a \propto \gamma_a u_a{}^2$ so that

$$\text{hp}_c \propto \gamma_a A_e u_a{}^3 \tag{116}$$

The heat to be dissipated per second is

$$Q \propto (\text{ihp})^n \tag{105}$$

The exponent n for engines is about 0.6.

The heat transfer from fins to air is the same physical process as the heat transfer from cylinder gases to cylinder walls. Combining expressions (98c) and (99) for cooling fins,

$$Q = \text{const} \times A_f \, \Delta T_f \, C_{p_a} (\gamma_a u_a)^n \left(\frac{l}{\mu_a} \right)^{n-1} \tag{117}$$

where A_f = area of fin surface exposed to the cooling air

ΔT_f = temperature difference between cooling fins and the air

a = subscript referring to air

For the range of cooling-air temperatures ordinarily encountered, C_{p_a} and μ_a are constant. The quantity l would vary with fin size and spacing, but the exponent n for cooling fins is about 0.8 so that the Reynolds-number term $(l)^{n-1}$ is not important and will be considered constant.

Equation (117) then becomes

$$Q \propto A_f \, \Delta T_f \, (\gamma_a u_a)^{0.8} \tag{117a}$$

If expression (116) is divided by (117a), we obtain

$$\frac{\text{hp}_c}{Q} = \frac{\text{hp required to cool}}{\text{cooling obtained}} = \frac{A_e \gamma_a u_a{}^3}{A_f \, \Delta T_f \, \gamma_a{}^{0.8} u_a{}^{0.8}}$$

or

$$\frac{hp_c}{Q} = \frac{A_e}{A_f} \frac{\gamma_a^{0.2}}{\Delta T_f} u_a^{2.2} \tag{118}$$

Expression (118) shows that to get the most cooling for the least expenditure of power A_e/A_f should be small. This could be accomplished by using a large number of long fins to increase A_f, but closely spaced to reduce A_e. Also, for efficient cooling, the cooling-air velocity u_a must be kept low and ΔT_f high.

The variation in cooling power required in terms of the ihp of the engine may be seen by equating (105) and (117a). Using $n = 0.6$ for engine and 0.8 for fins,

$$(\text{ihp})^{0.6} \propto A_f \, \Delta T_f \, (\gamma_a u_a)^{0.8}$$

from which

$$u_a^3 \propto \frac{(\text{ihp})^{2.3}}{(A_f \, \Delta T_f)^{3.75} \gamma_a^3}$$

Substituting in (116)

$$hp_c \propto \frac{A_e (\text{ihp})^{2.3}}{(A_f \, \Delta T_f)^{3.75} \gamma_a^2} \tag{119}$$

From expression (119) we see that for a given engine power a great reduction in required cooling power can be effected by increasing the fin area and temperature as much as possible. When cooling is critical, as in high-output air-cooled engines, fins are made as numerous and as long as manufacturing technique permits, thus increasing A_f. For a given Q the fin temperature may be increased by reducing u_a [see expression (117a)]. This reduces hp_c according to expression (116) or (119).

In order to reduce u_a, adjustable flaps are included in the cooling-air duct of air-cooled engines as shown in Fig. 94. In practice the flaps are closed and u_a reduced until the fin temperature is as high as permissible.

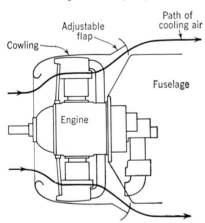

FIG. 94. Cowling for an air-cooled engine with adjustable flaps for control of cooling-air velocity.

The upper limit of fin temperature is reached when the lubrication of the cylinder wall or the structural integrity of the cylinder, valves, or piston is endangered.

SUGGESTION FOR FURTHER READING

McAdams, W. H.: "Heat Transmission," 2d ed., McGraw-Hill, New York, 1942.

PROBLEMS

1. A given diesel delivers its rated indicated power at a normal fuel-air ratio and at the maximum allowable engine speed. The power output can be lowered by:

(*a*) Reducing the quantity of fuel supplied per cycle, maintaining constant inlet conditions and engine speed.

(*b*) Reducing the engine speed, maintaining constant inlet conditions and fuel-air ratio.

(*c*) Throttling the air entering, maintaining constant engine speed and fuel-air ratio.

Discuss and compare the heat transfer from the gases to the cylinder wall when the indicated power is reduced from rated value to half rated value by each of the above methods. Write down any assumptions made in this comparison.

2. An engine develops 50 ihp at part throttle and rejects 800 Btu/min to its cooling system. If $n = 0.8$:

(*a*) How much heat would be rejected at twice the rpm (constant imep)?

(*b*) If opening the throttle increased the ihp to 100, how much heat would be rejected?

3. An engine operating at full throttle rejects heat to its cylinder head and walls equivalent to 15 per cent of the energy of the fuel intake. Assuming $n = 0.7$, what per cent of the energy of the fuel will be rejected if the air capacity of this engine is cut in half by:

(*a*) Throttling.

(*b*) Reducing the piston speed.

4. An engine similar to that of Prob. 3, running at the same piston speed, has twice the characteristic length.

(*a*) What per cent of the heat of the fuel will be rejected in this engine at full throttle?

(*b*) Calculate

$$\frac{\text{Area of cooling radiation required for large engine}}{\text{Area of cooling radiation required for small engine}}$$

assuming the same temperatures and air velocities in both cases.

5. A 6-cylinder engine develops 300 ihp. The heat rejected to the coolant amounts to 100 hp. A geometrically similar engine of 12 cylinders has such dimensions that it also develops 300 ihp at the same piston speed, other independent variables being unchanged. Estimate the heat rejected to the coolant. (Assume $n = 0.6$.)

6. (*a*) An engine running under standard conditions in the inlet manifold develops 600 ihp at 1,500 rpm. Under these conditions it uses 4,500 lb of air/hr and rejects 355 hp to the cooling system. By supercharging and raising the engine speed to 2,500 rpm, this engine can be made to use 8,000 lb of air/hr. Estimate the amount of heat rejected to the cooling system under the new conditions. (Assume $n = 0.7$.)

(*b*) A geometrically similar engine of half the piston displacement volume of the engine of part (*a*) also operates at standard conditions in the inlet manifold and at the same piston speed as in the first part of part (*a*). How many Btu per minute will this engine reject to its cooling system? If the temperature drop through the cylinder wall of the engine of part (*a*) was 50°F, what will it be for this engine? (Assume $n = 0.7$ and that ΔT through the gas film remains constant.)

7. A liquid-cooled engine (5 in. bore, 5 in. stroke) has a temperature drop through its $\frac{1}{8}$-in. cylinder walls of 60°F.

(a) A similar engine of $7\frac{1}{2}$ in. bore, $7\frac{1}{2}$ in. stroke will have what drop through its cylinder walls?

(b) If the first engine were modified by increasing the cylinder-wall thickness to $\frac{3}{16}$ in., what would the drop through the cylinder walls be?

8. With cooling air at sea-level conditions, an air-cooled engine cylinder with integral baffles gave the following test data:

mep = 200 psi, rpm = 2,000

Fin temperature = 450°F

Δp across baffles = 8 in. H_2O

(a) If constant Δp is maintained and engine conditions are changed to 180 psi and 3,000 rpm, what will be the fin temperature?

(b) What Δp will be required to keep fin temperature at 450°F under the new engine conditions?

9. In a liquid-cooled engine at 20,000 ft altitude ($p = 6.76$ psia, $T = 447$°R), cooling water must be kept at 160°F to prevent boiling. Prestone could be used at 240°F. What difference would this make in the relative area of radiator required for cooling at 20,000 ft? (Give ratio of area required with Prestone to area required with water.) Assume 10 per cent less heat flow from the cylinder gases to the coolant with Prestone.

CHAPTER 13

COMPRESSION-IGNITION ENGINES

Compression-ignition engines, or diesel engines as they are often called, are in a broad way thermodynamically similar to spark-ignition engines. The cycle for both types includes intake, compression, addition of heat, expansion, and exhaust. The combustion process and the method of power control in the compression-ignition engine are, however, very different from those in the spark-ignition engine.

In the CI engine usually a full unthrottled charge of air is drawn in during the intake stroke. A compression ratio between 12 and 20 is used, so that the temperature of the air near the end of the compression stroke is quite high. Just before top center, fuel is sprayed into the combustion chamber. Owing to the high temperature of the air, the fuel ignites and burns almost as soon as introduced. The combustion products are expanded and exhausted in the usual way.

Stages of Combustion

For convenience in analysis, the combustion process in a CI engine is usually divided into three stages, the delay period, the rapid-combustion period, and the period of controlled combustion.

The delay period. Figure 95 shows a typical pressure–crank-angle record for a CI engine. The duration of fuel injection is also indicated. Superimposed on this plot is a record made by motoring the engine without injecting fuel. An examination of these records shows considerable crankshaft travel between the start of injection and the start of combustion as indicated by the departure of the firing record from the motoring record. Apparently the first fuel to be injected must be heated to ignition temperature and must then undergo preliminary chemical reactions similar to the reactions which take place in the last part of the charge in a spark-ignition engine. In the CI engine this stage is called the delay period.

Delay time. The time interval between the start of injection and the start of combustion is called the delay time. Delay time, as in the spark-ignition engine, depends upon the temperature and pressure existing in the combustion space during the delay period. High pressures and temperatures shorten the delay. Delay time also depends upon the chemical structure of the fuel. Usually the degree of atomization of the fuel spray has little effect on the delay time. This would seem to indicate that the fraction of the delay time required for heating the fuel droplets to ignition temperature was quite small and that little would be accomplished by preheating the fuel. Changing the quantity of fuel injected during the delay period usually has no direct effect on delay time. In the boundary between the jet of injected fuel and the cylinder air there exists an infinite range of fuel-air ratios. There are

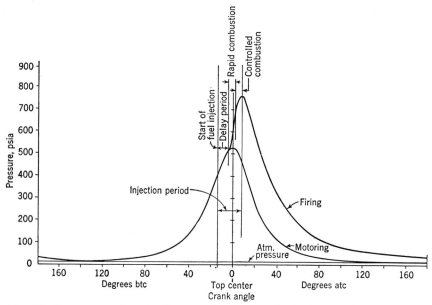

Fig. 95. Pressure–crank-angle diagram of a compression-ignition engine $3\frac{1}{4} \times 4\frac{1}{2}$. Waukesha Comet Head, $r = 13.5$, diesel fuel, $F = 0.04$, 1,400 rpm, 14.5°BTC injection advance. (*Loh et al., MIT SM thesis*, 1944.)

always several points where the fuel-air ratio is of the proper value for minimum delay time. Combustion starts at these points regardless of conditions elsewhere in the cylinder.

It is important to note that if the delay *time* is long, there will be more opportunity for the fuel and air to mix intimately before combustion starts. The delay *angle* is the number of degrees the crankshaft turns during the delay period and is the product of delay time and crankshaft speed. Since the fuel-injection pump is geared to the crankshaft, the quantity of fuel introduced before combustion starts is proportional to the delay *angle*.

Rapid-combustion period. During the delay period fuel has entered the cylinder and has to some extent evaporated or become more finely divided and mixed with the air. When combustion starts, the fuel in intimate contact with oxygen will burn with great rapidity. The speed of this reaction determines the rate of pressure rise (dp/dt) in the cylinder. A high rate of pressure rise means a sudden application of load to the engine structure, which often results in fatigue damage to the parts. A high rate of pressure rise also produces a violent pounding noise which is known as "diesel knock."

The rate of pressure rise during the second stage of combustion is affected by:

1. The degree of atomization of the fuel. This depends upon the design of the fuel-injection system.

2. How much fuel evaporates during the delay period. This depends primarily upon time. If the delay time is long, there will be more time for fuel evaporation.

3. How well the fuel is distributed throughout the cylinder and mixed with the air during the delay period. This depends upon the time available for this process to be carried out, upon the spray pattern, and to some extent upon the air motion in the cylinder. Long delay times and high engine speeds will increase the mixing.

4. How much fuel is injected during the delay period. In general, when a larger quantity of fuel is injected into the cylinder during the delay period, some of this extra fuel will become mixed with the oxygen present and will contribute to an increased rate of pressure rise.

To summarize: In order to avoid engine damage or diesel knock from high dp/dt, it is important to keep the delay time short so that there will be less time for fuel and air to come in contact before combustion starts. It is important to keep the engine speed low and the delay angle short so that there will be less air motion for mixing and less fuel injected before combustion starts.

The *magnitude* of the pressure rise during the second period may determine the value of the peak pressure of the cycle. For structural reasons it is important to limit the peak pressure as well as the rate of pressure rise. The amount the pressure rises during the second period depends primarily upon the quantity of fuel present. The number of crank degrees occupied by the second period is very short compared with the delay period, so that most of the fuel contributing to the pressure rise is injected during the delay. Therefore, to limit the pressure rise during the second period, it is important to keep the delay angle as short as possible.

From the above it is apparent that the rate of pressure rise (dp/dt) as well as the magnitude of the pressure rise in the second period depends upon conditions prevailing in the cylinder during the delay period.   Control of the delay period is therefore extremely important in compression-ignition engines.

Period of controlled combustion.   At the end of the period of rapid combustion, the temperatures within the cylinder are so high that any fuel injected after this time will burn as soon as it finds oxygen.   The shape of the pressure curve in the third period will therefore depend upon:

1. Rate of injection of fuel, especially if plenty of oxygen is still present in the cylinder.

2. Type and intensity of the air motion in the cylinder tending to bring fuel and oxygen together.   This depends upon the shape of the combustion space and the engine speed.

3. The motion of the piston.   If the third period occurs when the piston is well advanced on the power stroke, the rate of change of cylinder volume will be sufficient to affect the cylinder pressure.

For high efficiency it is necessary to complete the combustion process as near top center as possible.   Rapid mixing of fuel and air during the third period is therefore highly desirable.

The ideal compression-ignition engine.   The requirements for satisfactory performance during period 2 are seen to be in conflict with the requirements for satisfactory performance in period 3.   If the engine is designed to give poor atomization and mixing during the delay period, the rate of pressure rise in period 2 will be reduced.   The effects of this procedure will be disastrous, however, for the fuel and air will not completely mix and burn until well down the expansion stroke and the efficiency will be very low.   Furthermore, when atomization and mixing are poor, a great excess of air is required in the cylinder to burn the fuel completely.   This means that only a fraction of the chemically correct amount of fuel can be burned each cycle, with a resulting reduction in power.   In even the best adjusted CI engine the mixing of fuel and air is so poor that only about 80 per cent of the air present can be used to burn the fuel.   Attempts to use fuel-air ratios above about 0.05 result in dense exhaust smoke from unburned fuel.

If the quantity of fuel injected during the delay period is restricted in an attempt to reduce the pressure rise, there will not be time to introduce, mix, and burn this fuel during period 3; so smoke and inefficiency will again result.

The ideal engine would have an extremely short delay period and rapid air motion in the cylinder.   The fuel would burn as soon as injected, so that the rate of pressure rise would be controlled by the rate of injection, while the magnitude of the pressure rise would be controlled by the quantity injected and the injection timing.   Even after years of development the delay and mixing problems are still troublesome, especially in high-speed CI engines.

Effect of Operating Variables

The effect of operating conditions on CI-engine performance is sometimes difficult to predict with accuracy because of the large number of factors involved. The influence of these factors is often greatly affected by details of the combustion-chamber design. It is possible to draw certain conclusions from theory, however, which hold true for the general run of CI engines.

Injection timing. For *highest efficiency* the injection should be timed to cause peak pressure to occur about 10 to 15° after top center. For *minimum dp/dt*, the injection should be timed so that the delay period will be a minimum. Minimum delay is obtained when the cylinder pressure and temperature are high during delay. The delay period should therefore extend equally on each side of top center. Such an injection timing is too late for best efficiency, however, and a compromise position is generally used.

Early injection timing results in a long delay due to the lower temperatures and pressures existing during the delay period. The long time available for mixing of fuel and air during the long delay results in a high dp/dt. The long delay angle permits more fuel to be injected during the delay so that the pressure rise during period 2 will be high.

Late injection also results in a long delay; dp/dt will again be high, but the piston motion in this case will tend to reduce it. The maximum pressures will be lower owing to the position of the piston at the end of the combustion process. The effects of injection timing may be seen in Fig. 96.

Inlet-air temperature. An increased inlet-air temperature will reduce the delay period, reducing dp/dt and the pressure rise. As less air will be taken in, it will not be possible to burn as much fuel without smoke and the maximum power of the engine will be reduced.

Inlet-air pressure. An increased inlet-air pressure will reduce the delay period, reducing dp/dt. Since the compression pressure will increase with inlet pressure, the peak pressure will be higher. As the cylinder will contain more air, it will be possible to obtain more power by increasing the fuel injected per stroke. The effect of varying inlet pressure is seen in Fig. 97.

Compression ratio. An increased compression ratio will increase the compression pressure and temperature, reducing the delay period. This will reduce dp/dt, but the peak pressure will be higher owing to the increase in compression pressure. Efficiency will be increased as in all

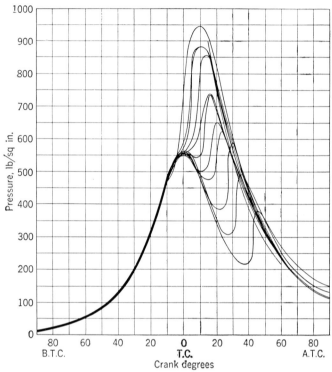

FIG. 96. Effect of injection advance angle on combustion. (*NACA T.N. 401 by A. M. Rothrock.*)

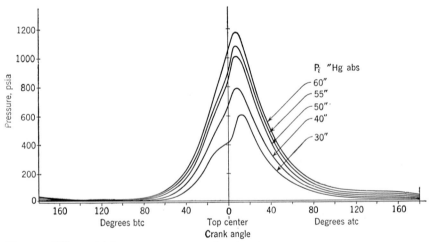

FIG. 97. Effect of inlet pressure on combustion in a compression-ignition engine. Waukesha Comet Head, $r = 13.5$, 800 rpm, 5°BTC injection advance, smoke limit. (*Morel, MIT SB thesis, 1949.*)

engines, because of the greater expansion of the gases during the power stroke.

Fuel quantity. Power control is achieved in the CI engine, not by throttling the air, but by varying the quantity of fuel injected per cycle. If maximum power is required, fuel is injected up to the point where objectionable exhaust smoke is produced or harmful deposits are formed in the combustion space. Since the cylinder air is very hot, there is no lean limit of combustion as in the spark-ignition engine and the smallest quantity of fuel may be injected and burned, reducing the output as much as desired. With no flame-speed problem, the CI engine should have a very high indicated thermal efficiency at light loads, much like the fuel-air cycle, since with small fuel inputs, the temperature rise is small and the specific-heat and equilibrium losses are greatly reduced.

Varying fuel quantity does not affect delay time directly, since a wide range of fuel-air ratios is always present in the cylinder. At *high* outputs (large fuel quantities), however, the cylinder walls tend to operate at higher temperatures. Under these conditions the cylinder air loses less heat to the walls during compression, shortening the delay period slightly. Large fuel quantities are usually injected by prolonging the injection period rather than by increasing the rate of injection. Thus, at high outputs, the amount of fuel entering the cylinder during the delay period will be reduced slightly as the delay angle is reduced. The dp/dt and pressure rise in period 2 might therefore be reduced slightly. If the additional fuel is injected rapidly during period 3, the peak pressure will increase. If, for *low* output, the fuel quantity is reduced sufficiently so that injection stops before the end of the delay period, the peak pressure will be greatly reduced.

Engine rpm. At low rpm the delay angle will be small even with a long delay time, so that there will be little fuel present in the cylinder to take part in the rapid-combustion period. The pressure rise and rate of pressure rise will therefore be moderate. Owing to the low rpm, there will be plenty of time during period 3 for mixing of fuel and air and for completion of combustion before the piston moves very far from top center. The conditions are therefore quite favorable for efficient operation and control of the combustion process. At high rpm, on the other hand, the crankshaft will turn through a relatively large angle during the delay time so that most of the fuel will have been injected during the delay, *i.e.*, before combustion starts. As the delay *time* will be approximately the same at low or high rpm, the time available for mixing will be the *same* regardless of speed. If the cylinder design is such that the inlet process results in considerable air motion within the cylinder, this motion will be greater at high rpm, increasing the mixing during the delay. Therefore at high rpm there will be a *large* amount of fuel in the cylinder at the end of the delay, with the *same* amount of time for mixing as at low speed, and *more* air motion available for mixing. Very high dp/dt and pressure rise will result in the second period. If the cylinder design is such that there is *little* air motion in the cylinder, then at high rpm there will again be a large amount of fuel in the cylinder at the end of delay. The time available for mixing will still be the same as at low speed, so that the dp/dt and pressure rise will be higher than at low rpm. In quiescent combustion chambers the rate of mixing is less likely to increase with rpm so that the crank angle required for final mixing and completion of combustion may become very large, resulting in low efficiency and smoky exhaust.

Engine size. As large engines operate at low rpm because of inertia-stress limitations, the control of combustion in large engines is much easier to achieve. The loss of heat from the cylinder charge during compression tends to be less in large engines owing to the smaller ratio of wall area to cylinder volume. The higher resulting compression temperature shortens the delay, which also improves combustion conditions. From the above it is apparent that the design of CI engines is less difficult when they are of large size.

Fuel quality. A diesel fuel with a short delay used in an engine with good provision for mixing the fuel and air should result in ideal combustion conditions. Burning will start before very much fuel has entered the cylinder so that dp/dt and pressure rise will be low in the second period. The good mixing will result in completion of combustion early in the third period while the piston is still near top center. In high-speed CI engines it is therefore very important to use a fuel having an inherently short delay and to provide carefully for rapid mixing of fuel and air after combustion starts.

α-methylnaphthalene

A diesel fuel is rated for its ignition quality by comparing it with mixtures of standard reference fuels, just as in the octane rating of gasoline. One of the primary standard fuels is hexadecane (more commonly called cetane). This is a straight-chain hydrocarbon like heptane except that it has 16 carbon atoms instead of 7.   Its formula is $C_{16}H_{34}$, and like all long straight-chain hydrocarbons it has a short delay.   The other primary standard is known as α-methylnaphthalene and is a double benzene ring with one methyl group as shown.   This fuel has a long delay and is rated zero "cetane number."

Under standard running conditions the compression ratio of a standard test engine is varied until the fuel being tested shows a delay angle of 13°. The percentage by volume of cetane in a mixture of cetane and α-methyl-naphthalene which also has a delay angle of 13° in the test engine at the same compression ratio is the cetane number of the test fuel.   Fuels of high cetane number ignite readily at lower compression ratios or have shorter delay periods at the same compression ratio and are therefore usually better fuels for CI engines.

Fuel Injection

In the most common type of fuel-injection equipment (see Fig. 98) a cam-driven plunger, operating in a closely fitting barrel, forces the fuel through a check valve into a small-bore tube.   The injection tubing carries the fuel to a nozzle which is mounted in the wall or head of the engine cylinder.   Here the fuel is injected into the engine cylinder at high velocity.   Usually there are a separate plunger, barrel, injection tubing, and nozzle for each engine cylinder.

Fuel pump.   The fuel pump has two main functions—it must start the injection at the proper engine crank angle, late in the compression stroke, and it must force through the nozzle and into the cylinder the exact quantity of fuel needed to produce the desired power.

In the operation of the fuel pump the pump plunger is moved in the barrel by means of a cam.   Early in the stroke of the plunger the inlet port is closed, and the fuel trapped above the plunger is forced into the injection line.   The start of injection is usually controlled by adjusting the position of the pump camshaft relative to the engine crankshaft. Fuel will issue from the nozzle shortly after port closing in the pump, the exact time interval depending on the length of the injection line and the elasticity of the entire system.

Injection may be stopped at any position of the pump plunger by arranging certain relieved portions of the pump plunger to uncover the inlet port and allow the fuel to return to the inlet.   The quantity of fuel injected per engine cycle, which determines the mep, may therefore be increased or decreased by allowing the plunger to move a greater or smaller distance in the barrel before reopening the pump inlet.   Since the fuel rate is the most important control variable in the diesel engine, this adjustment is designed to be made easily by the operator or automatically by the engine-speed governor.

Nozzle. It is the purpose of the nozzle to "atomize," or divide, the fuel into fine droplets and to direct the spray so that every fuel particle will be located where there is sufficient air to burn it completely.   Poor atomization and distribution will reduce dp/dt in the second period but will lengthen the combustion time so that only small quantities of fuel can be injected without exhaust smoke and inefficiency.   This is particularly true if the rpm is high.   Under these conditions both the mep and

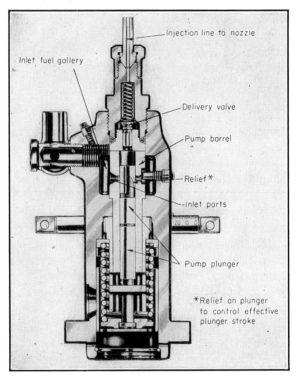

Fig. 98. Cross section of Bosch fuel pump.

horsepower will be low.   It is general practice to provide the best atomization and distribution possible, to depend upon fuel quality or hot spots to reduce the delay time and dp/dt, and to depend upon air motion to reduce combustion time in the third period.   Fuel spray must reach the air in the combustion space farthest from the nozzle, but it is not permissible for the spray to hit the cylinder wall.   Fuel on the walls will not burn completely and may form gummy deposits which will cause the piston rings to stick in their grooves.   The fuel may also dilute the lubricating oil on the cylinder walls and interfere with lubrication.

The nozzle is usually built with one or more small holes through which the fuel sprays into the cylinder at high velocity. The holes are carefully drilled to direct the spray most advantageously. Immediately behind the holes is a valve which is held on its seat by a stiff adjustable spring. The valve prevents cylinder gases from entering the injection system and remains seated until the motion of the pump plunger builds up a high pressure in the injection line. The line pressure acts on part of the valve surface, overcomes the spring force, and opens the valve. With this arrangement injection is made to start at high velocity, which ensures good atomization of the first fuel to enter the cylinder. A typical fuel nozzle is shown in Fig. 99.

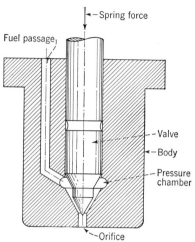

FIG. 99. Bosch fuel nozzle.

When the pressure in the fuel pump is relieved, the delivery check valve closes, increasing the volume of the injection line. The resulting sudden pressure drop at the nozzle causes the nozzle valve to close instantly, stopping the spray without "dribbling." Unless injection starts and stops suddenly, some of the fuel will not be atomized and will cause smoke in the exhaust and carbon deposits on the nozzle, which will further interfere with atomization.

When the pump check valve closes, some fuel pressure remains in the injection line. This residual pressure reduces the lag between the closing of the pump inlet port and the actual start of injection from the nozzle.

Spray formation. When a jet of liquid fuel issues at high velocity from a nozzle, it consists of a relatively solid stream with a sharply defined cylindrical boundary. Internal eddies may exist, which produce minute irregularities in the surface of the jet. These irregularities, striking the relatively motionless cylinder air, are torn away from the main body of the fuel stream and are drawn into drops by surface tension. The first droplets to form are quickly slowed down by the air, but the central core of the fuel moves ahead, and the process is repeated until all the fuel is broken up into droplets.

Although there is still much to be learned about spray formation, a number of general principles have been uncovered by analysis and experiment:

1. All nozzles produce millions of droplets, many of which are quite small. The time required to heat the envelope of fuel vapor surrounding

them to the self-ignition temperature is negligible, so that the delay time is principally a matter of the chemical make-up of the fuel and is almost independent of the spray characteristics.

2. Increasing injection pressure increases the issuing velocity. At higher velocity, more small drops and fewer large drops are formed. There is also more uniformity of drop size. Because small drops will be stopped more quickly by the air, spray penetration distance is not generally increased to any extent by increasing the injection pressure.

Evaporation is more rapid from small drops owing to the large surface area per unit of volume, so that high injection pressure tends to produce rapid combustion in the second and third periods. This improves engine efficiency and may increase the smoke-limited mep. On the other hand, the rate of pressure rise in the second period may be made undesirably high.

3. Increasing the diameter of the nozzle orifice increases the diameter of the solid core of the fuel so that by the time the cylinder air contacts the inner portion of the core it has attained some of the velocity of the spray and is unable to break this part of the fuel into very small drops. The average drop size and the penetration of the spray jet will therefore be increased by an increase in nozzle-orifice diameter.

4. With fuel of higher viscosity, the enlargement of the surface irregularities will be slowed down, and the fuel will therefore tend to break up more slowly and penetrate to a greater distance.

5. A more rapid breakup of the fuel and a wider spray envelope are produced by extending the nozzle valve into the orifice so that the fuel issues as a hollow cone. With the core eliminated the droplets are formed quickly, and the penetration of the spray is greatly reduced. This type of nozzle is often used in precombustion chambers, where great penetration is not desired.

Without air motion it is almost impossible to distribute the fuel throughout an open chamber so that fuel droplets are uniformly dispersed in the air. This requires bushy spray envelopes, nozzles with many holes, or several nozzles in each cylinder. As mentioned above, the spray must penetrate to the cylinder walls, yet must not touch the walls, or the fuel will dilute the lubricating oil or only partially burn, forming ring-sticking deposits. In open-chamber engines it is usually much simpler to arrange for some air motion. By moving the air at right angles to the spray plumes, fuel droplets will be continuously carried away by the air, giving a much better opportunity for mixing both before and during combustion. As the fuel droplets burn, they tend to surround themselves with layers of combustion products which can be removed and replaced with fresh air only when relative motion exists between fuel spray and air.

Many authorities feel that it is well to have both large and small droplets in the spray. Too much of the fuel in the form of small droplets may cause high rates of pressure rise in the second period. Too much of the fuel in the form of large drops will cause late burning in the third period.

Combustion Chambers

It has been pointed out that for low dp/dt there should be only a small quantity of fuel in contact with air at the start of combustion but that for high power and efficiency it must be possible to mix rapidly and burn completely large quantities of fuel while the piston is still near top center. These conflicting requirements are particularly troublesome in small, high-speed engines. To improve second-stage combustion, many methods have been devised to limit fuel-air contact during delay or to shorten delay time. Many schemes have also been devised to provide violent air motion after combustion starts, to satisfy the requirement for early termination of combustion. Several popular types of combustion chambers will be discussed.

Open chamber with directed spray. Figure 100 shows one of the simplest types of combustion chamber. The fuel nozzle has several orifices designed to distribute the spray as evenly as possible to all parts of the combustion space. With this type of chamber, the piston and cylinder head are usually made to fit the shape of the spray plumes. Sometimes the inlet valves are shrouded to produce a general air swirl past the fuel sprays. Rapid and complete burning requires finely atomized fuel. High injection pressures are therefore usually employed. The periphery of the piston is often raised as shown, to shield the cylinder wall from fuel droplets if they should travel this far, and to form a cavity from which drops of fuel may be reevaporated. Obviously the performance of this chamber is quite sensitive to the condition of the fuel nozzles.

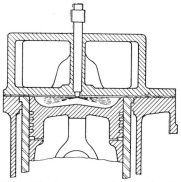

Fig. 100. Open chamber with directed spray.

As there is no provision for limiting fuel-air contact during the delay or for shortening the delay time, this chamber is more generally suited to low-speed engines.

Precombustion chamber. In this type of chamber, shown in Fig. 101, about one-third of the cylinder air is forced into the small chamber during the compression stroke. The fuel is injected into this air. The resulting combustion forces the burning fuel into the main combustion space at high velocity, where it combines rapidly with the rest of the air.   The chamber is designed to run hot in order to reduce the delay.   Note that the fuel is kept from contact with the main body of the air until combustion has started, to avoid a high dp/dt in the cylinder itself.   There is no delay with respect to the main combustion space, and combustion in the third period tends to be rapid and complete owing to the violent projection of the burning fuel into the cylinder.

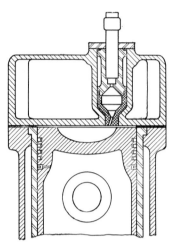

FIG. 101. Precombustion chamber.

In this type of combustion chamber, the fuel-injection pressure and spray pattern are relatively unimportant, as the introduction of the fuel into the main chamber is caused by the explosion in the precombustion chamber.

Turbulence chamber.   Figure 102 shows a turbulence chamber.   During compression practically all the cylinder air is forced into the turbulence chamber.   The chamber and passageway are shaped to give the air

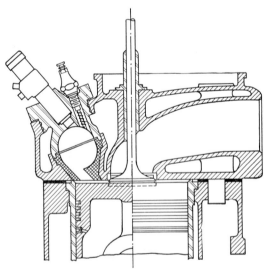

FIG. 102. Turbulence chamber (Waukesha Comet Head).

a rapid whirling motion in the chamber, and the chamber walls are in poor thermal contact with the cylinder-cooling system so that they operate hot. The high wall temperature reduces the delay time, which keeps the rate of pressure rise reasonable, while the rapid motion of the air past the spray results in rapid third-period combustion. As the engine speed increases, the chamber swirl velocity also increases so that relatively high engine rpm may be used without late burning. The injection pressure and spray shape are not particularly critical in this design, as the air swirl is the principal means for mixing fuel and air. Carbon deposits in the chamber improve engine performance, as they become very hot and reduce the delay time. When the engine is cold, the rapid air motion causes the air to lose heat to the chamber walls during compression. This may cause difficult starting and increases the delay, causing considerable knock until the chamber warms up.

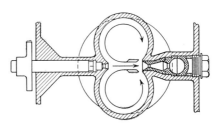

Lanova chamber. The Lanova system consists of a small precombustion chamber into which the fuel is sprayed from a single-hole nozzle on the opposite side of the cylinder. Figure 103 shows the general arrangement. The walls of the chamber run hot so that the injected fuel combines almost immediately with the small amount of air in the chamber. The resulting explosion forces the burning fuel out into the main combustion space at high velocity. The main

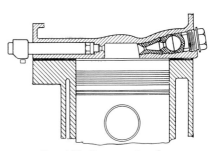

Fig. 103. Lanova chamber.

combustion space is shaped so that the burning fuel stream splits and forms two vortices for rapid mixing with the air in the third period.

In this chamber the mixing of fuel and air is minimized until after combustion starts, in order to avoid high dp/dt. The rapid, organized mixing of fuel and air which takes place in the third period tends to reduce late burning and ensure complete combustion.

Operation and Performance

Power. The CI engine is usually operated without a throttle, a full cylinder charge of air being admitted each cycle. To reduce the mep, it is necessary only to inject less fuel per cycle. The smallest fuel quantity will burn when injected, so that the only limit to low-power operation is the ability of the fuel-injection equipment to meter and inject extremely small quantities of fuel. There is usually little practical difficulty in this regard, and CI engines will usually idle satisfactorily for moderate periods of time.

When the fuel quantity injected per cycle is increased, a point is reached where there is not sufficient excess oxygen to ensure complete combustion of the fuel. Exhaust smoke and odor become noticeable, and fouling of nozzles and sticking of piston rings follow. This "smoke limit" limits the work which can be produced per cycle, *i.e.*, the mep.

The injected-fuel quantity which results in smoke depends upon the mixing conditions within the cylinder, *i.e.*, upon the particular cylinder design. In practice, CI engines can burn cleanly an amount of fuel which will use 60 to 80 per cent of the oxygen in the cylinder. Mean effective pressures will therefore be considerably lower than in spark-ignition engines, which can use all the oxygen in their cylinders. Super-charging of CI engines is fairly common and quite practical. With more air in the cylinders, more fuel may be injected before the smoke limit is reached, and higher meps will be obtained.

Efficiency. Well-designed CI engines usually show greater efficiency than spark-ignition engines, owing to their higher compression ratios. At part load the CI engine gains in efficiency, because of lower variable specific-heat and equilibrium losses at lower fuel-air ratios, as indicated by the fuel-air cycle. In the CI engine, however, the combustion-time losses do not increase at low fuel-air ratios so that the CI indicated thermal efficiency continues to increase as the fuel-air ratio is reduced. At low fuel-air ratios the indicated power is also low, so that eventually the reduction in mechanical efficiency will overcome the improvement in indicated efficiency and cause the brake thermal efficiency to fall. The part-load efficiency of the CI engine is one of its principal advantages, making it suitable for stationary power-plant and marine propulsion use.

Starting. A CI engine will not fire without a certain minimum compression temperature. When the engine block is cold and the inlet-air temperature is low, it is often difficult to start a CI engine. A compression ratio of at least 12 is generally considered necessary to give reasonable starting characteristics. A compression ratio of 14 to 16 is most common. Extremely high compression ratios are avoided because the resulting high peak pressures make the required engine structure too heavy. In starting or during periods of faulty operation, the fuel injected during one cycle may not fire. Some of this fuel may remain in the cylinder to mix with the air during the next inlet and compression strokes. A relatively large amount of fuel will then be in contact with oxygen; and the second-period combustion will result in very high peak pressures, particularly if the compression ratio is high.

To aid in starting, engines are often equipped with glow plugs, which contain electrically heated wires or are packed with smoldering material. The glow plug forms a local hot spot where combustion of the fuel will be initiated although the compression temperature of the air is insufficient. Special fuels such as ethyl ether, which do not require high compression temperatures, are sometimes useful in cold weather starting.

Friction. Because of the tendency of the upper piston ring to stick, and because of the higher cylinder pressures, CI-engine pistons are usually longer and heavier and carry more rings than those of spark-ignition engines. The greater oil-shearing areas of the piston and higher gas pressures make the mechanical friction of CI engines relatively high. The pumping friction tends to be less because throttling is not used. Total engine friction is usually somewhat greater than for spark-ignition engines running at the same piston speeds (see Fig. 46).

Supercharging. Since CI engines operate at relatively low fuel-air ratios (low energy input) and high efficiency (more of the energy converted into useful work), the exhaust loss is comparatively low. Low exhaust-gas temperatures make it mechanically easy to operate a small gas turbine with the exhaust gases. For supercharging the turbine is directly connected to a centrifugal or axial supercharger which increases the engine inlet pressure to about 20 psia, giving a corresponding increase in engine power. Of course, to realize this power increase, more fuel must be injected to use the extra air. The indicated thermal efficiency of the engine will be only slightly affected by supercharging, while the mechanical efficiency will be improved.

Advantages and disadvantages. The principal advantage of the CI engine is its high efficiency at part load. In large sizes the fuel quality is not important, and cheap fuels may be used as long as they are free from dirt and certain chemical impurities. As there is no detonation size limit such as exists for spark-ignition engines, they may be built in very large sizes. This is convenient for power plants or for the propulsion of large ships. Diesel fuel, being less volatile than gasoline, presents less fire hazard in general.

Compression-ignition engines must be built heavier to stand the high peak pressures and rates of pressure rise. Less power is produced compared with a spark-ignition engine of the same size because the CI engine cannot utilize all the air in the cylinders and cannot operate at as high rotational speeds. Careful and regular maintenance is necessary to keep a CI engine operating properly. First cost is higher for CI engines because the precision-made injection equipment is expensive. Large diesels are made in small quantities with considerable handwork, which adds to the expense. Small CI engines which may be produced in larger quantities require intricate combustion chambers, which add to the expense of construction.

The CI engine is most useful for constant-speed work at moderate bmep, where size and weight are not disadvantageous and where fuel cost is important.

SUGGESTION FOR FURTHER READING

Dicksee, C. D.: "The High Speed Compression-ignition Engine," Blackie, Glasgow, 1940.

PROBLEMS

1. A certain manufacturing company proposes to design a compression-ignition engine operating with premixed fuel and air instead of cylinder injection, as is the standard practice. You are assigned to investigate the feasibility of this project.

(*a*) Assuming that the mixture supplied to the cylinder is perfectly uniform, compare qualitatively the combustion process in the proposed design with that in an ordinary compression-ignition engine during (1) delay period, (2) period of rapid combustion, and (3) third stage of combustion.

(*b*) Compare the performance of the proposed engine with that of a standard CI design.

2. A new compression-ignition engine of 8 in. bore and 10 in. stroke is operated on test at constant inlet conditions and constant imep. This engine develops excessive peak pressure when the engine speed reaches 1,000 rpm. List the methods you would suggest to eliminate this trouble. Also list one disadvantage associated with each method suggested.

3. The same fuel is used for the following geometrically similar engines having quiescent, open-type combustion chambers: (1) 8-in. bore × 12-in. stroke, 700 rpm; (2) 12-in. bore × 18-in. stroke, 400 rpm; (3) 16-in. bore × 24-in. stroke, 450 rpm. It is assumed that the beginning and end of fuel injection occur at the same crank angles for each engine and that the amount of fuel injected is proportional to the fresh air supplied in each case.

(*a*) Which engine would you expect to show the greatest tendency to "knock" under the condition stated? Give complete reasoning for your answer.

(*b*) Which engine would have the greatest tendency to show a "smoky exhaust"? Give complete reasoning for your answer.

4. A four-stroke compression-ignition engine will operate up to 80 psi mep without smoke. What effect will you expect the addition of a gear-driven supercharger to have on

(*a*) Mean effective pressure which may be carried without smoke?

(*b*) Efficiency at mep = 40 psi?

(*c*) Efficiency at mep = 80 psi?

(*d*) Tendency to knock?

Explain.

5. A certain fuel gives 0.005 sec delay in a compression-ignition engine of 12 in. bore at 600 rpm. For similar engines of 4, 6, and 8 in. bore, running at the same piston speed, what would be the delay angle with the same fuel, other conditions remaining the same? To give similar combustion characteristics in the smaller engines, what should be the delay time of a fuel appropriate to each engine?

6. A CI engine with 20 in. bore and 25 in. stroke operates smoothly at 1,600 fpm piston speed if the delay period of the fuel does not exceed 0.006 sec. A geometrically similar engine with 8 in. bore is going to be operated at 1,800 fpm piston speed. If the injection period occupies the same number of crank degrees in each engine, what is the maximum permissible delay period for the fuel which is to be used in the smaller engine? (Show all calculations.)

7. (a) It is proposed to control the power of a spark-ignition engine by varying the fuel alone without altering the inlet pressure. Comment on this scheme.

(b) It is proposed to control the power of a compression-ignition engine by maintaining a constant fuel-air ratio, throttling the air supply along with the fuel supply at reduced loads. Comment on this scheme.

8. One of the primary objectives of the designers of diesel engines is to make compression-ignition engines that will burn richer mixtures satisfactorily; on the other hand, many attempts have been made to get rapid combustion of lean mixtures in spark-ignition engines. Explain in detail why these are important objectives.

9. It has been stated that, when each engine is run at a constant speed and inlet temperature and with a given fuel and fuel-air ratio, detonation in the spark-ignition engine is largely controlled by the maximum cylinder pressure, while "knock" in the compression-ignition engine depends largely upon the compression pressure. Do you agree with this statement or not? Explain your answer fully.

CHAPTER 14

TWO-STROKE ENGINES

A two-stroke engine is one which completes its cycle of operation in two strokes of the piston. The work of the inlet and exhaust strokes is done by a separate pump or blower while the engine piston is near bottom center. The engine piston needs only to compress the fresh charge and expand the products of combustion. Since a two-stroke engine will have twice as many cycles per minute as a four-stroke engine with the same number of cylinders, it will develop twice the power when operating at the same mep. As with the four-stroke engine, the power depends upon the number of pounds of air per minute available for combustion.

In many two-stroke engines the mechanical construction is greatly simplified by using the piston as a slide valve in conjunction with inlet and exhaust ports cut in the side of the cylinder.

The two-stroke category includes most of the very large marine engines, nearly all the outboard spark-ignition motorboat engines, and a large fraction of all the compression-ignition engines built.

Two-stroke Engine Types

One of the simplest types of two-stroke engine is shown in Fig. 104. In this engine the scavenging air is compressed in the crankcase by the underside of the piston during the expansion stroke. For this reason it is called a crankcase-scavenged engine. As the piston moves down, it eventually uncovers the exhaust ports, and the cylinder pressure drops to atmospheric as the combustion products leave the cylinder. Further motion of the piston uncovers the transfer ports, permitting the slightly compressed air or mixture in the crankcase to enter the engine cylinder. The piston and ports are usually shaped so that the fresh air will sweep up to the top of the cylinder before flowing to the exhaust ports. This is for the purpose of scavenging the upper part of the cylinder of combustion products and also to prevent the fresh air from flowing directly to the exhaust ports and being lost. The projection on the piston is called a deflector. As the piston returns from bottom center, the transfer ports and then the exhaust ports are closed and compression of the charge begins. Motion of the piston during compression lowers the pressure in the crankcase so that the fresh air or mixture is drawn into the crankcase through the automatic spring-loaded inlet valve. Ignition and expansion take place in the usual way, and the cycle is repeated. Owing to friction in the inlet valve and transfer ports something less than one cylinder

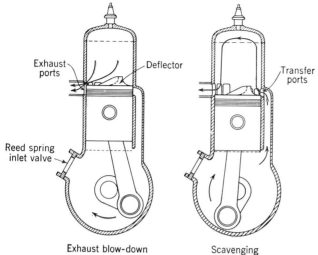

Fig. 104. Crankcase-scavenged two-stroke engine.

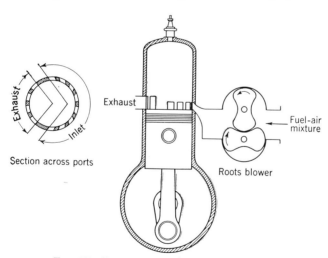

Fig. 105. Loop-scavenged two-stroke engine.

displacement volume of free air will reach the cylinder. Engines of this type seldom have meps of over 60 psi.

Figure 105 shows a loop-scavenged two-stroke engine. This type uses an external blower supplying a pressure of several pounds per square inch at the inlet manifold. As the piston moves down on the expansion stroke, it uncovers the exhaust ports at approximately 65° before bottom center. About 10° later, when the cylinder pressure has been considerably reduced, the inlet ports open and the scavenging process takes place. The inlet ports are shaped so that most of the air flows to the top of the cylinder on the inlet side and back down on the exhaust side before reaching the exhaust ports. This ensures scavenging of the upper

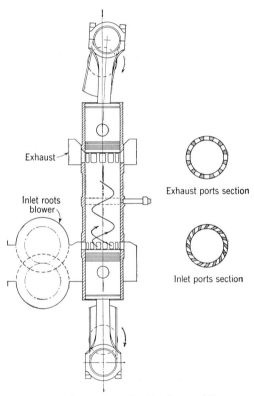

Fig. 106. Port arrangement of a two-stroke "end-to-end" scavenged compression-ignition engine.

cylinder volume. Piston deflectors are not used as they are heavy and tend to become overheated at high output. The scavenging process is more efficient in properly designed loop-scavenged engines than in the usual crankcase compression engine with deflector piston.

Figure 106 shows one type of "end-to-end" scavenged engine. In this type the exhaust ports or exhaust valves are opened first. The inlet ports are usually shaped to give the incoming air a swirl in a plane perpendicular to the cylinder axis. The swirl helps to prevent mixing of fresh charge and combustion products during the scavenging process.

Early on the compression stroke the exhaust ports close and the cylinder pressure may rise part way toward full inlet-manifold pressure before the inlet ports close. In the loop-scavenged engine the port timing is symmetrical, so that the exhaust port must close *after* the inlet port closes. This timing prevents this type of engine from filling its cylinder at full inlet pressure. In the end-to-end scavenged engines, counterflow within the cylinder is eliminated, and there is less opportunity for mixing of fresh and spent gases. The scavenging should therefore be more efficient.

Two-stroke Air Capacity

Unless large amounts of overlap are used, the average *four-stroke* engine retains all the air entering the inlet system; *i.e.*, none is lost out the exhaust valve. An air meter at the engine inlet will therefore measure w_a, the amount of air available for combustion, and the output will be

$$\text{hp} = \frac{(w_a/\text{min}) \times JFe_c\eta}{33{,}000} \tag{34}$$

The exhaust ports of a two-stroke engine must be open during most of the scavenging process, so that it is impossible to avoid some loss of fresh air or mixture at that time. The more air we force into the cylinder, the greater is the fraction of this air lost out the exhaust ports. The power output of a two-stroke engine is therefore proportional not to the amount of air *entering* the engine but to the amount of air *retained* in the cylinders.

Scavenging ratio. In the two-stroke cylinder the "ideal" air capacity would be

$$\text{rpm} \times \text{No. cyls.} \times V_t\gamma_i \tag{120}$$

where V_t = total cylinder volume = $V_d \dfrac{r}{r-1}$

γ_i = inlet-air density

The ratio of total air per minute entering the engine ports to the ideal air capacity is a measure of the excess air used for scavenging. This quantity is called the *scavenging ratio* R_{sc}. Thus

$$R_{sc} = \frac{(w_a/\text{min}) \dfrac{r-1}{r}}{\text{rpm} \times \text{No. cyls.} \times V_d\gamma_i} \tag{121}$$

To secure reasonably complete scavenging most two-stroke engines require scavenging ratios of about 1.2. Values higher than this result in excessive loss of fresh charge out the exhaust ports and require high scavenging (inlet) pressures.

Scavenging efficiency. For high outputs it is important that as much air as possible be *retained* in the cylinders. The ratio of air retained per minute to the ideal air capacity is called the scavenging efficiency η_{sc}. Thus

$$\eta_{sc} = \frac{(w_{ret}/min) \, \dfrac{r-1}{r}}{\text{rpm} \times \text{No. cyls.} \times V_d\gamma_i} \tag{122}$$

The scavenging efficiency therefore indicates the extent to which combustion products have been replaced with fresh air.

Power. If F' is the ratio of fresh fuel to fresh air retained in the cylinder after the ports close, then the indicated power of the two-stroke engine will be:

$$\text{ihp} = (w_{ret}/min)(F'e_c\eta_i') \frac{778}{33,000} \tag{123}$$

where η_i' is the thermal efficiency based on the fuel retained in the cylinder. Substituting in (122),

$$\text{ihp} = \text{rpm} \times \text{No. cyls.} \times V_d\gamma_i \frac{r}{r-1} \eta_{sc}(F'e_c\eta_i') \frac{778}{33,000} \tag{124}$$

A comparison of expression (61a) for the four-stroke and (122) for the two-stroke engine shows that for the same sized engine and same inlet density

$$\frac{\text{Air retained in two-stroke}}{\text{Air retained in four-stroke}} = 2 \times \frac{r}{r-1} \frac{\eta_{sc}}{\eta_v} \tag{125}$$

If the two-stroke engine came as close to its ideal retained air capacity as the four-stroke engine, it would develop something more than twice the power.

In the two-stroke engine

$$\text{Work/cycle} = V_d\gamma_i \frac{r}{r-1} \eta_{sc}(F'e_c\eta_i') \times 778 \times 12$$

The imep is therefore

$$\text{imep} = \gamma_i \frac{r}{r-1} \eta_{sc}(F'e_c\eta_i') \frac{778}{144} \tag{126}$$

Relationship between R_{sc} and η_{sc}. As seen above, the output of a two-stroke engine is proportional to the scavenging efficiency. To obtain a given scavenging efficiency, it is necessary to force a certain amount of air into the engine. The relationship between the amount of air forced in and the amount of air retained, *i.e.*, the relationship between R_{sc} and η_{sc}, depends upon the shape and arrangement of inlet and exhaust ports, the shape of the piston head, cylinder head, and combustion chamber, and upon the timing of the ports, the engine speed, etc. Obviously no two designs will have exactly the same curve of η_{sc} vs. R_{sc}.

If the scavenging process were perfect, the fresh charge would flow into the cylinder without mixing with the combustion products and without loss from the exhaust ports, so that the air retained would equal the air supplied. At a scavenging ratio of 1, the scavenging efficiency would also be 1, and no residual gases would be present. There would be no advantage in using a scavenging ratio of more than 1, as the additional air would have to flow out of the exhaust ports. This condition is shown as curve A in Fig. 107.

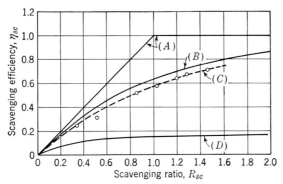

Fig. 107. Scavenging efficiency vs. scavenging ratio under different conditions. (A) "Perfect scavenging." (B) $\eta_{sc} = 1 - (\epsilon)^{-R_{sc}}$ for "perfect mixing." (C) Experimental points with MIT two-stroke engine, $4\frac{1}{2} \times 6$, 1,800 rpm, D ports, varying scavenging pressure. (*Rogowski et al., NACA T.N. 674 and 919.*) (D) "Short circuiting."

The opposite extreme would be the case where the entering charge crosses the cylinder without scavenging the combustion products and leaves immediately through the exhaust ports. This is called short circuiting and results in very low scavenging efficiency even at large scavenging ratios (curve D).

In most two-stroke engines part of the fresh charge displaces combustion products without mixing or loss, and part short-circuits without mixing. Other portions of the fresh charge mix with the products of combustion, part of them remaining in the cylinder and part being scavenged. The resulting curve of η_{sc} vs. R_{sc} for actual engines is therefore somewhat below the "perfect-scavenging" curve A and curiously enough is often quite similar to the theoretical curve obtained by assuming that as the fresh charge enters the engine, it immediately diffuses and mixes with all the combustion products present and is partially lost as the mixture leaves the cylinder.

The formula for this latter curve is

$$\eta_{sc} = 1 - \epsilon^{-R_{sc}} \qquad (127)$$

where ϵ is the base of the natural logarithms. This is called the "perfect-mixing" curve and is shown as curve B in Fig. 107. Unless the actual curve of η_{sc} vs. R_{sc} has been established for a given engine, this theoretical curve is often used in performance estimation.

Measurement of scavenging efficiency. No entirely satisfactory method has been developed for measuring the scavenging efficiency. One of the better methods, which may be used with diesel engines or other engines which inject their fuel into the cylinder, is to draw off a small sample of the products of combustion just before the exhaust valve opens or during the earliest part of blowdown. The sample is analyzed and compared with curves of exhaust products vs. fuel-air ratio such as Fig. 37. This determines the fuel-air ratio that must have existed in the cylinder before combustion. If the quantity of fuel injected per cycle is measured, the quantity of fresh air retained in the cylinder per cycle may therefore be calculated. Air in the residual gases need not be considered, as it represents a constant quantity which does not take part in the combustion.

In engines which use a fuel-air mixture for scavenging, the value of F' will be known, as it is the same as at the carburetor. If η_i' can be estimated for the values of r and F' being used and if the imep is measured, η_{sc} may be obtained from expression (126).

With a spark-ignition engine a mixture sufficiently rich to ensure combination of all the retained oxygen might be used and the exhaust gas analyzed for oxygen. This would indicate how much fresh mixture had passed through the engine into the exhaust during scavenging.

Scavenging pressure. A two-stroke engine may be conveniently considered as an orifice. The air flow through the engine will depend upon the port area, the pressure difference across the engine, the scavenging density γ_i, and the flow coefficient of the ports. The relationship may be expressed as

$$w_a/\text{sec} = AK \sqrt{2g\gamma_i \Delta p} \qquad (84b)$$

For a *constant scavenging ratio*, w_a/sec must be proportional to the rpm.

Assuming γ_i is constant, the scavenging-pressure difference required is $\Delta p \propto (\text{rpm})^2$.

In practice the scavenging-pressure difference is usually increased by raising p_i, which increases γ_i. At high rpm, on the other hand, the exhaust blowdown occupies more crank degrees, the pressure in the cylinder at the time the inlet ports open will be higher, and blowback into the inlet system may occur. These two effects tend to counteract each other so that in most two-stroke engines the scavenging pressure required varies nearly as the square of the engine speed.

In similar two-stroke engines running at the same piston speed and with the same scavenging ratio, the air used per unit of time would be $w_a/\text{sec} \propto V_t \times \text{rpm} \propto l^3 \times \text{rpm}$. But $l \times \text{rpm} = \text{constant}$ at constant piston speed. Therefore, $w_a/\text{sec} \propto l^2$ as in the four-stroke engine [see expression (72)].

From (84b), at constant γ_i

$$\Delta p \propto \frac{(w_a/\text{sec})^2}{A^2} \propto \frac{l^4}{A^2}$$

But $A^2 \propto l^4$; therefore, $\Delta p = \text{constant}$ (the same for all engines of the series). A value of Δp from 2 to 5 psi is usually required to give reasonable scavenging ratios at normal piston speeds.

The scavenging process may be seriously disturbed by pressure waves in the inlet or exhaust systems. The two-stroke engine is therefore much more sensitive to the design of the inlet and exhaust piping than is the four-stroke engine with its positive piston scavenging. To minimize dynamic effects, most two-stroke engines are provided with large surge chambers in the inlet and exhaust systems. When a two-stroke engine is to operate at only one speed, the piping is sometimes tuned so that the pressure fluctuations produced will assist the scavenging process.

Fuel loss. If fuel is injected into the cylinders after the exhaust ports are closed, the indicated thermal efficiency of the two-stroke engine can be made practically as good as that of a four-stroke engine. When a carburetor is used, however, the scavenging is done with fuel-air mixture and only the fuel mixed with the *retained* air is used for combustion. The fuel supplied per cycle will be $R_{sc}V_t\gamma_iF$, while the fuel retained will be $\eta_{sc}V_t\gamma_iF$. The fraction of the fuel supplied which is actually used will therefore be η_{sc}/R_{sc}. The *engine* efficiency η_i will be $\eta_i{}' \, (\eta_{sc}/R_{sc})$, where $\eta_i{}'$ is the efficiency with which the *fuel retained* is used in the cylinder. $\eta_i{}'$ might be estimated at 85 per cent of the corresponding fuel-air-cycle value based on the cylinder fuel-air ratio F' and the compression ratio actually used.[1]

At high scavenging ratios η_{sc} increases at a lower rate so that η_{sc}/R_{sc} becomes less. The engine efficiency at high scavenging ratios may therefore be very low.

Idling. The two-stroke spark-ignition engine may refuse to run at low scavenging ratios because of the high percentage of residual gas present. The four-stroke engine cylinder always contains the residual gas which occupied the clearance volume at exhaust pressure at the end of the exhaust stroke. This mixes with the amount of fresh charge which

---

[1] Except for distribution difficulties, $F' = F$ in a carbureted engine.

passes the throttle and enters the cylinder on the inlet stroke. In the two-stroke engine the residual gas in the cylinder at the start of scavenging is sufficient to fill the *entire cylinder* volume at exhaust pressure and may therefore be 5 or 10 times as much as in the four-stroke engine. If the scavenging ratio is low, most of the residual gas remains in the cylinder to mix with the small amount of fresh charge. An incombustible or slow-burning mixture is the result. Some spark-ignition two-stroke engines fire irregularly and finally refuse to run when the mep is reduced to 30 psi or so. At low scavenging ratios, the burning rate may be so low that flame is still present in the cylinder when the inlet ports open. The flame will then ignite the fresh charge if a fuel-air mixture is being used for scavenging. At low speeds this early ignition will cause backfiring into the inlet system, which will stop the engine. At higher engine speeds the inlet ports may close before ignition from the flame takes place. The result will be lowered efficiency, because of incorrect ignition timing, and difficulty in stopping the engine.

Fuel injection in two-stroke engines. By injecting fuel directly into the cylinder the fuel loss from the exhaust is eliminated. To obtain reasonable charge homogeneity in spark-ignition engines, it is necessary to inject the fuel as early as possible. Fuel is usually injected somewhat before the exhaust ports close. The additional time thus gained for mixing of fuel and air improves combustion enough to more than offset any slight loss of fuel through the exhaust ports. For CI engines, since the injection timing controls the combustion timing, injection must take place near top center and there can be no loss of fuel.

In spark-ignition engines idling is improved by fuel injection. Backfiring into the inlet system is eliminated since the inlet system contains no fuel. By using very rich mixtures and very advanced spark timing it is often possible to run well, at quite low meps. Two-stroke CI operation is usually quite satisfactory in the idling range. In CI engines it is not necessary to reduce the scavenging ratio when idling; there is therefore little residual gas to interfere with ignition or combustion.

Compression-ignition operation eliminates fuel loss at high scavenging ratios and idling difficulties at low scavenging ratios. As these are the two principal disadvantages of the two-stroke engine, many two-stroke engines are built for compression-ignition operation. The relative simplicity of two-stroke construction and the possibility of greater power output lead many builders of CI engines to choose the two-stroke cycle.

SUGGESTIONS FOR FURTHER READING

Rogowski, A. R., and C. L. Bouchard: Scavenging a Piston-ported Two-stroke Cylinder, *NACA T.N.* 674, November, 1938.
Scavenging of Two-cycle Engines, *Sulzer Tech. Rev.*, no. 4, 1933.

PROBLEMS

1. A two-cylinder 2- by 3-in. outboard two-stroke engine (19 in.³ displacement), $r = 6$, uses a carbureted gasoline-air mixture of fuel-air ratio 0.08. When running at 5,000 rpm it gives 20 ihp and uses 0.8 lb of fuel/ihp-hr at standard sea-level conditions. If its scavenging characteristics are the same as those given by curve B, Fig. 107, compute:
(a) Scavenging ratio.
(b) Scavenging efficiency.

2. A one-cylinder two-stroke engine has a bore of 4.5 in., stroke of 6 in., and compression ratio of 7.
bmep $= 100$ at 1,800 rpm
$\eta_i' = 0.30$, $\eta_{mech} = 0.80$
$p_{sc} = 19.7$ psia, $T_i = 620°$R
Air supplied $= 10$ lb/min
Fuel is injected after ports close
Cylinder fuel-air ratio $= 0.07$
Calculate:
(a) Scavenging ratio.
(b) bhp.
(c) ihp.
(d) Scavenging efficiency.
(e) η_i of the engine if a 0.07-fuel-air-ratio carbureted mixture were used.

3. A two-stroke engine using a carbureted mixture and running at 1,200 rpm, $p_{sc} = 16.7$ psia, $p_{ex} = 14.7$ psia, has an imep of 72 at a scavenging ratio of 0.8. The ihp $= 155$ and the isfc 0.85. p_{sc} is raised to 20.7 psia. If the fuel-air ratio and rpm are held constant,
(a) Calculate the new value of the scavenging ratio.
(b) Calculate the new scavenging efficiency, if curve B of Fig. 107 applies.
(c) Calculate the new imep and ihp.
(d) Calculate the isfc for the engine under these conditions.

CHAPTER 15

PERFORMANCE AND SUPERCHARGING

Performance is a rather loosely used term which has to do with the power and efficiency obtainable when an engine is operated at various values of piston speed, inlet pressure and temperature, fuel-air ratio, spark advance, compression ratio, etc. The useful range of all these variables is limited by high mechanical stresses, detonation, overheating, or other undesirable effects. For this reason there is always a practical limit to the maximum power or maximum economy which can be obtained with a given engine.

It is often possible to extend the useful range of one engine variable by using a less effective setting of another, as, for example, when a retarded spark or a very rich mixture is used to control detonation so that a higher inlet-manifold pressure may be used. The result of this compromise would be increased power at the expense of reduced efficiency.

Since output = input $\times$ efficiency, an analytical approach to performance is best made by considering first the effect of engine-operating variables on efficiency and then the effect of the operating variables on input.

Efficiency

Indicated efficiency. As previously shown, the indicated thermal efficiency of an engine depends primarily upon the compression ratio, the fuel-air ratio, and the spark-advance or fuel-injection timing.

In diesel engines the compression ratio is usually kept below 18 or 20 in order to avoid high maximum cylinder pressures with the resulting mechanical stresses in the engine structure. In spark-ignition engines the compression ratio is limited by detonation. With high-quality fuels and low inlet pressures, compression ratios of 10 or 12 are feasible. In supercharged engines or engines using lower grade fuels, the compression ratio is usually limited to 6 or 7.

In spark-ignition engines the fuel-air ratio for maximum indicated thermal efficiency is about 0.06 at high inlet pressures. Maximum efficiency occurs at somewhat richer mixtures at part throttle due to the effect of time losses (see Fig. 70). The carburetor is designed to provide the most economical fuel-air ratios when operating at part throttle. At full open throttle the carburetor will supply a fuel-air ratio of about 0.08 to ensure maximum power output. At high inlet pressures, mixtures richer than best power are sometimes used to prevent detonation or overheating.

In diesel engines the power output is controlled by varying the quantity of fuel injected per cycle. Thus the fuel-air ratio automatically varies with output, and higher indicated efficiencies will be obtained at low output because of the effect of lean mixtures on specific-heat and equilibrium losses.

For maximum efficiency in a spark-ignition engine it is necessary to adjust the ignition advance to minimize the time losses, at each engine speed, inlet pressure, or fuel-air ratio. For simplicity, some engines are operated with a fixed spark advance. Automobile engines are equipped with automatic control of spark timing which approximates optimum setting at high speeds and low manifold pressure where detonation is unlikely to occur. For other conditions of operation, the control retards the spark timing to prevent detonation, at the expense of some efficiency.

For best economy the injection timing in diesel engines should be set so that the major part of the burning process is completed just after top center. This injection timing will probably be too early for minimum delay so that an injection setting somewhat retarded from optimum may be necessary at high rpm to reduce the rate of pressure rise.

If the fuel-air ratio and compression ratio of an engine are known, it is possible to estimate the indicated efficiency by assuming the actual η_i to be 0.8 to 0.9 times the efficiency as calculated for the fuel-air cycle and plotted in Fig. 29. A more accurate estimate might be obtained by using a curve of actual η_i vs. F such as Fig. 39, for an engine of the same general design, correcting for any difference in compression ratio by assuming that the ratio of actual efficiencies at the two compression ratios is the same as the ratio of air-cycle efficiencies at the same compression ratios.

Brake efficiency. Since brake efficiency $\eta_b = \eta_i \times \eta_{\text{mech}}$, the mechanical efficiency is important in over-all performance. From (53) or (54a)

$$\eta_{\text{mech}} = \frac{\text{bmep}}{\text{imep}} = 1 - \frac{\text{fmep}}{\text{imep}}$$

Thus any change in operating conditions which increases the ratio of fmep to imep will tend to reduce the brake thermal efficiency.

An increase in engine speed at constant inlet pressure increases the fmep but usually reduces η_v and therefore the imep. As a result, the mechanical efficiency will be less at high speeds.

By lowering the inlet pressure (part throttle) at constant speed, the imep is reduced because of the lowered air capacity. The fmep may increase slightly owing to increased pumping losses. The net result will be a definite reduction in mechanical efficiency.

Changing the fuel-air ratio from the value which gives maximum imep will reduce the mechanical efficiency because the fmep is only slightly affected by changes in imep.

To estimate η_{mech} and η_b it is usually sufficiently accurate to assume that fmep depends only on piston speed. If a curve of true friction for the engine is not available, a curve of motoring fmep such as Fig. 46, from an engine of more or less similar design, may be used.

Output

Indicated power output. From expressions (34) and (61a)

$$\text{ihp} = \frac{\text{rpm}}{2} \times V_d \times \text{No. cyls.} \times \gamma_i \eta_v (Fe_c\eta_i) \frac{778}{33,000}$$

The indicated output is seen to depend primarily upon the air capacity, the fuel-air ratio, and the indicated thermal efficiency. As air capacity is not appreciably affected by fuel-air ratio, the input (air capacity × fuel-air ratio) will therefore vary with fuel-air ratio.

To obtain maximum indicated output in spark-ignition engines the fuel-air ratio is adjusted to give the maximum product of $F \times \eta_i$. The fuel-air ratio may have to be increased above this figure for cooling or detonation control. For any given fuel-air ratio, η_i is kept as high as possible by the use of optimum spark advance and the highest compression ratio possible without detonation or undue mechanical stresses.

In compression-ignition engines maximum output is obtained by increasing the quantity of fuel injected per cycle until objectionable exhaust smoke is produced. The "smoke limit" is reached at fuel-air ratios somewhat leaner than chemically correct, and it is impossible to operate rich enough for $F\eta_i$ to be a maximum.

From expression (72) the air capacity and input of a given design of unsupercharged engine will be maximum when the product of piston speed and η_v is maximum. If the inertia stresses are too severe at this piston speed, the designers will have to limit the piston speed to one low enough to ensure mechanical reliability and be satisfied with a lower air capacity.

The procedure for obtaining maximum air capacity (with a minimum of supercharging work) in supercharged engines is the same as in unsupercharged engines except that γ_i may be raised until detonation, cooling, or mechanical-stress limits are reached. It is possible to obtain an increase in detonation-limited indicated output by reducing the compression ratio and increasing the inlet pressure. Figure 108 shows the output obtainable with a particular engine by supercharging up to incipient detonation, for a range of compression ratios. Lowering the compression ratio greatly reduces the cyclic pressures with only moderate loss in η_i and

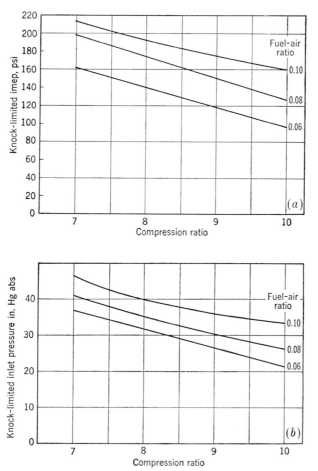

FIG. 108. Effect of compression ratio on detonation-limited imep and inlet pressure. Constant spark advance and engine speed. (*From NACA wartime report* E-124 *by R. E. Bolz and R. Breitwieser.*)

power. By supercharging, the power can more than be regained before the detonation limit is again reached.

It is also possible to increase the detonation-limited output by increasing the fuel-air ratio to control detonation and then increasing the inlet pressure to the detonation point again. The latter is a common method of increasing engine power for airplane take-off. The magnitude of the effect may be seen in Fig. 58.

Brake output. Brake output is indicated output $\times \eta_{mech}$. The previous remarks regarding the effect of engine variables on indicated output, therefore, apply to brake output except when changes in friction are too large to be neglected.

The engine variable which has the greatest effect on friction is piston speed (see Fig. 46). It is to be expected, therefore, that the curve of brake output vs. piston speed or rpm will be considerably different from

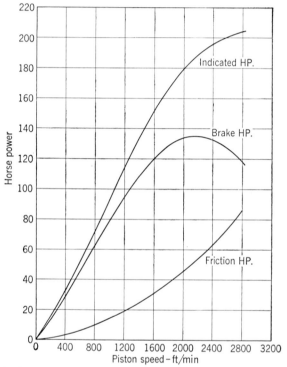

Fig. 109. Typical curves of full throttle ihp, bhp, and fhp vs. piston speed for an automobile-type engine.

the curve of indicated output. As may be seen in Fig. 109, the slope of the fhp curve increases with engine speed. When the fhp is increasing at the same rate as the ihp, the difference between these two curves is a maximum. This difference is the bhp, and the peak occurs at piston speeds much lower than for maximum ihp. Maximum bhp will occur when piston speed $\times \eta_v \times \eta_{mech}$ is a maximum.

Road performance. In a road vehicle the ratio between engine rpm and road speed is usually fixed by the gear ratio of the drive system and the effective diameter of the driving wheels. With a given gear ratio the full-throttle bhp may be plotted against miles per hour, as in Fig. 110. The resistance to motion of the particular vehicle is made up of such items as aerodynamic forces and rolling resistance of the tires. If the vehicle is not operating on level ground, the component of gravity parallel to the road surface must be included in the road resistance. The aerodynamic forces on the vehicle vary as the square of the speed; the

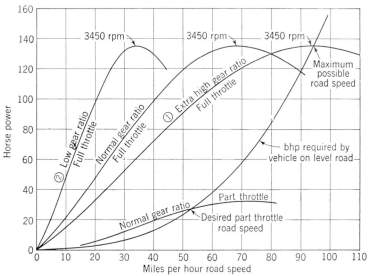

FIG. 110. Horsepower required and available for a typical automotive vehicle on a level road.

rolling resistance is nearly constant with speed. At each speed the horsepower required to drive the vehicle is

$$hp_{req} = \frac{\text{road resistance} \times \text{mph}}{375} \tag{128}$$

A typical curve of hp_{req} for a motor vehicle is shown in Fig. 110. In this figure the hp_{req} becomes equal to the full throttle bhp of the engine at 90 mph. This will therefore be the maximum speed of the vehicle at this gear ratio. If lower road speed is desired, the throttle is closed until the part-throttle bhp curve intersects the hp_{req} curve at the desired value of miles per hour. The highest possible maximum speed is obtained by changing the gear ratio so that the hp_{req} curve is intersected by the peak of the engine bhp curve. This condition is illustrated by curve 1 in Fig. 110.

Acceleration. The acceleration of a vehicle is, of course, proportional to the tractive force which acts at the ground on the driving wheels, minus the road resistance of the vehicle. Neglecting the losses in the drive system,

$$\frac{\text{Tractive force} \times \text{mph}}{375} = \text{engine bhp}$$

and

$$\frac{\text{Road resistance} \times \text{mph}}{375} = \text{hp}_{\text{req}}$$

The net force on the vehicle will then be

$$\text{Tractive force} - \text{road resistance} = \frac{\text{engine bhp} - \text{hp}_{\text{req}}}{\text{mph}} \times 375$$

A very large acceleration or drawbar pull is obtainable at low speeds by changing the gear ratio so that maximum engine bhp occurs at very low miles per hour. This is called shifting to a "lower gear" and is illustrated by curve 2 of Fig. 110.

Engine economy at constant brake horsepower. Often a certain horsepower is required, and the problem is to supply it at highest η_b, that is, with minimum expenditure of fuel per hour. From (44a)

$$\text{bhp} = \frac{\text{bmep} \times \text{rpm} \times V_d \times \text{No. cyls.}}{792,000}$$

The brake thermal efficiency $\eta_b = \eta_i \times \eta_{\text{mech}}$, and as η_i is relatively insensitive to rpm or imep, the highest brake thermal efficiency will in general occur when η_{mech} is maximum.

$\eta_{\text{mech}} = \text{bmep/imep}$, which may be expressed as

$$1 - \frac{\text{fmep}}{\text{imep}} \tag{54a}$$

so that η_{mech} will be maximum when the ratio of fmep/imep is a minimum.

Figure 111 shows typical curves of imep and fmep vs. rpm for an automobile-type engine. For maximum economy the engine should be operated at full throttle to give high imep. The fuel-air ratio should be adjusted to give best thermal efficiency (without too much loss in imep). A fuel-air ratio of about 0.065 would probably be optimum.

In a road vehicle, the gear ratio should be increased, or in an airplane the pitch of the propeller blades should be increased until the engine speed is just barely high enough to produce the required bhp [see expression (44a)]. At this low rpm, the fmep will be a minimum and the imep will be the highest possible (consistent with an economical fuel-air ratio). Thus the conditions for maximum η_{mech} are met. The great economy resulting from the use of very high gear ratios (overdrive) in automobiles is an example of these principles. This low-speed high-mep running condition sometimes results in detonation.   In this case a compromise adjustment must be made.   If the detonation is suppressed by retarding the spark or enriching the mixture, η_i will be reduced and the general economy will be less.   If lower imep and higher rpm are used, the mechanical efficiency will be lowered.

It may also be inadvisable to operate in the above manner at *extremely* low engine speeds, as η_i may be affected by the increased time available for direct-heat loss and by poor distribution of fuel due to low velocity in the inlet manifold.

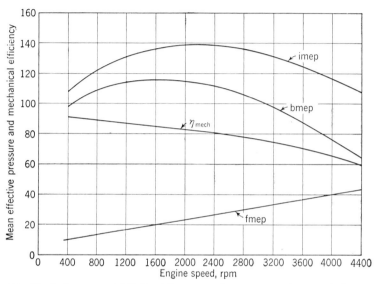

Fig. 111. Typical curves of full throttle mep and η_{mech} vs. engine speed, for an automobile-type engine.

Most economical road speed.   With an infinitely variable gear ratio between engine and driving wheels, it would be most economical to operate at an extremely low road speed.   Road resistance $\times$ distance traveled $=$ work done.   The work done directly affects the amount of fuel required. The engine speed would be kept as low as detonation and smooth operation would permit by means of a high gear ratio.   Engine friction would then be at a minimum.   The throttle would be opened enough to supply the required bhp.   Since the rpm is low, the resulting imep and η_{mech} would be high.   For acceleration, the gear ratio would have to be reduced.   This would permit higher engine speed at the same road speed. The bhp would then exceed hp_{req}, and the excess power would be used to accelerate the vehicle.

With a fixed gear between engine and wheels, the gear ratio must be low enough to provide reasonable acceleration.   That is, the full-throttle bhp must exceed the road horsepower required over a wide range of road speeds.

To operate at low road speed with a fixed gear ratio, it is impossible to reduce the engine speed to make the bhp equal to hp_{req}. Instead, the throttle must be closed, reducing the imep. At very low road speed, hp_{req} is so low that the imep will be reduced to such an extent that the ratio fmep/imep will become quite large. η_{mech} will therefore become low enough to overcome the favorable effect of low road resistance. At high road speeds the high road resistance reduces the economy. With a fixed gear ratio there will be a road speed (20 to 30 mph in automobile practice) where road economy will be best.

The Performance Map

It is always convenient to be able to reduce the performance of a device to a single set of curves. It is even more convenient when this plot is independent of the size of the machine, so that the same set of curves may be used to predict the performance of any one of a series of geometrically similar machines.

One such performance map may be made by using bmep as ordinate and piston speed as abscissa, as shown in Fig. 112. As in Fig. 111, the curve of full-throttle bmep vs. piston speed for the engine under consideration may be drawn in near the top of the plot. Any bmep under this curve is obtainable by varying the inlet pressure by means of the throttle or, in the case of diesel engines, by changing the quantity of fuel injected per cycle. Lines of constant bsfc are drawn on the plot so that, for the given operating conditions, the bsfc obtainable at any bmep or piston speed may be instantly determined.

The lines of constant bhp per square inch of piston area are independent of the particular engine, as they are merely mathematical lines which pass through all points where the product of piston speed and bmep is constant. This may be seen from the following: From (44a),

$$bhp = \frac{bmep \times rpm \times V_d \times No. \; cyls.}{792,000}$$

and since $V_d \times$ No. cyls. $\times$ rpm = total piston area $\times$ stroke $\times$ rpm and $s = (2 \times stroke \times rpm)/12$, if total piston area is A_p, then

$$bhp = \frac{s}{4} \times \frac{A_p \times bmep}{33,000} \tag{129}$$

or bhp per square inch of total piston area

$$\frac{bhp}{A_p} = \frac{s}{4} \times \frac{bmep}{33,000} \tag{129a}$$

Figure 112 would look much the same for spark-ignition or compression-ignition engines. The minimum bsfc point is located in from the edges of the plot. Increased bsfc is obtained by moving upward from this point in spark-ignition engines, because of mixture enrichment from the action of the economizer, and because of poorer distribution at full throttle. In CI engines the bsfc increases at high loads owing to the increased fuel waste (smoke) associated with high fuel-air ratios.

Moving to lower bmeps, the bsfc increases because of reduced mechanical efficiency.

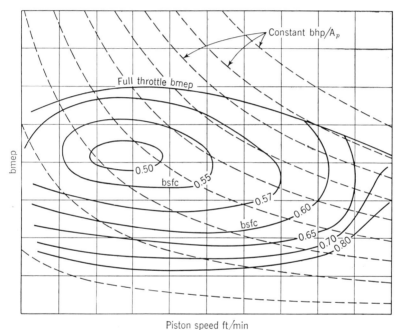

Piston speed ft/min
Fig. 112. Typical performance map.

Moving to the right, to higher piston speeds, the bsfc increases owing to increased friction.

Moving to the left, the bsfc increases in spark-ignition engines because of increased heat loss per cycle, poor distribution at low manifold velocities, and lowered efficiency due to the automatically retarded spark used for detonation control at low engine speeds. Compression-ignition engines also have increased bsfc at low piston speeds probably because the injection equipment cannot be set to give completely satisfactory characteristics over the entire speed range.

The inlet pressure or fuel quantity required for a given bmep will not be the same at different piston speeds because of changes in friction and volumetric efficiency.   Curves of constant p_i, constant fuel quantity per cycle, constant fmep, constant spark advance, etc., may be added to the plot as desired.   Usually it is of more interest to know the minimum bsfc obtainable at any combination of bmep and piston speed.

Figure 113 is a performance map for a typical automobile engine. Plotted on this map is the full-throttle bmep (the upper limit of power

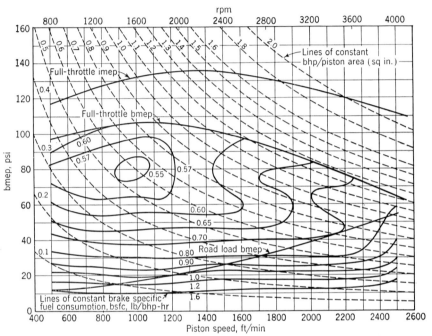

FIG. 113.   Performance curves of a Ford V-8 engine, 1946 model, $3\frac{3}{16} \times 3\frac{3}{4}$, 6.75:1 compression ratio, as installed, with fan, generator, muffler, and tail pipe, automatic spark-advance control.   (*Data from Ford Motor Company Research Rept.* 815, *August*, 1947.)

output).   The irregular shape of the bsfc curve is probably due to the action of the carburetor economizer as the throttle is opened.

The engine bmep required to keep a car running at various road speeds and a certain gear ratio is included on the plot.   The economy of a higher gear ratio may be shown by considering the bsfc obtainable with the gear ratio shown, say at a piston speed of 2,000 fpm.   From the plot, bhp/A_p is about 0.59 and the bsfc about 0.71.   If a higher gear ratio is chosen so as to give the same road speed at 1,400 fpm piston speed, the same bhp/A_p of 0.59 will be required to move the vehicle, but now the bsfc is only 0.60.

Figure 114 is a similar map for a single-cylinder compression-ignition engine.   The upper practical limit of output on this map is the smoke

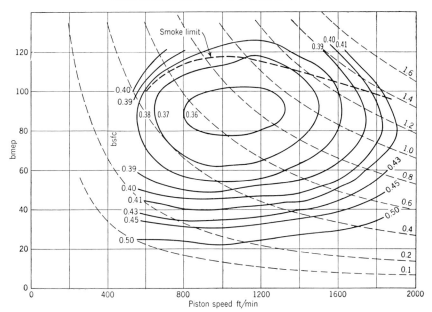

Fig. 114. Performance map of six-cylinder open-chamber diesel engine.

limit, shown in dotted line. Notice the similarity between Figs. 114 and 113.

Supercharging

It is always possible to increase the power of an engine by increasing the density of the air at the engine inlet. The resulting power will be almost directly proportional to the increased air capacity. The degree to which an engine may be supercharged is limited by detonation or by the additional mechanical stresses or cooling difficulties encountered.

Supercharging power. The power required to operate the supercharger may be supplied directly from the engine shaft by suitable gearing. The engine power will then be reduced by an amount equal to the supercharger power. The energy in the engine exhaust gases may be used in a small gas turbine to provide the power required to supercharge. In this case, the shaft output of the engine will not be reduced, as energy normally wasted will now be used to drive the supercharger.

Applying the general energy equation (28) to any supercharger, and realizing that there is very little heat loss from the supercharger to its surroundings, we have, using the symbols of Fig. 20,

$$E_1 + \frac{p_1 V_1 \times 144}{778} + \frac{\text{work input}}{778} = E_2 + \frac{p_2 V_2 \times 144}{778}$$

or

$$\text{Work input} = (H_2 - H_1) \times 778$$

Therefore

$$\text{Work input/lb of air} = C_p (T_2 - T_1) \times 778$$

This relationship is true *regardless of the amount of internal friction or the reversibility of the compression process.*

In an ideal compressor having no friction and with isentropic compression

$$\frac{T_2}{T_1} = \left(\frac{p_2}{p_1}\right)^{(k-1)/k} \tag{27}$$

$$\frac{T_2 - T_1}{T_1} = \frac{T_2}{T_1} - 1 = \left(\frac{p_2}{p_1}\right)^{(k-1)/k} - 1$$

Thus

$$\text{Ideal work input/lb air} = C_p T_1 \left[\left(\frac{p_2}{p_1}\right)^{(k-1)/k} - 1\right] \tag{130}$$

The ratio of ideal work input to actual work input is known as the adiabatic efficiency η_a.

$$\eta_a = \frac{C_p(T_2 - T_1)_{\text{ideal}}}{C_p(T_2 - T_1)_{\text{actual}}} = \frac{T_1[(p_2/p_1)^{(k-1)/k} - 1]}{(T_2 - T_1)_{\text{actual}}} \tag{131}$$

The power required to compress and deliver the air will be

$$\begin{aligned}
\text{shp} &= \frac{(w_a/\text{min})(\text{work input/lb air})}{33,000} \\
&= \frac{(w_a/\text{min})C_p(T_2 - T_1)_{\text{actual}} \times 778}{33,000} \\
&= \frac{(w_a/\text{min})C_p T_1[(p_2/p_1)^{(k-1)/k} - 1] \times 778}{33,000 \times \eta_a} \tag{132}
\end{aligned}$$

The above calculations are general and apply to *any type of compressor.* Note that the power required depends upon the quantity of air handled, the pressure ratio, and the initial temperature, as well as upon η_a.

The increase in engine power produced by supercharging will be many times the power required to drive the supercharger, but of course additional fuel will be used to produce this power, as well as to run the supercharger if the supercharger is engine-driven.

Efficiency of a supercharged engine. As the indicated thermal efficiency of an engine is not affected to any extent by increasing the inlet pressure, the brake thermal efficiency of a supercharged engine reflects only the change in mechanical efficiency due to supercharging. In an unsupercharged engine

$$\eta_{\text{mech}} = 1 - \frac{\text{fhp}}{\text{ihp}} \tag{54}$$

In a supercharged engine part of the indicated power is used to drive the supercharger so that

$$\text{bhp}_s = \text{ihp}_s - (\text{fhp}_s + \text{shp})$$

For a supercharged engine

$$\eta_{\text{mech}} = 1 - \frac{\text{fhp}_s + \text{shp}}{\text{ihp}_s} \qquad (133)$$

The fhp_s will usually be slightly lower than fhp owing to reduced pumping losses, while ihp_s will be much higher than ihp owing to the increased air capacity.

The net result with most engines is that, at full throttle,

$$\frac{\text{fhp}_s + \text{shp}}{\text{ihp}_s} \approx \left(\frac{\text{fhp}}{\text{ihp}}\right)_{\text{unsupercharged}}$$

so that η_{mech} is usually only slightly affected by supercharging and the brake thermal efficiency of supercharged and unsupercharged engines is about the same.

An engine with a gear-driven supercharger, which is throttled to give the same ihp as the same engine without supercharger, will have *less* brake power by the amount of the shp. The brake thermal efficiency will be lower also, as the fuel used is proportional to the ihp (which is the same) while the bhp output is lower. The supercharger should therefore be disengaged when not needed.

The temperature rise $(T_2 - T_1)$ of the engine air as it passes through the supercharger is conducive to detonation. When engines are highly supercharged, particularly when more than one stage of supercharging is used, an air intercooler is generally installed after the first supercharger. The intercooler is helpful in reducing the final air temperature at the engine inlet. In addition, by lowering T_1 for the second stage, it reduces the shp required [see expression (132)].

Centrifugal superchargers. The centrifugal supercharger is the type most commonly used with internal-combustion engines. The centrifugal compressor consists of an impeller which rotates in a close-fitting casing. A photograph of an impeller is shown in Fig. 115. It is seen to have radial blades. With the impeller running at peripheral speeds close to the speed of sound, these blades pick up the air near the hub of the impeller and carry it radially to the blade tips. Owing to the centrifugal field, the pressure of the air rises as it moves outward along the blades. The air is then thrown from the edge of the impeller at a velocity nearly equal to the peripheral velocity of the wheel. By slowing the air down in a diffuser passage, the kinetic energy of the air is used to raise the pressure further and deliver the air to the engine.

To determine the impeller speed required to obtain a given pressure rise

Fig. 115. Impeller of centrifugal supercharger.

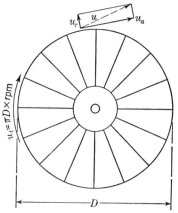

Fig. 116. Centrifugal-supercharger impeller showing tip speed u_t and tangential component u_a of air leaving impeller.

with a centrifugal compressor, it is necessary to calculate the shp in terms of impeller tip speed u_t and equate it to expression (132), which is shp in terms of the pressure ratio.

Figure 116 shows the air leaving part of the impeller with radial velocity u_r and tangential velocity u_a.

The force required at the tip of the impeller to give w_a lb of air/min a tangential velocity in feet per second of u_a would be, from Newton's law,

$$\text{Force} \times \text{time} = \text{mass} \times \text{velocity}$$

$$F = \frac{w_a/\text{min}}{g \times 60} u_a$$

The power absorbed by the impeller will be the tangential force times the tangential velocity of the wheel.

$$\text{shp} = \frac{(w_a/\text{min})u_a u_t}{g \times 60 \times 550} \tag{134}$$

where u_t = tangential velocity of the wheel, ft/sec
   550 = ft-lb/(sec) (hp)
Let $\zeta = u_a/u_t$ (usually about 0.9 for superchargers). Then

$$\text{shp} = \frac{(w_a/\text{min})\zeta u_t^2}{g \times 33{,}000} \tag{135}$$

Setting (135) equal to (132),

$$u_t^2 = \left[\left(\frac{p_2}{p_1}\right)^{(k-1)/k} - 1\right]\frac{gC_p T_1 \times 778}{\zeta \eta_a} \tag{136}$$

The product $\zeta \eta_a$ is sometimes called the pressure coefficient. The greater the pressure coefficient, the greater the pressure ratio which can be obtained with a given impeller tip speed. The quantity ζ is relatively constant for a given design of impeller, but η_a varies considerably with impeller speed and flow of air through the supercharger. Peak values of η_a may be about 0.75 to 0.80, so that with impeller tip speeds of over 1,100 fps, it is possible to obtain pressure ratios (p_2/p_1) of better than 2.5 with one stage of supercharging.

Supercharging the CI engine. The high inlet temperatures and pressures produced by a supercharger often cause detonation in a spark-ignition engine, but these very factors reduce the delay angle in CI engines and lower the rate of pressure rise. While supercharging increases peak pressures and cooling difficulties in all types of engines, the improved combustion characteristics resulting from supercharging make the process most attractive for CI engines. An additional factor in favor of supercharging is the low exhaust temperature of the CI engine due to its high expansion ratio and low fuel-air ratio. Because of the low temperature, the exhaust gases may be easily used in a gas turbine to produce sufficient power to operate the supercharger, as discussed on page 197.

PROBLEMS

1. A spark-ignition aircraft engine, operating unsupercharged at rated speed, develops a full-throttle output of 1,000 bhp at sea level. The corresponding bsfc is 0.52 lb/bhp-hr. The corresponding mechanical efficiency is 0.87.

(a) Make the best possible estimate of the full-throttle fhp of this engine at the same speed, at 10,000 ft altitude. (p = 10.1 psia, T = 483°R.)

(b) Estimate the full-throttle ihp, bhp, and bsfc of this engine at the same speed, at 10,000 ft altitude.

2. An automobile with a six-cylinder engine operating on a level road at 40 mph obtains 19.5 miles/gal of gasoline. The bhp required at this speed is 9.6. The engine rpm is 2,000, and the engine fhp is 14.5. A spark plug becomes fouled so that one cylinder no longer fires. The car starts to lose speed, but the driver opens the throttle until he is again running at 40 mph.

(a) Calculate the miles per gallon under these conditions. Assume negligible change in fuel-air ratio as the throttle is opened.

(b) Calculate the miles per gallon at 40 mph as above, if the piston, connecting rod, and valve-operating mechanism of the nonfiring cylinder were removed.

3. From an inspection of Fig. 113,

(a) Estimate the piston speed which will give maximum bhp for this engine.

(b) Calculate the value of maximum bhp.

(c) Calculate the pounds fuel per hour which the engine will use at maximum power.

4. (a) What piston speed and mep would you recommend for the engine of Fig. 113 if it is desired to operate at half of maximum bhp? Calculate the pounds fuel per hour which the engine will use at this point.

(b) How many pounds fuel per hour would the engine have used if it had been held at full throttle, but the rpm reduced by a gear ratio until bhp was one-half maximum bhp?

(c) How many pounds fuel per hour would the engine have used if it had been held at the same rpm as for maximum bhp but throttled at this speed until bhp were cut in half?

5. A one-cylinder two-stroke engine produces an ihp of 97. Its scavenging characteristics are given by curve B of Fig. 107. The bore is 4.5 in.; the stroke, 6 in.; F' = 0.08; compression ratio = 7; rpm = 1,800; η_i' = 90 per cent of the F/A cycle; scavenging pressure = 20.5 psia; inlet and exhaust pressure = 14.7 psia; atmospheric temperature = 520°R.

(a) Assuming the scavenging air leaves the blower at 600°R, calculate the pounds of air per minute required by this engine.

(b) Calculate the blower hp required if the adiabatic efficiency of the blower is 0.70.

(c) From (b) calculate the actual outlet temperature of the blower.

(d) How much engine mep will be used to operate the blower?

INDEX